Microcomputers in the Construction Industry

Microcomputers in the Construction Industry

James J. Adrian, Ph.D., PE, CPA, AIC

PROFESSOR, BRADLEY UNIVERSITY
PRESIDENT, CONSTRUCTION SYSTEMS CO.

RESTON PUBLISHING COMPANY, INC.
A PRENTICE-HALL COMPANY
RESTON, VIRGINIA

Library of Congress Cataloging in Publication Data

Adrian, James J.
    Microcomputers in the construction industry.

    Includes index.
    1. Construction industry—Management—Data processing.
    2. Microcomputers—Programming. 3. Basic (Computer
    program language) I. Title.
HD9715.A2A36   1985   624'.068   84-27628
ISBN 0-8359-4366-6

© 1985 by Reston Publishing Company, Inc.
A Prentice-Hall Company
Reston, Virginia 22090

1 3 5 7 9 10 8 6 4 2

Printed in the United States of America

to Christine, Douglas, and Kevin

Contents

11   Planning and Scheduling Applications   213

12   Equipment Management Applications   236

13   Bidding Strategy Applications   262

14   Selection of Hardware and Software   290

Appendix:

Preface

The use of microcomputers is virtually exploding in the construction industry. Contractors, designers, and project owners are making an increasingly wide use of computers to plan and control the time and cost of construction projects.

The rapid increase in the use of microcomputers in the construction industry has left many constructors "in the dark". Traditionally the industry has emphasized "bricks and mortar" more than scientific management techniques and the collection and use of data. The construction industry is now going through a transition. In the near future there is likely to be two types of constructors; the computer literate constructor and the computer illiterate constructor. Many would suggest that the successful constructor will need to be computer literate as well as know "how to build".

It is with this purpose that this book has been written. The book will enable the practitioner as well as the student to ready himself for the ongoing increase in the use of computers in the construction industry. The book assumes no prior computer knowledge.

Another purpose of the book is to give the reader a realistic view of just what a microcomputer can and cannot do in regard to the construction industry. All too often, the uninformed computer user has several misconceptions regarding the application of computers to his business. The computer cannot replace sound business practices or somehow take erroneous on-site job data and process it to yield accurate reports. In addition to setting out what a microcomputer can and cannot do, chapters in the book give the reader necessary organizational and data collection procedures that support a computer.

While the book does not promote the use of any specific brand of microcomputer or computer software, it does include chapters that will aid the reader in analyzing the benefits and disadvantages of computer hardware and software. This approach recognizes the fact that each and every potential microcomputer user may have specific needs that prevent the author from giving a single hardware or software recommendation.

The book is organized in five parts. After an introductory chapter, part two, to include chapters 2 and 3, address the technology of computer hardware and software. These chapters have the intent of illustrating how a microcomputer and accompanying software work.

Chapter 4, which can be considered part 3 of the book, has the intent of giving the reader fundamental BASIC programming skills. This is done via the presentation of a simple, but useable construction estimating program.

The intent of chapter 4 is twofold. For one, after studying this chapter, the reader should be able to write relatively simple construction industry application programs. However, perhaps of more importance is the fact that after studying chapter 4, the reader should be better able to understand how software programs work that the user purchases. This knowledge should put the reader in a better position to appraise such a program.

Chapters 5–13, the fourth part of the book, is perhaps the most important. These chapters set out many of the more beneficial computer applications to the construction industry. Accounting as well as job management applications are cited. In addition to discussing the applications, several of these chapters include actual computer programs. These are in a form such that the user can merely study them for his general interest, type them into a computer and actually use the programs, or modify the illustrated programs to meet the reader's own needs.

Part 5 of the book, chapter 14, includes a discussion of computer hardware and software selection. I have placed this chapter last with the idea that the reader can better appreciate the discussion and arguments in this chapter after having read the first 12 chapters.

The chapters are followed by an appendix of commonly used computer terms. Many of these terms are used throughout the book.

The book should prove useful to the practitioner as well as the student. In a teaching environment, the instructor might assign the student various programming assignments that go hand-in-hand with chapters 5–12. For example, an estimating conversion program might be assigned after studying chapter 9.

The author's interest in writing this book relates to his strong interest in computers, the construction industry, and his interest in implementing quantitative procedures to the construction process. The author has himself written the example computer application programs illustrated in the various chapters. The material included in the chapters has been taught by the author in his university classes as well as at numerous computer seminars taught around the country.

The author is indebted to many individuals for their indirect assistance in developing his thoughts for this book. Included in these individuals are the author's college professors that first got the author interested in computers many years ago and to his family members that once again have shown patience with him while he has devoted many hours to computer programming and the writing of this book.

James J. Adrian

1: Computers and the Construction Industry

INTRODUCTION

The construction industry is in great part an information collection, information processing, and information interpretation industry. In order to successfully plan and subsequently control the building process, the construction firm must collect, process, and interpret vast amounts of information and data. In fact, one might define a constructor as a "manager of information"—the building process being performed as a means of creating the information.

While the above definition of a constructor is not a dictionary-type definition, one could justifiably propose that the amount of information and data that is part of construction contracting is substantial. The fact that a contractor employs a large number of craftsmen results in a complex and time-consuming payroll process. The management of the payroll data and information is made more complex by the fact that the contractor experiences considerable employee turnover, and by the fact that the on-site craftsmen might be employed at numerous locations, perhaps each of which requires different wage scales and payroll deductions.

Owing to the relatively large number of vendors from which a contractor purchases material or services, the firm's accounts payable system entails a considerable number of accounts and data entries. One might argue that an effective (i.e., one that minimizes discounts lost and preserves cash) handling of a contractor's accounts payable is in itself a full-time job.

General ledger accounting, including payroll, accounts payable, and receivables, is not unique to the construction firm. However, the fact that the contractor's production process is decentralized (projects are constructed at numerous varied site locations) compounds the difficulty of these accounting tasks.

1

The information needs of the construction firms are not limited to the accounting functions. To be profitable, a construction firm must prepare accurate project estimates, schedules, and cost and time control duties. Each of these tasks requires a significant amount of data/information collection, processing, and interpretation.

The task of data and information management has often overwhelmed the contractor. The fact that most contractors are small, closely held companies has resulted in many firms being unable to cope with adequate and necessary data collection and processing. Instead, the contractor has on occasion focused more on the marketing or sales function and the necessary task of production, e.g., the pouring of concrete. Given the firm's insufficient attention to the record keeping and data/information processing aspect of its business, the contractor has often fallen victim to financial loss on a project and perhaps even financial ruin as a firm (contractors have one of the highest failure rates of all industries).

Enter the computer! The recent entry of the computer, especially the micro/personal computer, has given the contractor a potential tool for the efficient handling of the vast amount of information that is part of his business. Note our use of the word *potential*. A computer by itself does not solve the information handling problems of the contractor. It only provides the firm a tool for processing, manipulating, storing, and printing the information. It will not significantly enhance the collection of data. One should remember an often quoted characteristic of the computer: garbage in, garbage out!

While a computer is only a tool, not a solution, for the contractor, it is undoubtedly a tool the majority of contractors will utilize in the near future. While offering the potential to be a very useful and necessary tool, the computer has also become affordable for most builders. Given the relatively low price of microcomputer hardware and software, the computer has become almost expendable to the builder, often costing less than a small construction tool or piece of equipment. It is probably safe to say that the computer will soon become a necessary tool for the contractor, like his hard hat and construction shoes. It is not difficult to perceive a computer terminal in every job-site trailer in the near future.

THE ARRIVAL OF THE COMPUTER

The computer age has certainly arrived. One can hardly pick up a newspaper or periodical or watch television without seeing an advertisement for a new computer system. Parents are led to believe that they are depriving their children of a proper education if a computer is not purchased for the home! Businesses, including very small businesses, are projected as being nonmodern or out-of-date if they fail to have a computer in their office. Forecasts indicate that each and every business, and the majority of homes, will have a computer in the not too distant future.

The rapid interest in computers has not escaped the construction industry and the construction contractor. The rapid increase in computer technology, accompanied by a significant decrease in cost (relative to the high cost of large main-frame early computers), has resulted in the computer becoming affordable for the very small as well as large-sized contractor. The end result is that the number of construction contractors that are using a computer has been significantly increasing. A random survey performed by the author in 1980 of small- and large-sized contractors indicated that approximately 6 percent of the contractors surveyed were using a computer. However, a similar survey performed by the author in 1984 indicated that 18 percent were using a computer and another 22 percent were planning on implementing a computer within the next year. It is not difficult to comprehend the fact that the majority of construction contractors will be using a computer within the near future.

While many construction firms have already taken on computer capability, not all firms are using their computers for the same tasks. As one would expect, the most frequent use relates to accounting tasks, especially payroll accounting.

A survey performed in 1984 by the author of a random number of construction firms using a computer indicated usage of a computer for several tasks. These tasks and the summarized results of the survey are illustrated in Figure 1.1.

The predominance of usage of the computer for accounting functions relative to project management tasks likely is due in part to the abundance of available accounting computer software. On the other hand, until recently, there has been little off-the-shelf software unique to construction project management. However, this is likely to change as many software vendors recognize the large number of construction firms that are computerizing and have a need for industry-type software.

The construction contractor is not the only entity involved in the construction process that has turned to computers. Project designers, including architect/engineer designers, have taken on computer capability to aid them in their specification writing, estimating, and project control functions. While our emphasis in this book centers on computer applications and the construction contractor himself, the computer will likely continue to play an increased role in the entire construction project life, from the feasibility estimate for a project through the data processing necessary to support the project owner's final payment to the construction firm.

Percent of Construction Firms Owning and Using Computers	23%
Percent of Construction Firms Renting/Leasing and Using Computers	13%
Percent of Construction Firms Owning or Renting/ Leasing Computers	36%
NOTE: Following Percentages Expressed as a Percent of Firms Using Computers	
Percent Using for General Ledger Accounting	78%
Percent Using for Payroll Accounting	87%
Percent Using for Accounts Payable	64%
Percent Using for Accounts Receivable	36%
Percent Using for Job Costing	57%
Percent Using for Estimating Applications	21%
Percent Using for Scheduling Applications	24%
Percent Using for Equipment Accounting/Estimating	14%
Percent Using for Bidding Strategy	4%
Percent Using "Spreadsheet" Type Business Programs	34%
Percent Using "Data Base" Type Business Programs	37%

Figure 1.1 Survey of usage of computers by construction firms.

THE NEED FOR IMPROVED MANAGEMENT OF INFORMATION IN THE CONSTRUCTION INDUSTRY

There is little doubt that the construction firm is highly dependent on the collection and use of data and information. However, the fact is that the construction industry has often been characterized as an industry that lacks record keeping, management techniques, and a scientific approach to problem solving. While these criticisms are undoubtedly overexaggerated, especially in regard to the well-managed firm, it is true that the construction firm has likely placed more emphasis on the knowledge of the technology of the construction process than on the "number" and paper aspect of its business.

The contractor's emphasis on marketing and production versus accounting and control (essentially data collection and processing functions) likely stems from the fact that the contractor has to secure work to exist and must perform the production function to satisfy his contract requirements. In other words one might argue that the marketing and production functions are "must functions." On the other hand the contractor does not have to perform the "paper-based" functions of accounting and control. Perhaps the only function he has to perform is the payroll function. This is not to say that other paper-based tasks that include project management tasks are unimportant or unnecessary. They are; but the contractor may not view them as critical. One might argue that these paper-oriented tasks get placed on the "back burner."

What is the result of the construction industry's lack of attention to data/information collection and processing? It is difficult to relate contractor profits (or lack of profits) to any one task that includes data collection and data processing. However, one can state that contractor financial failure can be traced to data collection/processing functions more often than marketing or production causes. Evidence of this is illustrated in Figure 1.2. The figure lists the most common reasons a construction firm fails as compiled by Dun and Bradstreet. Inspection of the list, the first reason being the most frequent in occurrence, indicates that the majority of the reasons for contractor failure relates to functions that require the collection, processing, and analysis of data/information.

1. Lack of business experience	6. Insufficient advertising
2. Inadequate project estimating and/or cost control system	7. Lack of technical experience
	8. Wrong location for service
3. Inadequate working capital	9. Inventory control
4. Receivable difficulties	10. Fraud
5. Too much competition	

Figure 1.2 Reasons for construction firm financial failures.

The construction firm's need for efficient data/information collection and processing has increased during recent years. The contractor's profit margin has been on the decline while his risk has not decreased. This is illustrated in Figure 1.3 and Figure 1.4. Figure 1.3 illustrates the increasing cost of construction during the past decade. Unfortunately, as illustrated, there has been very little increase in construction productivity (units or dollars of work performed per man-hour) during the same time period.

The end result of the curves in Figure 1.3, illustrating the increased construction cost and the relatively flat construction productivity, is a decreasing contractor profit margin.

The author would propose that as the contractor's construction costs have increased, the contractor has been successful in only passing on a percentage of the costs. For example, assuming the construction contractor incurs a $1.00 raise for a craftsman, he might be successful in passing on

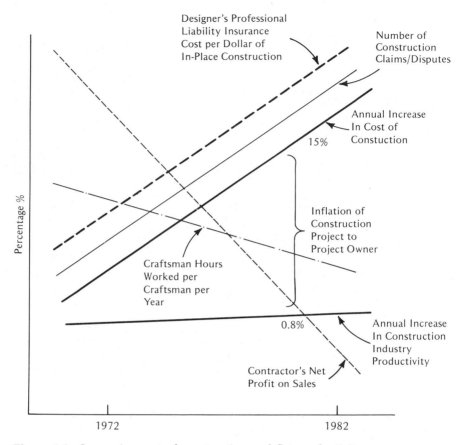

Figure 1.3   Increasing cost of construction and flat productivity.

90 cents of the increase to his project owner client. The end result is that the contractor absorbs the other 10 cents. Given this increase in cost without any offsetting revenue or productivity, the contractor's profit margin decreases. In other words, his profitability declines.

Figure 1.4 illustrates the decreasing profit curve of the contractor relative to the variation in a contractor's actual-to-estimated cost for a project. Over several years of performing financial CPA audits of construction contracting firms, the author has kept track of the actual cost of building a project relative to the contractor's initial estimate for the project. The author would propose that, on the average, a contractor builds a project for a 6 percent variation in cost relative to the project estimate. In other words a construction contractor cost estimate is accurate to a degree of 6 percent.

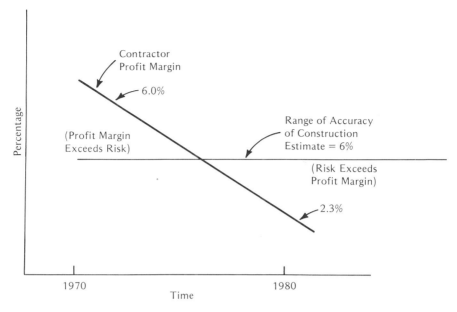

Figure 1.4 Decreasing profit margin relative to estimating risk.

Figure 1.4 illustrates that due to a decreased profitability (owing in part to low productivity) the typical construction bid submitted by a contractor now has more risk (6 percent) than profit (2.3 percent). Obviously, one has to call this a risky proposition! Unfortunately this has led in part to the increased number of contractor failures and an incentive for the contractor to do negotiated or construction management work.

What do these negative type of illustrations (negative in that they illustrate worsening profit and increasing risk for the builder) have to do with the construction industry's use of computers? The answer is simple. Hopefully, the use of the computer and its many applications offer the contractor an opportunity to increase his profitability and decrease his financial risk. For example, through accounting and project management computer software applications, the contractor may be able to increase the profit earned per dollar of work performed. Similarly, by using a computer and the appropriate software, the contractor may be able to develop a historical data bank regarding his costs such that he can decrease his estimating range of accuracy (and his financial risk) from the 6 percent range of accuracy illustrated in Figure 1.4 to a smaller number.

One might state that the goal of any firm, including the construction contractor, is to be in a position whereby its profit margin is greater than its financial risk. Given the many applications of computers to the construction industry that are described in later chapters, it may be that it is the computer that may afford the contractor this opportunity!

ORGANIZATION OF TEXT

The reader of this book is likely to have several objectives. Some readers may be interested in learning the "ins and outs" of how a computer and software work and how to select and implement hardware and software. Most readers also likely have the objective of viewing and learning the many applications of computers to the construction industry; in effect, this reader is interested in computer software application programs. On the other hand some readers may be interested in learning how to develop and write their own construction industry software application programs.

All of the above are worthwhile objectives (undoubtedly some more than others). The author has written chapters that essentially can be classified into four different sections/parts. They are as follows:

- Introduction to computer hardware and software
- Writing construction software programs using BASIC
- Application of computers to construction
- Selection of computer hardware and construction industry software

The following chapters are ordered according to the above sections/parts. Given the author's interpretation of the reader's needs, the majority of the chapters illustrate software applications to the construction industry. Reading and understanding all of the material should prepare the reader to cope with the coming computer age in the construction industry. More importantly, the material should equip the reader with the means to increase his profits and decrease his risk through the use of the computer!

2: Understanding Computer Hardware

INTRODUCTION

To many individuals in the construction industry, the word *computer* is a scary one. One must remember that the construction industry has historically not been a highly scientific, mathematically oriented industry. Instead, many owners of construction firms, and the construction worker himself, have made their living through knowledge of the building process and hard physical work.

The construction industry is witnessing a language transition. Words like *bits, microprocessor,* and *diskettes* are joining terms like *mortar, beams,* and *footings* as the vocabulary of the constructor. While computer words and terms may be new to many constructors, the computer language will likely be a necessity to the future successful constructor. Fortunately, the constructor can take comfort in the fact that in reality computer terminology is not as complicated as one might first believe. This chapter presents computer terminology in layman's language. Many of the terms introduced will be used intermittently in later chapters. Thus, it is important for the reader to understand the terms presented in this chapter.

A BASIC COMPUTER SYSTEM

There are numerous types of computers. Many computers in common use today are referred to as *desk-top* or *personal* computers. They are referred to as desk-top because they can easily fit on a desk. The name personal computer refers to the fact that they are often designed for use by a single person at a point in time. This differs from the huge business computers in common use in years gone by that were usually designed for use by several (multi) individuals at the same time.

While large business computers are still in use, the rapid growth in computers has been in the desk-top personal computers. These smaller, more affordable machines often have the same, if not more, capacity as the large, much more expensive computers. Computers costing only a few thousand dollars or less provide many construction firms the capability to perform both accounting and project management applications.

A variation of the desk-top personal computer is the hand-held or pocket computer. These small hand-held machines, while convenient especially for outdoor use or travel, usually have a few programming limitations relative to the larger desk-top models.

A computer is usually part of several pieces of equipment called a *computer system*. A computer system includes both a computer and accessories, called *peripherals*. A typical computer system is illustrated in Figure 2.1.

The computer itself can be thought of as the computer box and the *keyboard* shown in Figure 2.1. The *video monitor, printer,* and *floppy disk drive* shown are peripherals. A peripheral can be defined as any input or output device designed to be connected to the computer. Other peripherals include a cassette tape recorder, a modem, and joysticks. These and other peripherals will be discussed in the following sections.

COMPUTER HARDWARE

A computer system includes both hardware and software. The *hardware* includes keyboards, video monitors, disk drives, circuit boards, and all other electronic circuit equipment. On the other hand the *software* includes the programs, lists, operating instructions, and other documentation that is used in the operation of the computer system. This chapter will discuss hardware; the next chapter will discuss software.

The hardware of a computer system is basically made up of four separate elements or sections. They are as follows:

1. Microprocessor
2. Memory
3. Input Devices
4. Output Devices

No matter how big or small a computer system is and no matter what brand it is, the four elements noted above are included. A computer has an input device for getting information into it, a processor (referred to as

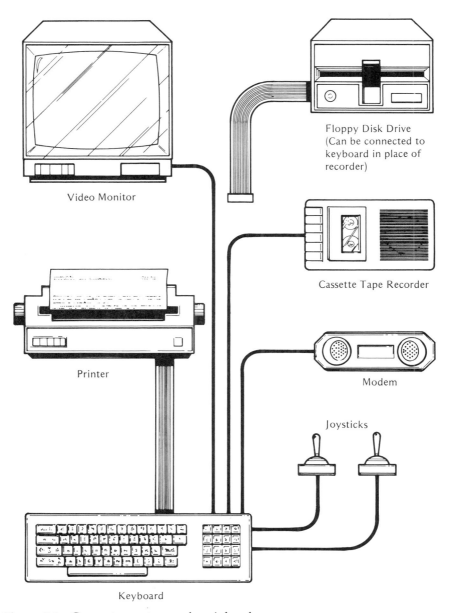

Floppy Disk Drive
(Can be connected to
keyboard in place of
recorder)

Video Monitor

Cassette Tape Recorder

Printer

Modem

Joysticks

Keyboard

Figure 2.1 Computer system and peripherals.

a microprocessor because of its size) for working on the information, a
memory to store information, and an output device for getting new information to the user.

MICROPROCESSOR

The *microprocessor* is the brain of the computer. In fact, it is fair to say that the microprocessor *is* the computer in that it does the computing. The fascinating thing about personal computers is that this powerful microprocessor is a tiny chip of silicon made from purified beach sand. The chip itself is usually no bigger than the nail on one's finger. Literally thousands of electronic transistors are on a single chip. The transistors can work millions of transactions per second.

A microprocessor can be thought of as a series of switches that can be switched to 0 or 1. A microprocessor can only understand the digits 0 and 1. The two-digit language is called the binary numbering system. A microprocessor gets and stores all its information in a continuous stream of these switches that are either in the 0 or 1 position. Each switch is referred to as a *bit*. If no voltage is in the switch, the switch is at 0. If there is voltage, the switch is at 1. An example of a series of these bits that form a number is illustrated in Figure 2.2.

Several companies manufacture microprocessors for the many computer vendors. One hears various names and model numbers associated with microprocessors. For example, Z-80, 6502, and 8802 have been popular microprocessors. Because new and faster microprocessors continue to be developed, we will not attempt to list them here. Suffice it to say that essentially all microprocessors serve the same function, that of working on data and information.

A microprocessor is sometimes characterized by the number of bits it has. This refers to how much information or data a microprocessor can handle at one time. Each bit is either a 1 or 0. Early microprocessors handled information 4 bits at a time. In recent years, about the time personal computers became popular, the 8-bit microprocessor was developed. Many of the personal computers, especially those used in the home, are 8-bit machines. More recently, the 16-bit microprocessor was developed. These 16-bit machines are gaining in popularity, especially in business-type machines. Given that the 16-bit microprocessor can perform operations faster

1	=	1	111	=	7
10	=	2	1000	=	8
11	=	3	1001	=	9
100	=	4	1010	=	10
101	=	5	1011	=	11
110	=	6	1100	=	12

Figure 2.2
Converting bits into a number.

and can also handle more *memory* (discussed in the following section), most business machines that will be used by the construction industry in the future are likely to be 16-bit machines. There is even talk of a 32-bit microprocessor. One will likely continue to see new technology develop in regard to microprocessors.

MEMORY

Similar to a microprocessor, a computer could not operate without *memory*. The memory of a computer system can be thought of as the circuits, components, and/or mechanical elements of the computer that store information.

In appearance, the memory within a computer is like a microprocessor. Memory consists of an array of small chips. Like a microprocessor, in each chip there are thousands of on and off switches, which take on a value of 0 or 1.

If a computer system includes a disk drive or a cassette, it has three types of memory: memory on a disk (referred to as a floppy disk) or on a tape if a cassette is used, random-access memory (RAM), and read-only memory (ROM); the last two types are internal to the computer. Because disks and tapes are discussed in a later section, we will only describe RAM and ROM memory in this section.

A computer's size is often characterized by the amount of random-access memory (often abbreviated RAM) it has. A 64K machine essentially means that the machine has approximately 64,000 bytes of memory size. A byte is a set of 8 bits of memory. In reality a 64K machine has somewhat more than 64,000 bytes of memory because 1K is 1,024 bytes.

RAM or random-access memory is integrated circuit chips that store and recall information. Unlike the read-only memory (ROM) discussed below, RAM requires electrical power. If the power of the computer is turned off, the information in the RAM is lost.

Computer software programs that are being written or predesigned programs loaded from disks or tape are stored in the RAM of the computer. As such, the amount of RAM a computer has in great part dictates the size and complexity of the software program it can store and run. It is no wonder that the amount of RAM a system has is so commonly used to characterize the computer size. To give the reader an appreciation of the great capacity of RAM, a 64K machine can store approximately 20 typed pages of information. In other words an entire chapter of a book can often be stored in the memory of a small personal computer.

Many personal computers are made such that additional RAM chips can be added. Additional RAM is usually relatively inexpensive. This is usually done by simply adding circuit boards. One of the advantages of the large-bit microprocessors (e.g., a 16-bit microprocessor) is that it can readily handle additional memory.

The other type of memory internal to a computer is read-only memory (ROM). This type of memory is built into the computer. Unlike RAM where information can be written in or read out, information can only be read from the ROM.

ROM stores permanent information. The information cannot be erased or changed. In fact, the information in ROM is not lost even if the computer (the electrical power) is turned off.

ROM is built into the computer. Because the computer user cannot change this memory or write to it, it is not essential for the user to understand how ROM works or is designed. However, ROM is an essential part of the computer. Every time the computer is turned on, the ROM goes through a series of steps, which includes checking all circuits to see that they work. These start-up and check procedures are often referred to as *bootstraping*.

ROM also serves another important function. Many personal computers are purchased with a high-level language called BASIC already built into the computer. The computer needs a way of understanding the BASIC commands a programmer gives it. It does this by having a BASIC interpreter stored in the ROM of the computer.

INPUT DEVICES

The third element in a computer system is an input device. Without an input device there would be no way of putting information into memory and subsequently have the microprocessor perform operations on the information.

By far the most common device for inputting information into a computer is a *keyboard*. A sample keyboard is illustrated in Figure 2.3. In appearance, a keyboard looks very similar to a typewriter, except that a computer keyboard usually has additional keys.

There are essentially four types of keys on a computer keyboard. For one, there are the typical keys that are on a typewriter that include letters of the alphabet and numbers. These keys are used to type in words and numbers. Another set of keys on computer keyboards include keys that let the user erase letters, move the *cursor* (the movable indicator on the screen of a video display that shows where the next character or symbol will appear), and various keys that operate the computer. The number and

Figure 2.3   Example computer keyboard.

types of these keys vary somewhat depending on the computer manufacturer.

A computer keyboard may or may not have a third and fourth type of keys. Some computers have a separate set of numerical keys that serve as a calculator. Rather than have to reach the top row (like on a typewriter) to obtain a numerical number, the separate numerical set of keys provides the user the convenience of direct entry.

The fourth type of keys that may be included on a keyboard are referred to as *functional* keys. If a computer has these functional keys, it is possible for the user to program a series of computer commands or statements and execute all of these by merely pressing a single functional key. This is a convenient feature if the same set of commands or statements are to be executed several times; it saves the time retyping the several commands and/or statements.

The number of keys and their purpose are not the only differentiating feature of the keyboards of various manufacturers. Essentially the pressing of any key sends to the computer memory or microprocessor a series of voltages that sets switches to a 0 or a 1. However, the "feel" of the keys differ depending on the manufacturer. Some keyboards "feel" like a typewriter when you hit a key. The key lowers and the user feels a type of click. On the other hand more economical keyboards tend to be more of a soft material or plastic type where the keys do not protrude. Instead, by pressing the location of the key printed on the material, or plastic, the voltage is sent to the memory or microprocessor. More inadvertent data entry errors are common on this latter type of keyboard.

Keyboards are also characterized as being either attached or non-attached to the computer console itself. In fact, some manufacturers produce a computer console, disk drive, monitor, and keyboard as a single unit. Many computer programmers prefer the unattached keyboard in that it provides the convenience of typing data entry at a distance from the computer console. For example, a programmer might enter information by typing data into the computer while holding it in his lap sitting in a comfortable chair. On the other hand a computer and an unattached keyboard usually take more space than if they were a single unit.

One final functional aspect about keyboards is that some computers (and the accompanying keyboard) allow the entry in uppercase and lowercase letters, while others allow only uppercase letters. The constraint of only having uppercase letter input is not prohibitive to writing programs. However, to use the computer as a word processor and be able to write and print letters, papers, and manuscripts, the entry of both uppercase and lowercase letters via the keyboard is required.

For business uses a keyboard is by far the most commonly used input device. However, other input devices are in use, including joysticks and various graphic boards, that enable a user to enter lines and illustrations directly into the computer. Because of the scarcity of their use in business applications, they will not be discussed here.

OUTPUT DEVICES

The fourth element of a computer system is an output device. Two output devices are in common use: a video display unit [sometimes referred to as a cathode-ray tube (CRT)] and a printer. Instead of using a video display unit, the user can substitute a television screen.

Most video monitors project green letters on a black image screen. Color monitors can also be utilized. However, similar to color televisions, the color screens tend to be significantly more expensive. For business purposes a video monitor projecting a single color image is usually sufficient. Green and black and amber and black video monitors are most common.

After the video monitor, the most popular output device is a printer. Unlike a monitor, a printer gives the user a hard copy of a program, information, or data processed in the computer. A printer becomes an essential computer peripheral.

A printer is essentially a one-way device. It prints information that the computer sends it. Printers can type words very fast, usually much faster than one could type the same printout.

The quality and speed of printers vary significantly. There are two different types of printers, *impact* printers and *nonimpact* printers. An impact printer uses a printhead that strikes a ribbon paper. A nonimpact printer uses special mechanisms that do not strike the paper.

Impact printers can be further divided into two types: fully formed character printers and dot matrix printers. Impact printers that produce fully formed characters work similar to a typewriter. There are two types of fully formed character printers: a daisy wheel and thimble-type printer. In a daisy wheel printer a hammer strikes a movable wheel that hits the paper. On the other hand, in a thimble printer, a cylinder covered with embossed characters hits the paper.

Fully formed character printers produce a quality of document similar to a typewriter. They are often referred to as *letter-quality* printers. While they produce superior quality documents relative to a dot matrix printer, they have two disadvantages relative to dot matrix printers. For one they are more expensive. Equally important, a letter-quality printer is usually significantly slower than a dot matrix printer in regard to the number of characters per second it can print. For example, letter-quality printers often print on the order of 20 to 50 characters per minute (cpm) whereas many dot matrix printers provide speeds approaching 300 cpm. Because of his added speed, dot matrix printers are usually preferred when printing long mailing lists, multiple documents, and computer program listings.

In addition to being less expensive and faster than letter-quality printers (fully formed character printers), dot matrix printers are usually more reliable, owing to the fact that they have a row of needlelike pins that are individually fired against a ribbon as they move across the paper. Each pin produces a single dot as it strikes the paper. They are relatively durable.

Nonimpact printers use various forms of heat, jets of ink, and electrical devices to form letters on a document. They are not as popular as impact printers. Part of the reason for this stems from the fact that they are not as dependable and may require more maintenance.

Several types of print styles can be purchased for both impact and nonimpact printers. Various carriage sizes can also be purchased to allow for printing varying size documents.

DISK DRIVES

An important, and almost essential, peripheral for using a computer system for construction industry applications is a disk drive. A disk drive, along with diskettes (often referred to as floppy disks), serves as both an input and output device to a computer.

A sample disk drive is illustrated in Figure 2.4. A disk drive is a motorized device that spins a magnetic disk at high speeds. The disk drive contains a sensing device that can both read information from and write onto the surface of the disk in the form of magnetized patterns.

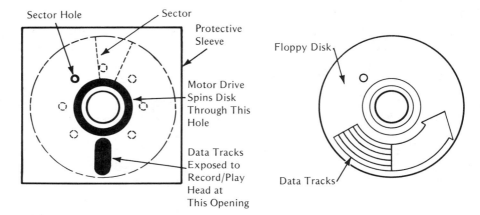

Figure 2.4   Example disk drive.

Information is stored and read on a diskette at very fast speeds. The information is stored on a diskette using the same 0s and 1s that are stored in a computer memory and microprocessor. However, in order to coordinate the transfer of information between the computer and the disk drive, you also need a special disk-operating system (DOS). The DOS may be stored in the disk drive, stored in the computer, or loaded into the disk drive or computer from a diskette.

Disk drives offer several advantages over other means of input/output devices, including cassette players. For one, most "off-the-shelf" software is only available on diskettes (floppy disks). It is necessary to have a disk drive to run the software. Another advantage of disk drives is their speed. Very large programs can be stored or read from disk drives in a matter of seconds. Equally important, data on a disk drive can be quickly accessed and input to the computer memory. This is an important plus because many construction industry computer applications require the computer to continually get information/data from a disk and put information/data on a disk.

The amount of information/data that can be stored on a disk is measured in "K," where a K is 1024 bytes of data. This is the same means used to measure the amount of computer memory. The actual amount of data that can be stored on a diskette depends on the circuitry of the disk drive.

When a computer application requires large amounts of data storage or requires the use of multiple programs simultaneously, it is advantageous to have two or more disk drives. Many computers that would be purchased for use by the constructor have two disk drives.

The most common disk drive uses 5¼-inch diskettes. A less popular disk drive uses an 8-inch diskette. Disk drives and diskettes are commonly referred to as *single-density* or *double-density* drives. Essentially, double-density drives store information on both sides of the diskette, whereas a single-density drive stores information on one side of the diskette.

3: Understanding Computer Software

INTRODUCTION

A computer system without computer software is like a television set without shows. Like television shows, computer software provides the interface between the user and the electronic hardware.

Computer software consists of instructions or programs that tell the computer what to do. Computer software essentially is one of two types: software programs developed by the user himself and programs written by someone other than the user that are purchased. These latter type of programs are also referred to as off-the-shelf programs or purchased software. In either case, in order to be successfully run by a computer, the software programs must be loaded into RAM (random-access memory) from ROM (read-only memory) or from an external device such as a disk drive.

LEVELS OF COMPUTER LANGUAGE

In describing the various levels of computer software languages, it is important to remember the languages of the sender and the receiver, i.e., the computer user and the computer hardware. One can assume that the language of the user is English (or some other spoken language). On the other hand the main "brain" of a computer, the microprocessor, is a binary number system consisting of 0s and 1s.

Given the two different communication capabilities, there is a need for a communication interface so that the user can write computer software programs. Let us start our discussion of this interface by proceeding from the language of the computer to the language of the user.

As noted above, the computer microprocessor can only understand binary numbering. However, by using various combinations of 0s and 1s, various "words" and "instructions" can be communicated. This combining of 0s and 1s to form words and instructions makes up what is referred to as *machine language.* If the user had to write computer software programs using machine language, the process would be very time consuming and difficult. For example, a few relatively simple computer instructions would require the user to specify the following machine language software codes.

Instruction	*Machine Software Code*
Get a number from memory	10110110
Get another number from memory	01101101
Add the two numbers	11110101
Place the total in memory	00110110

To appreciate the difficulty of writing a machine language software program, one should mention that any meaningful software program would likely entail writing hundreds or even thousands of machine language instructions and words. The task would be extremely difficult given that the user does not speak a "binary language" or has memorized the hundreds of difficult computer instructions or words.

While difficult, the fact remains that in the early years of computers, the user (called a programmer) did have to write programs using machine language. Fortunately, it is no longer necessary to understand machine language to write a program. This brings us to the next "level" of computer languages, *assembly* language. This level of computer language and the others are illustrated in Figure 3.1.

In an assembly language a short term or phrase takes the place of the string of 0s and 1s that characterize machine language. The following examples illustrate a few assembly language instructions (a program) that add two numbers.

Instruction	*Assembly Language*
Load a number from memory	LO,A,1
Load another number from memory	LO,B,10
Add the two numbers together	ADD
Place the total in a new memory location	LO,C

Machine language—for example, 10110110
>   The language by which a computer "thinks" and "stores" data.

Assembly language—for example, LO, ADD
>   An "intermediate" language between machine language and various high-level languages.

BASIC—for example, PRINT 23 + 56
>   A high-level language commonly used in personal computers. Its popularity stems from its similarity to the English language.

FORTRAN—A high-level language used primarily for engineering/ scientific applications.

COBOL—A high-level language used primarily for business-type applications.

Figure 3.1   Levels and uses of various computer languages.

An assembler program internal to the computer acts as an interface between the assembly language and the machine language. In effect this go-between program changes assembly language instructions into machine language.

While assembly language is an improvement (relative to machine language) in regard to a computer programmer being able to understand instructions like LO, ADD, etc., the language is still relatively difficult and time consuming in regard to writing a software program. Given this time and difficulty, computer specialists sought yet another level of computer software language. This effort resulted in what we today commonly refer to as *high-level languages.* High-level languages are close (but not exactly the same) as the English language of the user. A computer has the ability to convert high-level languages to an assembly language, which in turn is converted to machine language.

There are several high-level languages in common use today, e.g., FORTRAN (an abbreviation for *FORmula TRANslation*) and COBOL (an abbreviation for *COmmon Business-Oriented Language*). However, by far the most common high-level language in use today is BASIC. BASIC is an abbreviation for *Beginner's All-Purpose Symbolic Instruction Code*.

BASIC is easy to learn and use. A previous nonuser of a computer or a nonprogrammer can usually quickly learn how to use BASIC, including writing software programs with the language. Many off-the-shelf software programs are written in BASIC. Because of the popularity of the language, many computers are sold with a BASIC compiler built into the machine such that the user can write programs in BASIC without any complications. In other words the computer has a program built into the machine that interprets BASIC words and instructions and converts them into machine language. This "compiler" program is built into the ROM (read-only memory) of the computer.

BASIC and other high-level languages are vast improvements on assembly and machine languages. It is much easier to understand, and most importantly, to write computer software programs using the high-level languages. For example, the following illustrates the previously noted computer software program to add two numbers using BASIC.

Instruction	*BASIC*
Get a number from memory	INPUT A
Get another number from memory	INPUT B
Add the two numbers and	
Place the total in memory	C = A + B

Not only is it easier to understand BASIC in that the words and instructions are similar to English, but there are usually far less computer statements or instructions necessary in BASIC relative to the same program written in assembly or machine languages. For example, a single BASIC instruction might represent two or three separate assembly language instructions.

The introduction of high-level languages, and in particular BASIC, has enabled the noncomputer specialist to write his own application software and to modify off-the-shelf programs. It has become realistic for a construction firm to write its own software programs for estimating, scheduling, cost control, and some of the other applications discussed in Chapters 5 through 14.

One should not infer that BASIC is the only high-level language in use today. Other specialty-type high-level languages in wide use include PASCAL, LOGO, and others. However, these languages are not that useful relative to construction industry applications. As such, the following chapters will limit themselves to BASIC and the illustration of programs written in BASIC.

In practice, there are several versions of BASIC. For example, the BASIC supplied with the IBM-PC is slightly different from the BASIC supplied with the Apple computer. However, the versions differ only ever so slightly. One might consider the different versions like different dialects of the English language. Usually, the computer programmer has little difficulty in adapting from one version of BASIC to the next.

The author does not consider this a BASIC programming book in itself. However, with the intent of providing the fundamentals of BASIC such that the reader might begin writing relatively simple construction industry software programs, or modify existing ones, the next chapter will present somewhat of an overview of BASIC with an emphasis on words and instructions relative to construction industry applications.

OPERATING SYSTEMS

Probably the most important and vital software that is part of a computer system is the *operating system.* Actually, most computer systems designed for business applications, including construction industry applications, have two operating systems, one that is built into the computer itself and one that accompanies the use of a disk drive.

Essentially, the operating system built into the computer serves as the go-between for the application software the user loads into the computer and the computer itself. The operating system works with the microprocessor to keep all the electrical signals organized. In effect the operating system "runs" the circuitry of the computer. It is essential software internal to the computer. Because it is internal to the computer, there is little need for the user or programmer to understand the "ins and outs" of the operating system itself. However, it is the quality, size, and speed of the operating system software that characterizes the efficiency of the computer system.

If the computer system utilizes a disk drive (as it likely would for construction industry applications), a special disk-operating system (DOS) is needed. The DOS coordinates the transfer of information to and from a floppy disk or diskette that is placed in the disk drive. The DOS system is actually a computer software program, one that is again internal to the computer system. It may be built into the disk drive itself or may be installed in the computer's memory.

Many computers have a DOS unique to their own hardware. Manufacturers continue to update the DOS, and each update is given a version number, e.g., DOS 1.0, DOS 1.1, DOS 2.0, etc. With each new version the ability of the programmer to carry out new and expanded programming options improves.

Given the fact that each computer vendor might have his own DOS, off-the-shelf software will not run on every computer system. One must purchase software specifically designed for the DOS unique to one's computer. This problem is somewhat alleviated by the fact that most software vendors have written popular programs in several versions such that the program is available for several different computer DOS. The software usually is labeled as to the DOS on which it will run.

Several computer vendors are now designing their computers such that they can use more than one operating system. This enables the computer to run a wider variety of off-the-shelf programs. It is also becoming possible to buy software programs on diskettes that load a DOS into the computer's memory.

Given the problems associated with computers having unique DOS (and therefore creating software programs compatible with the DOS), one would think that computer vendors would organize and attempt to develop a "standard" DOS. To date this has not happened. However, an operating system has evolved titled CP/M (an abbreviation for Control Program for Microprocessors) that has been written to work on several computers. Software vendors have written thousands of programs to run on the CP/M. As such, many computer vendors have installed CP/M as a DOS within the computer.

Even though CP/M is in wide use, it is by no means available on each and every computer. It is difficult to predict whether or not a standard DOS will evolve for all computers. In the meantime the variability of various computers relative to their DOS is a point of concern to the computer programmer and to the individual or firm attempting to design and market off-the-shelf software.

SOFTWARE PROTECTION

The problem of computer vendors having their own DOS is not the only problem confronting the computer programmer who is attempting to develop and market software, including construction industry application programs. Another problem is the illegal copying and resale of software. Because of this problem, programmers are finding means of protecting their programs from being copied. By writing various relatively complicated programming procedures, they prevent an individual from making a copy of the program.

However, attempts to copy protect a software program have at least two problems. For one, the fact that a program has been copy protected prevents the purchaser/user from making a backup copy in case the original is damaged. But perhaps more importantly, no matter how well a program has been copy protected, a sophisticated programming expert can usually determine the programming code to copy it. In other words a person really intent on committing software piracy can usually find a way of copying the program. The person that is prevented from copying a copy-protected program usually will not be interested in the illegal copying of it anyway. To complicate the problem of software piracy, software programs called *emulators* are being developed that enable one to copy programs written for one computer onto yet another computer.

The potential problem of computer piracy is not a problem for the construction firm devloping its own software program. However, if the firm intends to subsequently market the software to other firms (and this objective is in part one reason the firm goes to the expense of developing its own software), then the potential for computer piracy is a concern.

SOFTWARE CONCERNS

Given the significant number of small computers purchased by business and households alike in recent years, many companies that design and sell computer software programs have evolved. Some of these companies are large, multiownership, national firms. On the other hand the majority of software programs are developed and sold by small firms and entrepreneurial individuals. Some of the most sophisticated software programs have been developed by "part-time" programmers.

Owing to the large number of computer software vendors and the fact that the computer software buyer usually purchases the software without the advantage of personally knowing the seller (most software is purchased off-the-shelf as one purchases a music record), the buyer should be attentive to several concerns. For one, the most obvious concern relates to the capability of the software. Does the software do what the buyer needs? Does the program have flexibility such that it serves varying needs of the buyer.

The capability or scope of application of the software under consideration usually can be appraised by the potential buyer. Given the fact that the market literature for an off-the-shelf software program stipulates the capability and scope of application, seldom is the buyer vulnerable to a misunderstanding. However, the same is not true of some of the other concerns a potential buyer should keep in mind.

The potential buyer of off-the-shelf software also needs to be concerned about software documentation, software "bugs," and software compatibility with other programs. Software documentation is essentially written instructions as to how to use the software, what the software does and does not do, what to do if there is a computer or software failure, instructions on how one might modify or expand the software (assuming this is possible), and instructions on how to contact the software supplier if there are problems. Some software vendors provide excellent software documentation while others essentially provide none. To a degree this is also true of computer hardware vendors.

Another concern of the potential off-the-shelf software buyer is referred to as computer "bugs." It is often stated in regard to software that "there never has been a software program that doesn't have a 'bug' in it somewhere." What this means is that there is something the user might do that can cause a major computer input or output error. For example, the incorrect hitting of one of the keys on the keyboard might cause a program to "hang-up" or loop. This may result in the user losing part or all of his previously input data.

Yet another concern relates to software compatibility with other software. Ideally, the software programs of a firm should be fully integrated. This means that to the extent possible, each and every program the firm has uses the same input data and data base. This eliminates the need for double entry of data and reduces the potential for errors when data is entered. One of the major advantages of the computer is that it enables a user to integrate various information systems of the firm. Therefore, programs that tend not to be integrated with other programs tend to be inefficient.

Obviously selecting a program is more than merely determining if the program performs a certain function. There is a difference between a program that works, and a program that works efficiently.

4: Writing Application Programs Using BASIC

INTRODUCTION

There are essentially three different approaches a constructor might take in utilizing computer software. They are as follows:

- Use purchased off-the-shelf software as designed
- Modify off-the-shelf or purchased software to meet the specific needs of the user
- Design and develop one's own software to meet the specific needs of the user

The advantage of the first option, purchasing and using software as designed and developed by another, eliminates the need to understand software programming or the cost associated with hiring a firm to develop the custom-designed software.

Many readers will want to modify software designed by another individual or design/develop their own construction industry software programs. With this in mind, this chapter will present the fundamentals of the high-level computer software language referred to as BASIC. BASIC is the most commonly used software language in use today. It is not only popular but also relatively easy to understand and learn.

This chapter assumes no prior knowledge of the BASIC language. However, the material provides the reader sufficient skills so that, upon completion of the chapter, he can write his own BASIC programs. In particular, those aspects of BASIC that are important in designing/developing construction industry software applications are presented.

BASIC: THE THREE IMPORTANT STEPS FOR
DESIGNING CONSTRUCTION INDUSTRY PROGRAMS

A computer can be essentially used in one of two ways: an *execution* mode or a *deferral* stage. A computer working in an execution mode is like a calculator. One puts in instructions or commands and the computer responds almost immediately. For example, the user might enter the following:

PRINT 9 + 4

and hit the return (enter) key on the computer. The computer screen or printer will almost immediately respond with the following:

13

This type of execution mode has limited applications to the individual using the computer for construction industry applications. While the computer can be used in this mode to add a series of numbers, this is not a high benefit/cost use of a computer. In addition, the computer, via the use of a written software program, can perform the same functions in the deferral mode.

The deferral mode of a computer is by far the most common use. In effect, the computer defers the running of an execution mode software program until the user executes or "runs" the program.

A deferral mode computer software program is written using *line numbers*. Each instruction or command that is part of the software program is preceded by a line number. For example, the following illustrates an instruction in a BASIC deferral mode program.

110 PRINT "LABOR COST"

The purpose of the line numbers in a software program is to give an order to the execution of the various software instructions and commands. By the use of line numbers, it is possible to have the execution of the program "jump back and forth" so that a program will operate efficiently and effectively. This will be illustrated later as we discuss subroutines and GOTO statements.

As we start our presentation of the fundamentals of BASIC, the reader should be forewarned that our presentation will differ somewhat from the presentation style in most of the how-to-learn BASIC programming books available in local bookstores. These books often start with a discussion of constants and variables and proceed to more advanced issues, culminating with a discussion of data files.

Given our interest in limiting our presentation to fundamentals and skills needed to write construction industry software, we will present BASIC fundamentals in the order the programmer is likely to confront them. In particular, we have divided our presentation into the following three categories.

- Strings
- Mathematical calculations
- Data files

NARRATIVE STATEMENTS AND STRINGS

We will start our short course in BASIC with a discussion of strings. A string is essentially a way of having the computer print on a screen or printer various narrative terms, sentences, and paragraphs. By using strings, the programmer can print statements for a program user on the computer monitor, print sentences or paragraphs, and format headings for various forms, including estimating spreadsheets.

Let us demonstrate the use of strings and the TAB instruction to write a small program to print an estimate spreadsheet. The program shown in Figure 4.1 utilizes several strings and uses the TAB instruction to space/align various spreadsheet headings. The running of this program will result in the report shown in Figure 4.2. Let us now discuss the program that yields this report.

The first line in the program introduces a BASIC statement we have not previously discussed. The statement CLS in line 100 is used to clear

```
90 KEY OFF
100 CLS
110 PRINT TAB(26);"ESTIMATE SPREADSHEET"
120 PRINT TAB(26);"ABC HOTEL PROJECT"
130 PRINT ""
140 PRINT "DESCRIPTION";
150 PRINT TAB(15);"LABOR COST";
160 PRINT TAB(27);"MATL. COST";
170 PRINT TAB(39);"SUBCONTR";
180 PRINT TAB(51);"TOTAL COST"
190 PRINT "-----------";
200 PRINT TAB(15);"-----------";
210 PRINT TAB(27);"-----------";
220 PRINT TAB(39);"-----------";
230 PRINT TAB(51);"-----------";
240 END
```

Figure 4.1 Using strings and the TAB instruction.

```
                        ESTIMATE SPREADSHEET
                        ABC HOTEL PROJECT

DESCRIPTION     LABOR COST   MATL. COST   SUBCONTR    TOTAL COST
-------------   ----------   ----------   ---------   ----------
```

Figure 4.2   Output from example program.

the monitor of any typing that was previously on the monitor before the execution of the CLS statement. The CLS statement enables the printing of the estimate spreadsheet at the top of the monitor. Some versions of BASIC use the CLS statement to do this while other versions use the instruction HOME.

The TAB statement in line 110 enables the printing of ESTIMATE SPREADSHEET in column 26. This is done to center the statement.

The PRINT statement followed by the two double quotes in line 130 results in the program placing a space (skips a line) in the spreadsheet. The programmer can use the PRINT " " one or more times to skip one or more lines in the printout.

The semicolons between the TABs and the terms in quotes in lines 110, 120, 150 through 180, and 200 through 230 are necessary in order for the computer to execute the TAB instruction and the printing of the term in quotes as two separate instructions. The semicolons at the end of lines 140 through 180 and 200 through 230 serve a different purpose. Without these semicolons, each of the terms in a quote in a line would be printed on a separate line. The placing of a semicolon at the end of each of these lines results in any narrative in the next instruction line to be printed on the same line.

Actually there are three different ways to control the printing of a string. Placing a semicolon after the string will force the next string or printout to be printed on the same line. If one placed a comma after a string instead of a semicolon, the next print statement would also print on the same line. However, the printing of the next print statement would be at a designated point on the monitor. Most versions of BASIC divide the monitor horizontally in four equal parts. When a comma follows a string, the next print statement is executed at the next quarter point on the screen. If the programmer uses neither a semicolon or a comma after a string, as noted before, the next print statement is executed on the following line.

The program illustrated in Figure 4.1 is completed with the BASIC statement END. The END statement informs the computer to end the execution of the program. While it is not required in that the execution would end at the last program statement anyway, the use of the END statement is considered good programming because it avoids the computer entering a never ending execution loop should the program be poorly written.

The narrative terms enclosed in the double quotes are referred to as *strings*. Actually, there is another way of writing the program statements such that the various strings would be printed. A string can be represented by a variable name by assigning it one or more letters followed by a dollar sign ($). For example, the following are acceptable BASIC variable names:

A$	B$
AA$	BC$
ABC$	ZX$

Let us illustrate one application of using a variable for our spreadsheet program. In the program in Figure 4.1 the dashed lines enclosed in quotes in lines 190, 200, 210, 220, and 230 were used to underline the labor, material, etc., headings. The number of dashes in each line matches the number of letters (and spaces) in the terms they underline.

Instead of underlining each letter and space, let us assume that we prefer that each underlining be of equal number of dashes, regardless of the term underlined. Let us assume each underline is to be 14 dashes long. In that case we could rewrite our previous estimate spreadsheet program as is shown in Figure 4.3.

The reader will note the new lines 105 and 190 and the elimination of lines 190 through 230 in the previous program. Actually, the fact that lines 190 through 230 have been condensed into one line, line 190, has nothing to do with using a variable to represent a string. In the old program lines 190 through 230 could have been combined by merely placing the tab instructions, then a semicolon, then a string, then a semicolon, then a tab

```
100 CLS
105 A$="--------------"
110 PRINT TAB(26);"ESTIMATE SPREADSHEET"
120 PRINT TAB(26);"ABC HOTEL PROJECT"
130 PRINT ""
140 PRINT "DESCRIPTION";
150 PRINT TAB(15);"LABOR COST";
160 PRINT TAB(31);"MATERIAL COST";
170 PRINT TAB(47);"SUBCONTRACT";
180 PRINT TAB(63);"TOTAL COST";
190 PRINT TAB(15);A$;TAB(31);A$;TAB(47);A$;TAB(63);A$
200 END
```

Figure 4.3   Use of variable instruction.

instruction, then a semicolon, etc., all on one line. However, given the requirement to type out each string, such an approach may prove awkward in that the program line would be very long. Nevertheless such an approach to condensing the various print statements could have been taken.

What is new in our estimate spreadsheet program is the use of lines 105 and 190. In line 105 we assign the string we will print several times to the variable A\$. Then, in line 190, instead of having to type out the 14 character string four times, we can merely instruct the computer to print the variable A\$ four times. This is a more convenient approach than printing the string several times. The execution of the program by the computer instruction RUN will yield the same estimate spreadsheet illustrated in Figure 4.2.

One other point about line 105 is noteworthy. Many manuals on BASIC programming would introduce the statement LET in line 105. Instead of line 105 being as it is, such a manual would use the following:

105 LET A\$ = "_____"

The LET statement tells the computer to "let" A\$ equal the string in the double quotes. Actually the LET instruction is not necessary. By writing the line as A\$ = "_____", the computer also assigns the string to variable A\$. In fact, the author has found very little use for the LET statement. For the most part, the reader can avoid its use.

There is a second and better use of strings and variable names in conjunction with one another. Let us illustrate this second use by means of expanding our estimate spreadsheet program.

Having successfully printed the estimate spreadsheet illustrated in Figure 4.2, let us now expand the program to allow the user to enter construction work item descriptions underneath the "description" heading. By work item we mean a piece or phase of the overall project. For example, concrete footings, concrete slabs, masonry walk, etc., might be example work item descriptions.

We would like to modify the previously described software program to enable a user of the program to print work item descriptions on the estimate spreadsheet. Once we have accomplished this, we can then discuss programming procedures that enable the user to enter dollar amounts for the labor, material, and subcontractor columns.

There are several programming approaches that one can use to print work item descriptions. While some are more efficient than others, let us illustrate an approach that uses strings and variables for strings.

Let us design the estimate spreadsheet program to enable the user to input and subsequently print three work item descriptions in the estimate spreadsheet program. The program to do this is shown in Figure 4.4.

```
90 KEY OFF
100 CLS
110 PRINT "ENTER YOUR FIRST WORK ITEM"
120 INPUT WI$
130 PRINT "ENTER YOUR SECOND WORK ITEM"
140 INPUT WK$
150 PRINT "ENTER YOUR THIRD WORK ITEM"
160 INPUT WJ$
170 REM TURN PRINTER OFF
180 CLS
190 A$="--------------"
200 PRINT TAB(26);"ESTIMATE SPREADSHEET"
210 PRINT TAB(26);"ABC HOTEL PROJECT"
220 PRINT ""
230 PRINT "DESCRIPTION";
240 PRINT TAB(15);"LABOR COST";
250 PRINT TAB(31);"MATL. COST";
260 PRINT TAB(47);"SUBCONTR.";
270 PRINT TAB(63);"TOTAL COST"
280 PRINT A$;TAB(15);A$;TAB(31);A$;TAB(47);A$;TAB(63);A$
290 PRINT WI$
300 PRINT WK$
310 PRINT WJ$
320 END
```

Figure 4.4 Program to input three work items.

The reader will observe that lines 110 through 160 are new lines added to the program. Line 110, a print instruction followed by a string, is used to instruct the user that he will be requested to input a work item name or description.

Line 120 introduces us to a commonly utilized BASIC instruction, the INPUT instruction. When the computer confronts this instruction when executing the computer program, it stops the execution and prints a blinking question mark or cursor (depending on the type of computer) on the video monitor. This question mark or cursor informs the user that the computer is awaiting input from the user. Because we have followed the INPUT instruction on line 120 with the WI$, the computer is awaiting a string to be input by the user. If the programmer had followed the INPUT instruction with the variable WI (leaving off the $ sign), then the computer would await a numerical input from the user.

When the user responds to the request for input via the INPUT instruction on line 120, the computer will assign the typed-in string to the variable WI$. For example, the user might type CONCRETE FOOTINGS when confronted with the request for input on line 120. Thereafter, any time the variable WI$ is used in the program, it will represent or equal CONCRETE FOOTINGS.

Lines 130 and 140 and lines 150 and 160 request and receive two more work item names or descriptions. It should be noted that many versions of BASIC will accept letters and numbers when a string variable such as WI$ is used. On the other hand the user is usually limited to inputting numbers when a nonnumeric variable such as WI is used.

The REM instruction following line 170 serves no real purpose when the program is run or executed. In fact, the computer ignores the instruction. The REM instruction, followed by a remark such as TURN PRINTER ON, is merely a way for the programmer to place some remarks within his program such that he or another user of the program can better understand the organization of the program itself.

The next set of new lines in our program illustrated in Figure 4.4 are lines 290, 300, and 310. Each of these lines prints the work item descriptions that were entered when the INPUT instruction was encountered in lines 120, 140, and 160. For example, if CONCRETE FOOTINGS was entered as a response to the INPUT instruction in line 120, the variable WI$ was assigned to the string and subsequently printed when WI$ followed the PRINT instruction in line 290.

The reader should note that unlike the programming for printing a string, the variable WI$ is not enclosed in double quotations in line 290. A variable, numerical or nonnumerical, is not enclosed in double quotes when used with an INPUT or PRINT instruction.

The running of the program illustrated in Figure 4.4 yields the printout shown in Figure 4.5. The three work item descriptions shown were assumed to be entered in response to the INPUT instructions in lines 120, 140, and 160.

The reader should observe one serious constraint to the program illustrated in Figure 4.4. The program limits the user to inputting and

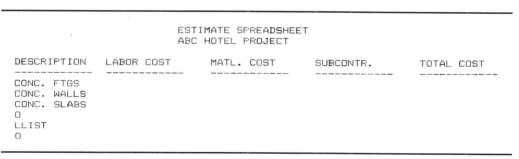

Figure 4.5   Output of example program.

subsequently printing three work items. Naturally, we could program additional PRINT and INPUT lines to enable more variables. However, this would require two or three additional lines for work items. Even more importantly, what if the user wanted to input and print more or less work items than requested by the program?

Our apparent dilemma can be eliminated by the use of a few new BASIC instructions: the FOR (along with the NEXT instruction), IF, and DIM instructions. What we do is create a "loop" in the program to input work items, check to see if the user wants to exit the loop by indicating he does not want to add more work items, and then he does print the work items and terminates the program.

We will now modify one estimate spreadsheet program to do this. The modified program is illustrated in Figure 4.6.

There are several new lines (and some we have deleted) in the new program illustrated in Figure 4.6. While the first new line is line 105, let us first describe the programming loop we have created via lines 110 through 200. This is the loop that enables us to enter a varying number of work items.

Line 110 starts the loop. The BASIC instruction FOR is used on this line. By using the FOR instruction followed by a counter (in this case 1 to 50), we perform each programming instruction up through the line with

```
100 CLS
105 DIM W$(50)
110 FOR N=1 TO 50
120 PRINT "ENTER WORK ITEM NUMBER";N
130 INPUT W$(N)
140 CLS
150 PRINT "DO YOU WANT TO ENTER ANOTHER WORK ITEM ?"
160 PRINT "ANSWER YES OR NO"
170 INPUT B$
180 IF (B$="NO") THEN 210
190 CLS
200 NEXT N
210 A$="--------------"
220 PRINT TAB(26);"ESTIMATE SPREADSHEET"
230 PRINT TAB(26);"ABC HOTEL PROJECT"
240 PRINT ""
250 PRINT "DESCRIPTION";
260 PRINT TAB(15);"LABOR COST";
270 PRINT TAB(31);"MATERIAL COST";
280 PRINT TAB(47);"SUBCONTR.";
290 PRINT TAB(63);"TOTAL COST"
300 PRINT A$;TAB(15);A$;TAB(31);A$;TAB(47);A$;TAB(63);A$
310 FOR M=1 TO N
320 PRINT W$(M)
330 NEXT M
340 END
```

Figure 4.6 Program to enable variable amount of data input.

the instruction NEXT (in this case through line 200) numerous times. In the program in Figure 4.6 we have put an upper ceiling on the number of times of 50. In other words the user could enter (and subsequently print) up to 50 work items with the program.

Each time the loop (starting in line 110 and ending with line 200) is executed, the variable N defined in the FOR instruction increases in value by 1. Each time the loop starts in line 120, the PRINT instruction would be executed. Note that the PRINT instruction in line 120 is followed by a string, a semicolon, and the variable N. The value of N in line 120 would increment by one each time the loop is performed.

Line 130 introduces the concept of an array. An array variable, the W$ (N), allows the programmer to designate a collection of data values or strings with a single variable name. One might view an array as a group of empty location cells, each cell capable of holding a data or string entry. In our case we would like to have the capability to input as many as 50 work item name strings. In other words we would like to set aside or reserve as many as 50 "empty cells." This is accomplished by using the DIM instruction in line 105. A DIM instruction tells the computer how much memory or "cells" should be set aside for an array. In our case, by using line 105, we inform the computer that we will be using an array named W$ (the dollar sign meaning we will input strings), and that the computer should set aside 50 memory locations or cells for the array.

Let us now return to our loop and line 130 in particular. The INPUT instruction, like our INPUT instructions in the previous program in Figure 4.4, stops the program and requires the user to input a work item. The N in the brackets following the array name W$ in line 130 identifies the specific array location for each entered work item. In effect, each location can be viewed as a separate variable, W$ (1), W$ (2), W$ (3), etc.; the value of N being incremented each time the loop is executed. After each work item name is entered in line 130, the CLS instruction in line 140 is used to clear the screen.

Lines 150 through 180 introduce yet another BASIC programming concept referred to as an IF instruction or a conditional operation. An IF instruction enables the programmer to instruct the program to carry out different options depending on the value of an inputted variable.

We would like to enable the user to enter as many work items (actually any number from 1 to 50) as he chooses. We can do this by asking the user (with the two PRINT instructions and strings in lines 150 and 160) if he wants to enter another work item. When confronted with the blinking cursor caused by the INPUT instruction in line 170, the user would enter YES or NO. This line is followed by the IF instruction in line 180. The IF instruction "tests" the inputted variable, B$, against the string in the double quotes in line 180 and if the variable is the same as the string, the program proceeds to the line number following the THEN instruction in line 180. Each IF instruction is accompanied by a THEN instruction that directs the program to a line number.

If the value of the variable in the IF instruction does not equal the string in the double quotes, the program execution proceeds to the next line in the program, in this case line 190. For example, if the user responds to the YES/NO question by inputting YES for the variable B$, the program proceeds to line 190 and clears the screen. Upon encountering line 200, a NEXT instruction, the program returns to line 110 to increment to the next value of N. This continues until the 50th loop occurs, at which time the program proceeds to line 210 when it encounters the NEXT instruction.

Note what happens if B$ is equal to NO. When this is confirmed by the IF instruction in line 180, the program jumps to line 210. In effect, the program leaves the loop, and N has a value equal to the last incremented loop. The program then proceeds to print the estimate spreadsheet headings as instructed via lines 210 through 300.

Line 310 starts yet another loop, the print loop. We would now like to print all the work items previously inputted. How can the program know how many to print? This is accomplished by the fact that we know that N (the counter in the previous loop) has a value equal to the number of work items regardless of whether or not we entered all 50 work items. Given this fact, we can now start another loop in line 310 by using another loop counter variable, say M, and increment by 1 up to and including N.

Each loop executes the PRINT instruction in line 320 such that each location or cell of the W$ array is now printed. In this manner each and every work item is printed on a line. The loop continues via the NEXT instruction in line 330 until M equals N at which time the loop is complete and the program ends.

The FOR and IF instructions provide the programmer many options that streamline programs and enable conditional options to be performed. In more sophisticated programs, a programmer might include several FOR statements within one another, called nested loops.

There is another way of programming the YES/NO option in lines 170 through 210. Let us assume that for some reason we tested the variable B$ against the string "YES" instead of "NO". In that case we want the loop to continue if the variable equals YES but jump out or leave the loop if it equals NO.

In that case lines 170 through 210 can be changed as follows:

```
170      INPUT B$
180      IF (B$ = "YES") THEN 190
185      GOTO 210
190      CLS
200      NEXT N
REM:     TURN PRINTER ON
210      A$ = "_____"
```

Note that we have introduced another BASIC instruction, the GOTO instruction. When this instruction is encountered, the program execution proceeds to the line number following the GOTO instruction.

The reason we have used the GOTO instruction in the above programming relates to the fact that we tested against "YES" instead of the previous NO. If B$ equals "YES", we want to continue the loop and as such we jump to 190, execute the clear screen instruction, and reiterate via the NEXT instruction. On the other hand, if the variable B$ is not equal to YES (and in particular is NO), we want to jump out of the loop. However, the fact that B$ does not equal YES results in the program proceeding to the next line, line 185. In order to prevent the loop from continuing, the GOTO instruction then directs the program execution outside the loop, and in particular to line 210.

While the GOTO instruction is not necessary for the pertinent spreadsheet program as illustrated in Figure 4.6, the instruction is frequently used in many programs. It may or may not be used in conjunction with an IF instruction.

We now have completed our discussion of strings. As part of our discussion we have introduced several commonly used BASIC instructions that include PRINT, IF, FOR, CLS, NEXT, INPUT, and GOTO instructions. We will now proceed to discuss the performing of mathematical calculations using BASIC so that we can expand our estimate spreadsheet program.

MATHEMATICAL CALCULATIONS

Perhaps the most beneficial applications of the computer for the constructor is in the computer's ability to store, calculate, and process mathematical calculations quickly and accurately. While we have observed how the computer can print various strings, which include estimating spreadsheet headings, this application is more of a necessity to support mathematical applications.

A computer can essentially do three things better than an individual: it can store more data via a large memory; it can process information, including mathematical calculations, very rapidly; and it tends to make few if any errors when carrying out calculations. These are three desirable attributes in regard to construction industry computer applications.

Programming mathematical calculations using BASIC is made simple by the fact that BASIC instructions used to perform calculations are very similar to those used when performing math calculations manually. For example, if one wants to add numbers using BASIC, one uses the BASIC instruction " + ". Similarly, the " − ", " * ", and " / " symbols are used in BASIC for subtracting, multiplying, and dividing numbers, respectively. Even though they are not commonly used in construction industry applications, mathematical calculations such as squaring numbers, taking square roots, and performing trigonometric calculations are also easy to program using BASIC.

Perhaps the only difficulty in performing mathematical calculations using BASIC relates to the formatting of numbers and the treatment of significant figures. For example, if one multiplies two numbers such as 243.33 times 342.34, one obtains a result equal to 83301.5922. If this is a mathematical calculation involving dollars and cents, we would like the computer to print the result as $83,301.59. However, the computer may not know to insert the "$", the ",", and round off the "22" in the decimal term .5922.

Similarly, when one adds two dollars and cents numbers such as 349.26 and 246.54 using BASIC, one might obtain the result as 595.8. The computer may not print the zero that results as the right-most digit when it adds the numbers. When the computer then prints the number without the zero, the printout may appear awkward and may in fact result in a staggered column of numbers.

The "housekeeping" problem of formatting numbers to yield a report that prints numbers in a dollar and cent format depends on the version of BASIC the programmer is using. As was noted earlier in this chapter, various versions of BASIC have a few minor differences in regard to available instructions. In some versions the programmer can use a BASIC instruction, PRINT USING, that enables the programmer to format printed numbers using the single instruction. On the other hand versions of BASIC that do not include this instruction require the user to program a more complex set of instructions to ensure desired printing results. BASIC instructions such as MID, STR, and UN are required. We will now demonstrate the two different approaches to formatting printed number results and the programming of mathematical calculations by returning to and expanding our estimate spreadsheet example.

The reader will remember that we wrote a program to place the headings on an estimate spreadsheet. In particular, in Figure 4.4 we wrote a program that allows the user to place the project heading at the top of a printout, print a description line, and enable the entry of a variable number of work item names.

We now want to expand the program to allow the user to input labor and material costs for each work item and have the program run them. The inputting of the labor and material costs causes us no new problem. We simply need to code some BASIC instructions similar to the program segment for inputting the work items.

Let us look at the program illustrated in Figure 4.7. The reader will note that we have only illustrated the program segment that inputs information. We will illustrate the print segment later. Program lines 230 through 260 enable the entry of the labor and material amounts for each work item. The input variables LA( ) and MA( ) do not include the $ symbol following the variable name. The omission of the $ symbol indicates that the program is requesting a numeric input. Remember that the inclusion of a $ symbol indicates the inputting of a string; i.e., nonnumerics. When BASIC awaits a numeric value such as the INPUT LA(N), the program indicates an error if anything but a numeric is input.

Line 270 in the program illustrated in Figure 4.7 adds the inputted labor cost and material cost for a work item and assigns the sum to the variable TOT(N). This program instruction eliminates the need for the user to have to input the sum himself. A good computer software program

```
100 CLS
110 PRINT "ENTER PROJECT NAME"
120 INPUT NA$
130 PRINT "ENTER PROJECT LOCATION
140 INPUT LA$
150 CLS
200 FOR N=1 TO 50
210 PRINT "ENTER WORK ITEM NAME ";N
220 INPUT W#(N)
230 PRINT "ENTER LABOR AMOUNT"
240 INPUT LA(N)
250 PRINT "ENTER MATERIAL AMOUNT"
260 INPUT MA(N)
270 TA(N)=LA(N)+MA(N)
280 PRINT "DO YOU WANT TO ENTER ANOTHER
290 PRINT "ANSWER YES OR NO
300 INPUT B$
310 IF (B$="N") THEN 400
320 CLS
330 NEXT N
400 REM STARTS PRINT OPTION
410 PRINT "THIS IS THE END OF THE PROGRAM
420 END
```

Figure 4.7 Program to enable entry of labor and material amounts.

should not require the user to input a value or make a calculation himself if the program can do it instead.

The program segment from lines 280 through 320 in Figure 4.7 is the exit option we had in the previous program in Figure 4.6. This exit option enables the user to enter less than the maximum number of work items if he so chooses.

Having completed the input of work item names, labor dollar amount, and material dollar amount, we could proceed to print these on an estimate spreadsheet. However, we would only be able to print the total cost (labor plus material cost) for each work item. It would also be desirable to be able to print the total labor cost and total material cost for all the work items plus the total cost for all the work items. In other words we would like to sum the columns in our spreadsheet programs as well as the rows (work items).

In order to modify the program illustrated in Figure 4.7 to enable the summing of the columns, we will have to introduce a "counter" variable. Let us assume we introduce new variables, LAT, MAT, and TAT, each of which will be the sum of the labor, material, and total columns, respectively. Let us illustrate the programming technique of a counter via the modified program in Figure 4.8.

```
100 CLS
110 PRINT "ENTER PROJECT NAME
120 INPUT NA$
130 PRINT "ENTER PROJECT LOCATION
140 INPUT LA$
150 CLS
191 LAT=0
192 MAT=0
193 TAT=0
200 FOR N=1 TO 50
210 PRINT "ENTER WORK ITEM NAME ";N
220 INPUT W$(N)
230 PRINT "ENTER LABOR AMOUNT "
240 INPUT LA(N)
250 PRINT "ENTER MATERIAL AMOUNT"
260 INPUT MA(N)
270 TA(N)=LA(N)+MA(N)
275 LAT=LAT +LA(N)
276 MAT=MAT + MA(N)
277 TAT=TAT + TA(N)
280 PRINT "DO YOU WANT TO ENTER ANOTHER WORK ITEM
290 PRINT "ANSWER YES OR NO
300 INPUT B$
310 IF (B$="NO") THEN 400
320 CLS
330 NEXT N
400 REM STARTS PRINT ROUTINE
410 PRINT "THIS IS THE END OF THIS PROGRAM
420 END
```

Figure 4.8 Modified program to add columns of numbers.

The totaling of the labor, material, and total columns is performed by lines 275 through 277 in the program illustrated in Figure 4.7. Each time the program loop from line 200 to line 340 is executed, the last inputted work item labor cost, material cost, and sum of labor and material cost is added to the variables LAT, MAT, and TAT, respectively. For example, in line 275, the labor cost for each work item is accumulated to the variable LAT by adding each value of LA(N).

The reader will observe an unfamiliar bit of mathematics in lines 275 through 277. In these lines a variable is set equal to itself. For example, in line 275, LAT is set equal to LAT plus LA(N). The variable LAT is on both sides of the equation. This is what we might refer to as a "counter." What happens is that each time such a programming line is executed, the variable is set equal to its value the last time the line was executed plus the new inputted variable. For example, each time the loop in Figure 4.8 is executed, the value of LAT is set equal to its value the last time through the loop plus the new inputted work item labor cost. When the user terminates the loop, the value of LAT will equal the sum of all the inputted work item labor costs.

There is one problem associated with letting a variable such as LAT equal the last inputted value of itself. The first time the loop is executed, the value of the variable (e.g., LAT) on the right side of the equation has no previously assigned value. This problem is eliminated by initializing the counter variables to zero. This is done in lines 191 through 193 in the program illustrated in Figure 4.8. Note that it is necessary to initialize the counter variables outside of the loop. If this initializing is performed within the loop, the counter variables would be "turned back" to zero each time the loop is executed.

The input loop and mathematics of our estimating spreadsheet program is now complete. We will now turn our attention to the printing of the input information. We will illustrate the formatting of output in this program segment.

Having inputted the estimating spreadsheet information, we can now have the program print the information we previously outlined. Note that we would want to defer the printing of the output until we have inputted all of the input information, otherwise we would clutter the monitor or hard-copy printout with mixed input and output information.

The revised estimate spreadsheet program, which includes the input program segment and the output print segment, is illustrated in Figure 4.9. The printing of the headings and project name and location is performed via program lines 400 through 470. This program segment was described previously in this chapter.

```
100 CLS
110 PRINT "ENTER PROJECT NAME
120 INPUT NA$
130 PRINT "ENTER PROJECT LOCATION
140 INPUT LA$
150 CLS
191 LAT=0
192 MAT=0
193 TAT=0
200 FOR N=1 TO 50
210 PRINT "ENTER WORK ITEM NAME ";N
220 INPUT W$(N)
230 PRINT "ENTER LABOR AMOUNT "
240 INPUT LA(N)
250 PRINT "ENTER MATERIAL AMOUNT"
260 INPUT MA(N)
270 TA(N)=LA(N)+MA(N)
275 LAT=LAT +LA(N)
276 MAT=MAT + MA(N)
277 TAT=TAT + TA(N)
280 PRINT "DO YOU WANT TO ENTER ANOTHER WORK ITEM
290 PRINT "ANSWER YES OR NO
300 INPUT B$
310 IF (B$="NO") THEN 400
320 CLS
330 NEXT N
400 CLS
405 F$="$$#####,####.##"
410 PRINT TAB(32);NA$
420 PRINT TAB(32);LA$
430 PRINT ""
440 PRINT "WORK ITEM DESC.";TAB(20);"LABOR $";TAB(40);"MATERIAL $";TAB(60);"TOTA
L $"
450 PRINT "---------------";TAB(20);"---------------";TAB(40);"---------------";
TAB(60);"---------------"
460 FOR K= 1 TO N
470 PRINT W$(K);
475 PRINT TAB(20);
480 PRINT USING F$;LA(K);
485 PRINT TAB(40);
490 PRINT USING F$;MA(K);
495 PRINT TAB(60);
500 PRINT USING F$;TA(K)
510 NEXT K
520 PRINT "---------------";TAB(20);"---------------";TAB(40);"---------------";
TAB(60);"---------------"
530 PRINT "TOTALS";TAB(20);
540 PRINT USING F$;LAT;
545 PRINT TAB(40);
550 PRINT USING F$;MAT;
555 PRINT TAB(60);
560 PRINT USING F$;TAT
```

Figure 4.9 The completed spreadsheet program.

The printing of the inputted work item names, dollar amounts, and summed totals is performed via the program loop from lines 460 through 560. The reader will note the introduction of new program instructions in lines 405 through 560.

Line 405 is used to control the formatting of printed dollar amounts on the estimate spreadsheet. This format instruction along with the PRINT USING commands in lines 480, 490, etc., enable the program to align numbers vertically in a column, including lining up the decimal point, inserting commas where appropriate, and inserting the $ symbol in front of the printed numbers.

The format variable in line 405 in Figure 4.9 and the PRINT USING instruction are not available in all versions of BASIC. Without these instructions, the formatting of a column of numbers is somewhat difficult and requires a somewhat complex programming routine. We will not describe such a routine.

When the PRINT USING instruction is available, the formatting of numbers is relatively simple. The instruction and variable, FA$, in line 405 indicate that each time a number is printed in the program it will be printed with a $ in front of the number (the double $ does this), commas will be inserted by the program (every three spaces to the left of the decimal point), and two numbers (cents) will be printed to the right of the decimal. The comma that is part of the string in line 405 tells the program and computer to insert commas every three places to the left of the decimal. Actually the comma in line 405 could be placed anywhere in the string to the left of the decimal. The # symbols shown in the string merely indicate that numbers are to be printed in these locations.

The PRINT USING instruction in line 510 is followed by the string variable FA$. This variable is used in line 500 to identify the desired print format. The FA$ in line 510 is followed by a semicolon and the variable name [LA(M)] that is to be printed.

Once the print loop is complete, the program continues to lines 570 through 630. Here the program prints the value of the counter variables that have been used to sum the labor, material, and total columns. Assuming the data shown in Figure 4.10 is input to the program illustrated in Figure 4.9, the program prints the output illustrated in Figure 4.10.

One might view the BASIC estimating spreadsheet program illustrated in Figure 4.9 as complete. For the most part, it is complete. However, an improved one would address two additional issues: the handling of erroneous input and the possible saving/storing of the program input via data files. Let us address each of these issues independently.

The user of the estimating spreadsheet program would encounter no problems if in fact he inputted what the program requested. However, any time a program segment uses an INPUT instruction, and thereby requires the user to input data, a potential program execution problem arises. What if the user inputs something other than requested? The user runs the risk

```
                          OFFICE BUILDING
                          PEORIA ILLINOIS

WORK ITEM DESC.    LABOR $             MATERIAL $          TOTAL $
----------------   -----------------   -----------------   -----------------
WALL FTGS            $34,534.00          $34,755.00          $69,289.00
PAD FOOTINGS         $93,434.00          $34,232.00         $127,666.00
WALLS                $94,594.00          $34,343.00         $128,937.00
BEAMS                $93,434.00          $34,232.00         $127,666.00
SLABS                $34,343.00           $9,343.00          $43,686.00
KEYWAY                $3,434.00           $5,454.00           $8,888.00
----------------   -----------------   -----------------   -----------------
TOTALS              $353,773.00         $152,359.00         $506,132.00
0
```

Figure 4.10 Output from program using example data.

of the program hitting a noncorrectable error routine message. A well-designed software program contains many error prevention routines to prevent a program from "bombing out" upon the input of erroneous input or unwanted input.

Let us consider the program segment in lines 280 through 330 in the program illustrated in Figure 4.9. This program segment is used to determine if the user wants to enter another work item; he is supposed to enter YES or NO to the question. If he enters YES, the program proceeds to the NEXT instruction, which in turn returns execution to the next iteration of the loop, i.e., line 200. On the other hand, if the user responds NO, the program execution branches to the print segment.

What if the user mistakenly inputs something other than YES or NO? For example, he might mistakenly input MO for a NO. The way our program is written (Figure 4.9), the program would incorrectly proceed to the NEXT instruction and start another loop.

An improved program would inform the user of his incorrect data entry and enable him to reenter the requested YES or NO. This program modification is relatively simple to do. After line 310 in Figure 4.9, we could add the following "error-routine" lines.

```
311   IF (B$ = "YES") THEN 330
312   CLS
313   PRINT "YOU HAVE MADE AN INPUT ERROR,
              YOU MUST ENTER YES or NO"
314   PRINT " "
315   GOTO 290
```

If the user mistakenly entered an MO, the program would not respond to the IF instructions and clear the monitor in line 312. Line 313 would inform the user of his erroneous data entry, and after skipping a line, use the GOTO instruction in line 315 to branch back to the question in line 290. The user would then have a second chance to input the YES or NO. The error routine would continue to be executed until the user finally input a YES or NO.

Error routines such as the one illustrated are a necessary part of a well-designed software program. A software program developer should always assume that the user might mistakenly enter an incorrect response to an INPUT request.

There are other error routines the program designer would likely want to be attentive to in designing a program. Owing to the fact that several of these routines are complex and somewhat unique to a specific type of hardware, we will limit our discussion of error routines to the above discussion. Perhaps one other point about our estimating spreadsheet program should be noted before completing our fundamental overview of programming with the BASIC language. Should we input data to our spreadsheet program illustrated in Figure 4.9, run the program, and then turn the computer off, our inputted data (including the work item names, labor costs, and material costs) would be lost. They would not be retained in the computer memory or on our program disk. This would prove very detrimental if we would subsequently want to access or reuse the input data.

DATA FILES

If we want to retain or store the program input (as we often would in construction industry applications), it is necessary to introduce what is referred to as *data files*. Data files provide the user with a means of storing data on diskettes or a hard disk.

Software program instructions using BASIC vary depending on what type of computer the user is operating. In addition, many computers can be programmed to handle random-access or sequential data files. Owing in part to the fact that the programming of data files is somewhat unique to each and every type of computer, and also to the fact that the programming for data files is rather complex, we will not go into an exhaustive discussion of data files here. However, let us illustrate the programming required for an unnamed example computer system.

We will limit our discussion of data files to the storing of the work item names entered in the program in Figure 4.9. The reader will remember that the program input routine counts the number of work items entered, i.e., the value of N would correspond to the number of entered work items.

A program segment to put the entered work item names onto a data file on a data disk is illustrated below. We have omitted the program line numbers in illustrating the program segment.

```
OPEN "NAMES" as    $1, LEN = 30
FOR K = 1 TO N
FIELD #1, NA$(K) = 30
NA$(N) = WI$(K)
PUT#1, K
NEXT K
CLOSE #1
```

Owing to the fact that the program segment shown is somewhat "machine" dependent, we will not go into detail as to the explanation of each line. However, the OPEN instruction "opens" a file #1 for input. The LEN instruction sets aside 30 spaces for the name of the work item (the 30 is assigned by the programmer; it could be 20 or 40 as well).

Inside the loop (the K loop), the FIELD instruction identifies the variable name that is to be stored; in this case NA$(K) is set equal to the previously inputted work item names represented by WI$(K).

The PUT instruction "puts" the work item onto a record on the data file disk. In particular the first work item name is stored in record 1 (i.e., K = 1), the second in record 2, etc. Finally, after inputting all the work item names, the previously open file is closed with the CLOSE instruction.

Once a data file is created, the stored data can be recovered by the program itself. This would be accomplished by again opening the data file with an OPEN instruction, identifying the FIELD, and then getting the data via a GET#1,K instruction instead of the previously discussed PUT instruction. The file would again be closed with a CLOSE instruction.

Once the inputted data file data is "read" by the program, the data can be used by the programmer, updated, or again stored.

Computer or versions of BASIC that do not have data file capabilities severely limit the use of a computer for construction industry applications. Almost all useful construction industry software applications would require the use of data files.

We have now completed our somewhat overview presentation of BASIC fundamentals. Actually we have done more than give an overview of BASIC. The knowledge and use of the instructions discussed in this chapter give the user the capability to design and write relatively complex programs should he have this objective.

5: Computer Applications— An Overview

INTRODUCTION

Applications of computers to the construction industry are likely to continue to evolve as computer technology continues to develop and the industry increases its sophistication in regard to data collection and management techniques. Nonetheless, the industry is already using the computer for a wide range of applications.

Some computer applications offer the construction industry a higher benefit/cost ratio than others. With the objective of identifying the many present-day applications of computers to the construction industry and also discussing the benefit/cost ratio of each application, this chapter will identify a wide assortment of applications. We will not give details of each application or illustrate any computer software programs for individual applications. This will be done in individual computer application chapters that follow this chapter.

USING THE COMPUTER AS A CALCULATOR

The management of a construction firm or construction project entails the performing of many numerical calculations. This fact, along with the fact that a computer is a fast and accurate number processor, results in numerous applications of the computer relevant to collection and processing of data. Listed below are a few different applications of using a computer as an efficient calculator for construction industry applications (note: the list is by no means all-inclusive).

1. Performance of mathematical formulas to convert estimating take-offs.
2. Performance of "engineering"-type formulas that are part of design or contracting calculations.
3. Extending and crossfooting mathematical calculations that are part of accounting or estimating.
4. Calculations relevant to the preparation of billing requests.
5. Performing mathematical calculations to support management tools or formulas to aid the firm in decision making.

We will now illustrate examples of each of the above-identified "calculator" applications.

Construction firms have programmed their computers to perform a wide number of estimating takeoff formulas that enable them to determine a quantity amount for a defined type of work. For example, let us assume that a construction firm is confronted with calculating the cubic yards of concrete in many rectangular-type sections that include walls, beams, etc., as part of their estimating function. Given the need to perform such a calculation many times, it may be advantageous to write a small computer software routine that transforms the takeoff of linear dimensions given in feet into a cubic yard calculation. Such a small software program written in BASIC is illustrated in Chapter 9. Example input and the resulting software program output are also illustrated.

The number of similar types of estimating conversion programs is extensive. Each type of firm, including the general contractor, plumbing contractor, and homebuilding contractor, has specific application needs when it comes to takeoff calculation transformations.

Another efficient use of a computer as a calculator relates to "engineering"-type calculations. For example, a construction firm that performs concrete work may have a requirement to design its concrete forming system for supporting the concrete work as it is cast in place.

Concrete forming systems have to be designed as structural members to enable them to structurally "hold" the cast-in-place concrete. Form design entails the use of various structural-engineering-type formulas, including formulas to determine the forces and stresses in the members. For example, the stress in a member may be calculated as the force or weight on a member (expressed in pounds) divided by the cross-sectional area.

Similarly, engineering-type formulas are needed to determine the reenforcing needed in a concrete member to resist the imposed loads on the member, to determine the size of steel members, or the quantity of cut-and-fill-type excavation work. Any of these calculations are easy to program as part of a computer software program.

Given the vast number of mathematical calculations, including the adding of a long list of numbers, it is easy to understand why construction firms, on occasion, have made mathematical errors in their calculations. Company personnel may spend numerous inefficient hours attempting to find a math error in an accounting ledger or perhaps an estimating spreadsheet.

The use of a computer as a device for adding and subtracting numbers, and most importantly as a device for "double-checking" the calculations, can alleviate headaches and risk for the construction firm.

The reader might refer back to our estimating spreadsheet program illustrated in Chapter 4. In particular, let us refer to the final version of the program illustrated in Figure 4.9. In this program we had the computer add the labor cost and material cost for each entered work item and in turn print the total in a total column. Similarly, we designed the program to add the entered labor amount entrys as a column and the entered material amounts as a column. These two totals (labor and material) were then added to yield a total dollar amount for the project in question.

The way we performed the calculations internal to the program leaves little or no potential for a math error. Nonetheless, we could make a slight program modification to enable us to check that the "total cost" for the project is correct. This "check" could be made by determining the total in two independent ways. For one we could have the program add the total labor amount and the total material amount. We could also program the computer to add all the totals in the total column to yield a total cost for the project. The two independently calculated totals could then be compared via the computer to ensure that the mathematics was performed correctly. This process is often referred to as *crossfooting* numbers. These types of crossfooting checks are easy to program and are a convenient and efficient means of performing many accounting as well as estimating calculations.

Another calculator application previously identified was that of making routine billing request calculations. Construction contractors are often required to submit their payment billing requests according to a defined billing format set out by the project owner. The process of performing this takes time and may be tedious owing to the relatively long list of "billable" items. In addition, when performed manually, there is the possibility for the contractor to make embarrassing and sometimes detrimental calculation errors.

Given a defined billing format, it is relatively easy to write a software program to make the necessary calculations and print out the payment billing request.

Effective management of a construction firm or project is often dependent on timely decision making. There are many management tools, algorithms, or formulas available to the construction firm to enable it to make timely and optimal management decisions. Management tools (algorithms that include breakeven analysis formulas, overhead allocation formulas, and linear optimization models) are all useful and relative to the construction firm.

The construction firm sometimes has argued against the use of these management-type tools based on the fact that the mathematical calculations that are part of the individual techniques/algorithms may be time consuming and cumbersome. The use of a computer in great part alleviates these concerns.

A good example of how the computer can make a management tool/ technique available and efficient for the construction firm is the performance of a planning and scheduling technique, one of the more popular being the critical-path method (CPM). Contractors have sometimes argued against CPM based on their conception of the benefits of the technique relative to the many hours required to perform the mathematical calculations that are part of CPM.

It is relatively easy to program CPM calculations for computer processing. An example of such a computer software program is illustrated and described in Chapter 11. Using the computer to perform CPM calculations is just one example of how a computer can "bring good management tools/ techniques to the construction firm."

The above discussion of the computer as a calculator tool for construction industry applications is by no means an all-inclusive list. There are many more similar applications. Independent of how many similar applications one might list, the author does not feel that the use of the computer as a calculator-type machine is one of the more advantageous applications of a computer from a benefit/cost standpoint. In reality, one could perform similar applications via the use of an inexpensive hand-held calculator. Nonetheless, if one views the calculator-type applications as a fringe to the more advantageous applications (to be identifed in following chapters), then these calculator-type applications are another argument in favor of using a computer in the construction industry.

USING THE COMPUTER AS A GRAPHICS TOOL

Perhaps one of the most "glamorous" applications of the computer relates to its use as a graphics tool. Computers can and have been programmed to both prepare and "read" drawings. This application of computers, while indeed impressive to the layman, may not be as practical as one might think relative to the construction industry.

Given the graphics capability of a computer, one of the more obvious applications one might think of is using the computer to read the construction drawings (blueprints) to actually perform the quantity takeoff function. Given the many hours a contractor expends performing the takeoff function, this reading of the construction drawings to determine takeoff quantities would appear to be a high-benefit computer application.

It is in fact possible to program a computer, via the use of a graphics pen, to actually read the construction drawings and determine quantities. However, at the present time, there are two major problems relevant to making this a cost-effective application of computers to the construction industry. For one, given any degree of construction project complexity, the computer software program that needs to be programmed to read the vast amounts of different types of materials and work items that would be included on a single set of construction drawings would be extremely complex and long.

The end result would be that it would take literally thousands of hours to develop a flexible software program to read even relatively simple construction drawings. Perhaps even more importantly, the size and complexity of such software programs would require the use of relatively large computers with extensive computer memory capacity. Such a computer is relatively expensive; a computer that may be outside the reach of the average-sized contractor.

A second difficulty of developing or applying a computer software program to read costruction drawings relates to the wide range of variation in the symbols and style various project designers use in preparing construction drawings. One might argue that no two architects prepare construction drawings using the exact same symbols or style. The end result is that it is difficult, if not impossible, to develop a computer software program that would successfully be able to read each and every set of construction drawings prepared by the many project designers that prepare drawings.

It is true that there have been software programs developed that read relatively simple drawings, e.g., highway and bridge structures. However, these types of structures are relatively simple in terms of the number of materials that are part of the design. Even for these relatively simple drawings, the cost of a computer software program to read the drawing takeoff quantities may be prohibitive relative to the time savings.

The end result is that the author does not foresee in the immediate future an extensive application of computers to actually read the drawings. Perhaps his view will change as computer technology continues to change and become more sophisticated. However, even if this happens, given the importance a contractor associates with the quantities takeoff function, many contractors would double-check the computerized quantity takeoff via a manual takeoff anyway.

While the use of the computer as a graphics tool to read the drawings has not, and may not, gain widespread popularity, the use of a computer to actually prepare a design and an accompanying set of drawings has been a highly viable application. Most computer-aided design (CAD) has evolved in the manufacturing industries. For example, via the use of a computer and appropriate computer software, an automobile designer prepares futuristic car designs that minimize wind resistance, maximize fuel economy, etc. CAD is a fast growing application of computers.

While most CAD applications have been limited to the preparation of manufacturing-industry-type applications, some project designers (architects) have taken to the use of a computer to prepare construction drawings. It is not difficult to foresee the day when the majority, if not all, construction drawings are prepared via a computer and a graphics pen.

Perhaps one of the advantages of using a computer for CAD is that it results in more uniform sets of construction drawings in that several designers would utilize the same CAD software program. If this trend continues, then perhaps one of the concerns about using the computer as a tool for reading drawings will diminish. In particular, the more the trend continues toward a CAD uniform set of construction drawings, the easier and more cost-effective it becomes to use the computer to read a set of drawings to determine the quantity takeoff quantities. However, we are years away, if it indeed ever happens, from witnessing the use of a computer as a tool to read drawings. While capable to do the task, the low benefit/cost ratio of the application may limit its usefulness.

APPLICATIONS OF DATA MANAGEMENT PROGRAMMING

Whereas we have indicated that the use of computers relative to calculator- and graphic-type applications may offer the construction industry only marginal benefits, the same is not true regarding the use of the computer relative to data base application. It is this type of application that can easily justify the construction firm's use of a computer. In fact, one might argue that it is the data filing management capabilities of a computer that provide the construction industry the potential to alleviate, or at least partially eliminate, many of the risk factors of managing a construction project and firm.

Many aspects of successful management of a construction project and firm entail the collection, storage, and interpretation of considerable amounts of data. Given the fact that the successful management of a construction project or firm is so dependent on the reliance on estimates of future uncertain events, estimating of uncertain events becomes a critical component of construction management.

Various individuals have proposed "mystery"-type formulas and theories for the estimating/predicting of future uncertain events. However, the fact remains that there is one, and only one, way of estimating/predicting future uncertain events. This entails the collection, processing, and interpretation of past data regarding the event being estimated. The science of mathematics tells us that the more historical data we have regarding a past event, the more accurate the data is for predicting a future occurrence of the event. For example, an individual who has collected a considerable amount of data regarding the weather in June in a specific city is better able to predict the weather in June for the city in a future year.

One might argue that past records are never an absolute basis of predicting a future event with certainty. This is true given the fact that future events are never predictable by the very definition of a "future uncertain event." However, one's ability to improve on the ability to predict future events with increased accuracy is in part dependent on having a large data bank of historical data to draw upon.

There are numerous examples of the need for a construction firm to collect, store, and subsequently interpret historical data. Listed below are just a few of the instances for which a historical data bank would aid the construction firm.

1. Historical data regarding the labor productivity under varying conditions for performing various types of construction work activities, e.g., man-hours to place a given amount of square feet of concrete wall forms.
2. Historical data regarding the cost of owning and using construction equipment, given various defined work environments.
3. Historical data regarding the amount of job or company overhead required to support various types of construction projects, e.g., the amount of job supervision required to support a dollar's worth of residential-type construction versus industrial-type construction.
4. Historical data regarding the bidding activities of a firm's competitors on past projects.

The above list of instances for which historical data would be useful to a construction firm is not all-inclusive. However, the availability of a historical data bank for each of the above circumstances has the potential to offer the construction firm significant benefits relative to managing a project on time and cost and serving the contractor's profit objective.

While few individuals would argue against the benefits of having historical data available to perform the individual tasks outlined above, one might argue that the cost and time required to develop such a historical data base may be prohibitive relative to the benefits of having such a data base at one's disposal. Typically, the argument given against the development of a useful historical data base is that it may take a considerable number of man-hours to gather and process the data, man-hours that might be better spent overlooking the construction process itself.

Enter the computer. A computer can be considered as having an almost infinite size memory for storing historical data. This almost infinite memory capacity, along with a computer's ability to access the data instantaneously via the use of floppy disks or a hard disk drive, enables data management. As discussed in Chapter 2, even small computers can access years of historical data in less than a second. For example, a labor productivity history record, gathered several years past, can be returned almost instantaneously by a computer. In effect it becomes possible for the construction firm to access years of historical data in less time than it would previously take to open a file cabinet that contained thousands of pages of past project data.

Perhaps equally important, via the use of software application programs, the construction firm is able to have the computer perform various data correlations, mathematical calculations, and printing routines that enable the user to utilize the historical data to the user's best advantage. As the construction firm is able to gather more and more data and store the data in the computer memory or on data disks, the construction firm should be able to improve its ability to better predict and control future events. If and when this happens, the "risk" of contracting and managing a construction project should be substantially reduced. Data file management is one of the most advantageous computer applications the computer age offers the construction industry. Several data-management-type computer software applications are discussed in following chapters.

GAMING APPLICATIONS

When one thinks of computer games, one's thoughts usually center on the numerous entertainment games available for home computers and video games. However, the concept of "gaming" and computers offers the construction industry yet more potential applications; applications that can yield the industry a significant benefit/cost ratio.

When one gives some thought to the building of a construction project, it is easy to visualize the process as a game of fighting and reacting to uncertain and unpredictable events. Similar to the game in which a video game player has to quickly react to spaceships, missiles, and monsters (all of which keep popping up at random), the construction firm is continually confronted with unpredictable weather, uncertain material deliveries, labor strikes, change orders, and disputes. Using its technical knowledge of construction and its available management tools and techniques, the construction firm must quickly react to these uncertain and unpredictable events if it is to successfully construct a project according to a time and cost budget. In effect, the construction industry is an industry of fighting against a foe called "uncertain events."

One of the attributes of a computer is the fact that it can be programmed to simulate uncertain events. Random generator numbers can generate uncertain weather patterns, labor strikes or shortages, material delays, disputes, etc.

Perhaps the most obvious benefit of being able to have a constructor "play a game" against a computer that simulates construction uncertainties is the ability to train constructors, such as project superintendents, how to react to uncertain events before they have to actually do this in the real world. In effect, many years of construction experience can be achieved by a simulation tool, the computer.

Computer gaming applications also provide the constructor the opportunity to evaluate risk, both for a project and for his firm. The random number attribute of the computer can be programmed to present "what if" conditions on a model, such as a construction estimate or schedule, such that the firm can evaluate a range of possible outcomes. The study of the possible outcomes enables the firm to evaluate the financial risk of a project relative to time, cost, or profits or loss.

Several gaming applications of computers to the construction industry are discussed in Chapter 13. Computer gaming applications offer significant potential for the construction industry; a potential that may in the not too distant future result in gaming being the highest benefit applications of computers to the construction industry.

OTHER APPLICATIONS

Our discussions of computer applications to the construction industry have centered on the following four applications.

1. Use of computer as a calculator-type device.

2. Graphical applications of computers.
3. Data base management applications.
4. Gaming applications.

In this chapter we have stressed the potential benefits of the latter two types of applications.

Computer usage is not limited to the above four applications. Individuals and firms utilize the sound, color, and communication features of computers, even the small inexpensive personal computer. While these computer features/attributes have on occasion been utilized by a few constructors, the majority of construction firms seldom utilize these features.

One computer feature many constructors do use is for the correspondence and letter writing functions of the firm. Numerous software vendors have developed word processing software packages that enable the user to store, correct, and print letters, newsletters, correspondence, and even construction reporting forms. These types of software programs facilitate the construction firm's paper processing functions.

Other more select computer software programs have been utilized by some constructors for yet other applications. For example, some construction firms, via mailing list and sorting software programs, maintain large mailing lists of potential customers, subcontractors, and even competitors. Such mailing lists are easily stored on computer data disks. Having developed such mailing lists, the construction firm can then use the computer to print subcontractor bid invites, letters to potential owner clients, and perhaps even a list of former employees—to which the firm may send notice of these activities.

Mailing lists, word processing, spelling error programs, and data sorting programs are just a few more of the many computer software applications that are continually finding a way into the construction industry. The list of these applications is likely to grow as the construction firm settles into its computer usage and advances in computer technology occur.

6: Getting One's Manual Procedures in Place First

INTRODUCTION

One of the most frequent phrases one hears when discussing the negative side of computers is "garbage in, garbage out." Perhaps there is no industry that better fits this phrase than the construction industry.

A computer can only output what is input to it. Indeed it can transform, manipulate, store, and print inputted information; it *cannot* by itself improve the quality or accuracy of the inputted data. Given the "mystical" attributes that often characterize one's view of a computer, there is a tendency to look at a computer's output as correct. In other words one sometimes views a computer as a means of taking bad or "garbage" data, manipulating it, and printing out accurate data and reports. Obviously a computer cannot do this! The garbage in, garbage out criticism is especially noteworthy in discussing the construction contractor's use of a computer. The nature of construction contracting is such that the firm builds projects at decentralized sites away from its main accounting/data processing center, i.e., the firm's main offce. The end result is that the construction firm has to have production people (e.g., foreman) play the role of data collectors. One might argue that this production person may not be attentive to performance of the data collection task. The end result is that he may not perform the task with a high priority and thus input inaccurate data. If this is the case, no computer can improve his accuracy.

The author is reminded of the contractor who spent approximately $30,000 on a computer to eliminate his lousy, inaccurate manual information system. Because the contractor did not focus on improving his jobsite information, the fact is that the contractor's $30,000 computer expenditure resulted in the firm having a $30,000 *faster* lousy information system!

Given the above possibility, this chapter discusses improving contractor's job-site information gathering. Accurate and timely job-site input information is a necessary part of an effective computer information system for the construction firm.

Self-Evaluation Quiz for Evaluating Procedures
To Support A Computerized
Job Management Information System

One of the best routes to improvement is through self-evaluation. All too often one gets into a rut of doing things one way, even if it is inefficient or wrong. This is often true of the construction firm. Once it gets into a pattern of set procedures, the firm continues to utilize the same procedures even if the environment in which the procedures are applied changes and makes the procedures inappropriate.

In order to lay the groundwork for an effective and efficient computerized information management system for the construction firm, this section includes a project management self-evaluation quiz written by the author. The intent of the quiz is to have the reader/firm periodically take the quiz and evaluate their score (the preferred solutions are given for each exercise along with a short explanation of the preferred practice). Note that the reader should not merely attempt to solve the exercise correctly for the sake of getting it correct. Instead, the intent is that the firm continue to implement procedures over a period of time such that it can respond correctly to each of the situations. When in fact the firm has procedures in place whereby it can solve each exercise correctly, one might suggest that the firm has its "house-in-order" to successfully support a computerized system for project management.

EXERCISE 1

Labor hours at the job site are recorded relative to job phases or work items on the time card; e.g., a carpenter's time might be recorded as 3 hours on wall forming, 2 hours on forming beams, and 3 hours on rough carpentry.

SUGGESTED SOLUTION 1

The only way to accurately estimate (budget) and subsequently control construction labor costs is to collect historical labor productivity records from past jobs, use the data for estimating future jobs, and monitor and control the costs on an ongoing job by recording labor hours on a work item basis.

Example work items might be as follows:

Wall forming	Beam forming	Footing forming
Concrete walls	Concrete beams	Concrete footings
Reinforcing		

EXERCISE 2

The firm uses common job phases or work items for each and every job; e.g., the firm might have a standard 50 work items that it uses to budget labor hours and subsequently monitor labor costs.

SUGGESTED SOLUTION 2

If the firm can create a standard set of work items and use them for each and every job, it is likely to get more accurate estimates as time progresses.

Naturally, each job might require the firm to create one or more new work items for a new job; nonetheless, the firm should not have to start a totally new list of work items for each job.

EXERCISE 3

The firm uses a daily time card for recording direct labor hours instead of a weekly time card.

SUGGESTED SOLUTION 3

If an estimating and cost control system is to be effective and accurate, it is necessary that accurate data be collected at the job site.

If the firm uses a weekly time card, the field personnel are likely to only fill it out weekly, leading to inaccurate data entry.

EXERCISE 4

The same job phases or work items that are used for taking off work items are also used for monitoring direct labor costs during the construction process.

SUGGESTED SOLUTION 4

There is no reason for a firm to use different work items for estimating and cost control.

By using the same work items for both functions, the firm is able to develop an integrated estimating and cost control system.

EXERCISE 5

The direct labor hour distribution to the job phases or work items on the time cards is reviewed for accuracy by the project superintendent or project manager.

SUGGESTED SOLUTION 5

One of the easiest means of destroying an estimating and control system is to allow a worker at the job site to enter incorrect or bad data and not have a management person reprimand the individual.

If an estimating and cost control system is to be effective, it is absolutely necessary that a management individual review the time cards.

The worker/individual filling out the time card should be made aware of the fact that the time cards will be reviewed.

EXERCISE 6

Labor time cards used list the allowable job phases or work items to which a worker can charge time written or typed on the time card.

SUGGESTED SOLUTION 6

One has to remember that construction field personnel are essentially production-oriented individuals who do not necessarily like to fill out forms, including a time card.

As such, anything that can be done to aid the worker in filling out the time card, including printing the allowable work codes on the time card, may aid in the collection of accurate data.

EXERCISE 7

Nonproductive work codes as well as productive work codes are used. For example, a worker may be allowed to charge travel time when going from one job to another or may be allowed to charge actual work time.

SUGGESTED SOLUTION 7

This situation is indeed a controversial one. However, if the firm does not have nonproductive work codes defined in its estimating and cost control system, a worker will incorrectly charge actual nonproductive time to productive work codes and will destroy the accuracy of the productive work codes, which may in turn lessen the accuracy of future estimates.

EXERCISE 8

The symbols for job codes infer the type of work performed. For example, the code CWF might be used to refer to the concrete wall forming job phase or work item.

SUGGESTED SOLUTION 8

As noted previously, job-site personnel usually do not like filling out accounting-type forms, including a time card.

Anything that can be done to aid the field personnel in filling out a time card accurately, including having work codes used on the time card infer the name of the work item, may aid in the accuracy of the data collection.

EXERCISE 9

Every individual required to fill in job forms, including the time card, is instructed in the use of the form, shown by example how the data is used, and given a return feedback report.

SUGGESTED SOLUTION 9

Inaccurate data from the job site is a common complaint of the constructor. However, the constructor often promotes this inaccurate data by not instructing the worker as to the use of the form or data and not giving a feedback report to the worker or individual that inputs data.

One should not overlook the need to design a feedback report for the worker in the field as well as reports for management.

EXERCISE 10

The individual workers at the job site are given a man-hour budget for individual work items. For example, the budgeted man-hours for each work item might be preprinted on the time cards used in the field.

SUGGESTED SOLUTION 10

Communicating standards in the construction industry is a controversial issue. Some might argue that if a worker knows how many hours he has to perform a task, he might pace himself to this amount. While this pacing might in fact take place, one could argue why should the constructor be concerned as long as the budget yields a profit. One might also argue that if a budget is not established and communicated, then how does the worker know what is expected of him; no one, including the construction crafts-man, likes to work without a measuring system.

EXERCISE 11

The project superintendent or project manager who has the responsibility for reviewing time cards is required by company policy to reprimand an individual for submitting erroneous data as soon as the erroneous data is detected.

SUGGESTED SOLUTION 11

An estimating and cost control system is only as good as it is enforced. Management must enforce the need for accurate collection of data at the job site.

If a worker is not reprimanded for inputting inaccurate data, then the worker will lose any confidence he had in the reporting system.

EXERCISE 12

A worker at the job site is able to input a request for a new work item, to which direct labor time may be charged, as he sees the need for such a new work item or job phase.

SUGGESTED SOLUTION 12

Perhaps the best person to know that the firm needs a work item not previously identified is the worker in the field. It is the worker himself who confronts the problem of some of his expended hours not fitting into any previously defined work item. One way of enabling the workers to input a new work item would be to provide a space labeled "other" on the time card with a description space for naming the work item and the reason for the work item.

EXERCISE 13

Historical direct labor hour productivity or unit costs are summarized on a work item basis from previous performances, and the summary is available on a form or piece of paper at the firm's office, where estimates are prepared.

SUGGESTED SOLUTION 13

Some firms only have access to historical productivity or unit cost data for a work item available by reviewing or inspecting past job cost reports or ledgers.

 The preferred practice would be to summarize the data regarding a work item on separate work item forms when jobs are completed. This type of summarized data would be more accessible and usable for estimating a future project.

EXERCISE 14

The firm prepares its direct labor estimate for a project by using historical direct labor hour productivity records instead of using historical direct labor unit cost data.

SUGGESTED SOLUTION 14

Some construction firms keep historical unit cost data while others keep historical productivity data. Costs in the construction industry change rapidly as a function of time. On the other hand labor productivity in the construction industry has been relatively constant over the years. Therefore, the use of productivity data would be less subject to error or variation as a function of time and would be preferred for estimating.

EXERCISE 15

The project superintendent hours and the project manager hours for a proposed project are estimated by analyzing the degree of supervision required as a function of time. The estimated hours are then multiplied by the hourly rates of the individuals to determine the supervision estimate.

SUGGESTED SOLUTION 15

Each project requires varying efforts and amounts of supervision per dollar of direct labor hours or project cost depending on the complexity of the project. If this effort is not analyzed and budgeted, the firm is likely to incur different supervision costs than were estimated. A good rule to remember in estimating is that one cannot control something that has not been properly budgeted.

EXERCISE 16

Project superintendents are required to review the direct labor hour estimate and overall methods of construction assumed by the estimator for a project as a means of validating the accuracy of the assumption made by the estimator.

SUGGESTED SOLUTION 16

All too often an estimator prepares a project estimate in isolation. Upon obtaining the project in a bidding process, the superintendent is given the project to build without a prior review of the estimate.

The failure to have the superintendent review the estimate prior to the submitting of the estimate/bid can lead to erroneous estimating assumptions. For example, the estimator may assume the use of a concrete pump when in fact the superintendent may use a crane.

EXERCISE 17

Material quantities and costs for a project are estimated or budgeted to the same job phases or work items as are used for estimating and monitoring labor costs.

SUGGESTED SOLUTION 17

To integrate the company's estimating and cost control systems, it is preferable to use the same work items for direct labor and material. This would enable the firm to calculate percent complete in regard to material put in place for a work item and compare this with the percentage of direct labor hours expended for the same work. Such a comparison would provide the firm a control tool.

EXERCISE 18

Work put in place is documented weekly by work item; i.e., the amount of material for a specific work item put in place such as square feet of contact of wall forming is documented.

SUGGESTED SOLUTION 18

If the construction firm is to effectively monitor the progress of a job and individual work items, it is necessary to document the quantity of work put in place as a function of time.

As a means of doing this, the material put in place for a work item should be documented weekly or in some cases even daily.

EXERCISE 19

The percentage of completion for a project as a function of time as the project progresses is determined weekly or monthly by means of determining the percentage of completion for each job phase or work item and summarizing them into an overall project percent complete.

SUGGESTED SOLUTION 19

Some firms calculate percent complete for a project as the percent of costs expended to date divided by the initial estimated cost. Such an approach not only fails to recognize changes in the total estimated cost for a project but also makes the assumption that costs expended are correlated to work performed. Given the fact that it is hard, if not impossible, to look at the project as a whole and determine percent complete, the most accurate means is to calculate it by a work item analysis.

EXERCISE 20

Weekly or monthly progress billing requests to the project owner as the project progresses are determined from an analysis of work items as their percent complete.

SUGGESTED SOLUTION 20

One of the advantages of an integrated estimating and cost control system is the use of work item data to perform several related tasks, including purchasing and the preparation of progress billings to the project owner. Naturally, the contractor may choose to modify somewhat his billings from a straight mathematical calculation as a means of some strategy in managing his project cash flow.

EXERCISE 21

The firm prepares a weekly or monthly job cost report as the job progresses that summarizes the following for each work item:

Budgeted Work Quantity For Job	Actual Work Quantity To Date	Budgeted Labor Hours For Job	Actual Labor Hours To Date

SUGGESTED SOLUTION 21

In order for a firm to effectively monitor work put in place and determine if there is a possible cost overrun, it is necessary to compare the percentage of work put in place with the percentage of budgeted effort expended to date. The firm should produce a report that gives it this type of information for each work item as the job progresses.

EXERCISE 22

The firm prepares a revised estimate of an in-progress job, including a revised labor estimate to complete as the project progresses based on the known events to date. Such a revised estimate is prepared weekly or monthly.

SUGGESTED SOLUTION 22

A construction estimate should not be viewed as unchanging. As a project progresses, events become known that should be reflected in the cost to complete a project. In effect, one could view the work to be completed for a project as a new job to be performed. As such, there may be another estimate, a revised estimate, made at periodic times. Without this revised estimate, a firm cannot determine a realistic measure of the actual percent complete at a point in time.

EXERCISE 23

Owner equipment cost for a project is budgeted/estimated based on an analysis of the time any piece of equipment is required and the use of established hourly rates for the various pieces of equipment. For example, if a machine coded 101A is required for 80 hours at a job being estimated, and the established hourly rate is $40.00 per hour, the cost estimate for this equipment for the job would be $3200.00.

SUGGESTED SOLUTION 23

Many firms determine owner equipment costs for a project by allocating a percentage of their total annual equipment costs to a project as a percentage of some cost—such as direct labor cost. Such an approach often leads to inaccuracies because actual equipment costs at a project are not always the same percent of another cost such as direct labor cost.

EXERCISE 24

For major pieces of owner-purchased equipment, the firm has established an hourly rate for its use by determining the annual cost of ownership and dividing this amount by the estimated hours of use of the equipment for the year. The annual cost of ownership of the equipment would include depreciation, operating costs, including maintenance and repair, taxes, and interest cost.

SUGGESTED SOLUTION 24

The hourly rate for an owner-purchased piece of equipment should be determined such that the firm can properly charge jobs for the use of the equipment and also determine if the equipment should be rented. The hourly rate should be determined as the annual cost of the equipment divided by the hours of use. The annual cost should include an annual depreciation rate, operating costs, and interest related to financing the equipment. The firm might also consider a replacement cost as part of the annual cost, recognizing the fact that the equipment will cost more to purchase when it is replaced at a later date.

EXERCISE 25

Owner-purchased equipment hours expended at a job site are recorded and summarized to determine the number of hours a piece of equipment is used at a job and also to determine the total number of hours a piece of equipment is used in a given time period, e.g., a year. This information is then available to establish an hourly rate for the equipment.

SUGGESTED SOLUTION 25

In order for an equipment estimating system to be effective, it is necessary to establish actual equipment costs and actual equipment use at job sites. Naturally, this requires that field records be maintained. Some firms merely document how many hours a given piece of equipment is at a job site on a given day, while other firms document the number of productive hours a piece of equipment is used at a job site on a given day.

EXERCISE 26

The firm prepares a time plan and schedule for a proposed job, usually a bar chart or a CPM (critical-path method) diagram, using the same set of job phases or work items used for estimating direct labor costs. Such a project plan is prepared as part of the estimating process.

SUGGESTED SOLUTION 26

A plan for time is nearly as important as a plan for cost if a project is to be properly planned and subsequently controlled. Such a plan should be prepared when an estimate is prepared in order to aid in the determination of accurate costs. For example, in order to determine the cost of placing wall concrete in Chicago, it would be necessary to determine when the concrete was to be placed, e.g., in June or in December.

EXERCISE 27

As a project progresses, a revised project plan, usually a bar chart or a CPM, is prepared that reflects events performed to date and revised times to complete the remaining work. Such a revised plan is prepared weekly or monthly.

SUGGESTED SOLUTION 27

Just as it is necessary to revise an estimate in order to reflect events and effectively control future costs, it is necessary to revise a project plan as a function of time. One might argue that a plan that is not revised/updated is worse than no plan at all. In actuality, an accurate initial plan and frequent revisions/updates should be made to reflect progress and a plan of action to complete the project.

EXERCISE 28

As part of the estimating task, the firm prepares a chart or form showing the proposed cash flow for the project expenditures and the proposed receipt of cash from the project owner as a function of time. The same job phases or work items that are used for estimating direct labor costs are used as the basis for preparing the cash plan. In effect, a cash plan is prepared as part of estimating.

SUGGESTED SOLUTION 28

Interest cost related to the expending of cash before receipt of progress billing is a cost of doing construction. In order to determine this interest cost and also in order to determine one's cash need as a function of time, it is necessary for the firm to prepare a cash flow plan for a project that is ja function of the actual work that will be performed.

EXERCISE 29

There is a form or report at the company's office that identifies the location of each and every piece of equipment the firm owns.

SUGGESTED SOLUTION 29

The preparation of an estimate assumes various resources to be used for a job are in fact available for the job, including various pieces of equipment. Unfortunately, it is often difficult for a construction firm to locate its equipment. This inability can relate to theft as well as the potential for an error in an estimating assumption, which will subsequently lead to an inaccurate estimate.

EXERCISE 30

Interest or finance cost associated with expending funds during the construction of a project is analyzed and calculated for a project rather than applied as a percentage of some other cost when preparing an estimate for a new project.

SUGGESTED SOLUTION 30

As was discussed relative to the estimating of equipment costs for a project, any time a cost is allocated (determined as a percentage of another cost), this is a potential weak or inaccurate segment of the overall estimate. Interest is as much a direct cost to a project as are other job overhead costs. It should not be allocated to a project; it should be analyzed and calculated for the specific job being estimated.

EXERCISE 31

Bond costs, insurance costs, and temporary job facilities, including job trailors, are line itemed as job overhead costs as part of the estimating process instead of being allocated to the project costs as a percentage of some other costs.

SUGGESTED SOLUTION 31

Job overhead costs are direct costs to a project. Costs such as bond costs, insurance costs, and temporary job facility costs are job overhead costs and should be analyzed and calculated as individual items for a project.

EXERCISE 32

As a project progresses, actual job overhead is determined as a function of time and compared with budgeted job overhead costs. Any potential job overhead items that are overrunning are investigated.

SUGGESTED SOLUTION 32

A firm does not have control over any cost, including job overhead costs, if it does not react to apparent overruns in an item.

The objective of budgeting these types of costs as individual items is to provide a basis of comparing actual costs against the budget such that the firm can react to apparent cost overruns.

EXERCISE 33

Company overhead costs, including home office secretarial costs, supplies, and home office utility costs, are allocated to a project as a function of some other cost such as direct labor cost or direct labor hours.

SUGGESTED SOLUTION 33

While it might be possible to design an accounting system that would trace individual types of home office or company overhead costs to specific jobs, such a system would likely require effort and costs in excess of the benefits.

An acceptable and preferred practice is to allocate company overhead costs to a project as a function of some base such as direct labor cost or hours.

EXERCISE 34

The firm uses the same company overhead application rate, e.g., 18 percent, from one year to the next and for each and every project when preparing project estimates.

SUGGESTED SOLUTION 34

The amount of company overhead application should be dependent on the projected company overhead for a given time period and a projection of the amount of the base by which the company overhead is applied for the same time period. Therefore, it is likely that the application rate would and should vary from one year to the next and from one job to the next. To the degree possible the company should attempt to determine the amount of company overhead it actually takes to support various types of projects; e.g., it may take more support per dollar of work to support a small dollar project versus a large project.

EXERCISE 35

The company reviews its needed company overhead allocation rate at least quarterly and makes adjustments if necessary.

SUGGESTED SOLUTION 35

The process of determining and applying company overhead to jobs is based on an estimate of several variables, including the firm's estimated volume for a period of time.

However, these estimates often prove inaccurate because of uncertain events. For example, the firm may not realize the anticipated volume that was used in the company overhead rate calculation. As such, the firm should continually review the overhead allocation rate and make adjustments to the rate such that the company covers or applies all of their overhead at year-end.

EXERCISE 36

In determining the amount of company overhead and profit to add to a project estimate, the firm considers them separately; i.e., company overhead is determined via an application process, and profit is determined via a strategy process. The company does not combine these two bid components as a markup rate.

SUGGESTED SOLUTION 36

All too often a construction firm determines all project direct costs and multiplies this total amount by a markup percentage to cover its company overhead and profit for the project estimate. However, the firm should remember that company overhead is a cost, whereas the firm should use the added profit as a means of strategy to be low bid and maximize its profit.

EXERCISE 37

The firm does not vary its company overhead rate for a project as a means of being low bidder on a project just because it needs work.

SUGGESTED SOLUTION 37

Company overhead is a cost, a cost that the firm absorbs as a result of being in business. One should not adjust cost as a strategy to be low bidder unless in fact the cost will be reduced.

The only bid component that should be manipulated as a means of strategy to get a job is the profit component.

EXERCISE 38

The firm records the bids of its competitors when they become known and compares these bids with the firm's estimated costs. This bid/cost information is subsequently used by the firm when the firm prepares its bid against the competitors.

SUGGESTED SOLUTION 38

One can argue that any information available to a firm can be useful information in future planning and strategy. The concept of collecting information about one's competitors and then using this information to prepare a strategy against them is commonly referred to as bidding strategy.

EXERCISE 39

When the firm completes a project, the firm performs a review of actual labor and material costs expended versus budgeted and analyzes differences to include overruns. This analysis is summarized and used in preparing subsequent estimates.

SUGGESTED SOLUTION 39

All too often a firm completes a project and then directs its efforts to preparing a new estimate without ever reviewing the data collected from a completed project. Experience is perhaps the best teacher. The construction firm can learn a significant amount of information from the analysis of a completed job that it can use in estimating a future project.

EXERCISE 40

The difference between the firm's estimated costs for jobs versus the firm's actual costs for jobs (calculated as a percentage) has been decreasing as a function of time.

SUGGESTED SOLUTION 40

Perhaps the best measure of the improvement in a firm's estimating practices and system is whether or not the accuracy of the estimates is improving as a function of time. If the accuracy of the estimating process is improving, the difference between the estimated cost and the actual cost becomes smaller and hopefully approach zero.

INFORMATION COLLECTION AND PERSONNEL MANAGEMENT

One sometimes hears the contractor make the statement, "My information system is weak because I can't get good information in the field." This statement is usually based on the premise that field personnel, including craftsmen, foremen, and even superintendents, do not like to fill out forms. These construction personnel are often viewed as individuals who would rather be pouring concrete, driving nails, or placing bricks instead of filling out forms.

It is true that production individuals probably enjoy watching the result of their work effort take shape, e.g., a building come out of the ground. However, one might also propose that these production personnel like to fill out forms! Let us explain what might appear to be an absurd statement.

The construction industry is sometimes characterized as a "we–they" industry. The owners of the construction firm are characterized as the "we," and the employees, in particular the field workers, are viewed as the "they." This we–they characteristic results because some view the craftsmen (and other field personnel) as having goals and objectives different from those of the project owner/management.

In contrast to the premise that workers have goals and objectives different from those of the owner/management of the construction firm are several personnel mangement theories, including a theory referred to as theory X and Y. In particular, advocates of theory Y suggest that every worker, including the construction craftsmen, foremen, superintendents, and company owner, have similar goals and work objectives. Included in these goals and work objectives are challenge, responsibility, pride in work, achievement, and a means of measuring their work efforts.

If the above theory Y is valid, one might also argue that many construction field personnel (craftsmen) have not been given the opportunity to achieve theory Y goals or objectives. Perhaps the main reason for this has been field personnel's inability to have a means of setting and subsequently measuring their work efforts and results. Perhaps a creative information system, one that is properly communicated to the workers and also enables the workers to participate in it, could be used to bridge the apparent gap between the "we" and "they" that characterizes the industry.

The author would propose that each and every worker, including the construction craftsmen, foremen, and project owner, is best motivated in regard to his work effort if offered the following motivations:

- A means of measuring how one is progressing relative to a budget
- A plan of what is expected of one in regard to work effort
- An open channel of communication whereby one can express his knowledge and ideas.

In many cases the construction craftsmen and foremen are not given any of the above three motivators. For example, the construction foreman and craftsman (the craftsman in particular) is not given any information as to what's expected of him, how he is doing, or where he is going. Similarly, he seldom has an invitation or the ability to input his knowledge regarding construction methods and better ways to do things. Again, one might suggest that a creative information system, one that requests and gives information to each and every employee, including field personnel, might be used to motivate each worker and at the same time improve the collection of accurate field data.

If our above premises are true, including our notion that job-site personnel like to fill out forms, and that workers like to contribute, know where they're going, and have a measuring system, then why does it follow that it is still difficult to get job-site personnel to input accurate field data—data that is needed to support an effective computer system for a constructor? One might propose that the answer is that the information systems that have been unsuccessfully implemented have not actively involved the worker himself. As a result, more often than not, the owner/management of the construction firm has witnessed the difficulty of getting information/data, especially accurate data, from the job site. The author's experience indicates that few individuals, including construction job-site personnel, are prone to fill out data forms correctly unless each of the following three events have occurred:

- The individual is shown (explained) the purpose of each information/data form he is required to fill out.
- For each form the individual fills out, he is given feedback, preferably a report that relates back to the requested input form.
- The individual is shown, by example, how his inputted information/data was utilized by the firm.

Absent any of the above three events, the author would suggest, job-site personnel may lack the incentive to fill out forms, input accurate data, or believe the information system is worthwhile.

Given our discussion, how does one then turn the problem of inaccurate or untimely job-site data around? Obviously, if there was any quick solution to the problem, it would have already been implemented universally by the construction industry. Nevertheless, the reader should not conclude that the task of getting accurate and timely construction job-site data is impossible. If he does, he is in effect saying that computers are ineffective in regard to the construction industry; one must remember that the computer can only process inputted information/data—if the information/data is inaccurate, the computer printout will output inaccurate reports.

What is needed in a job-site information system is a creative, new approach to getting the job-site personnel involved with the system. The reader should refer back to our points about explaining the information system, forcing feedback reports, and illustration of the use of the inputted data when attempting this creative approach. New ideas such as allowing the job-site personnel to set work goals and objectives, having the workers play a role in designing the information system, and giving the workers a budget of hours (which includes a company profit built into the budget) to perform their work may improve the accuracy and timeliness of job-site information/data as well as aid in the motivation of the job-site personnel.

The construction firm is often characterized as a relatively small company, often having only a few full-time personnel. In addition, the firm's priorities often center around production. This is due in part to the fact that the owner of the firm likely originated as a field production individual, e.g., a foreman or superintendent.

These two characteristics—a small closely held firm and personnel who originated from a production background—often result in the firm having inefficient and weak general ledger accounting practices and controls. This is evident when one views the redundant procedures some construction firms follow in performing their payroll function, in a loss of income due to a failure to optimize the accounts payable function, and the loss of timely collection of revenue owing to an ineffective receivable system.

In order to effectively computerize the accounting function, one must first streamline one's general ledger accounting practices. Many firms have redundant practices, inaccurate data collection procedures, and antiquated information control procedures. A computer by itself will not eliminate these types of practices.

In order to implement efficient general ledger accounting practices to support turning over some of the accounting to a computer, the following practices/procedures should be reviewed first by the reader. It is suggested that the elimination of these type of practices/procedures will aid in the implementation of a computerized system.

A. General Organization and Systems Points

1. Duplication of activity.

There may be
 a. excessive checking for accuracy.
 b. reports handwritten and then typed.
 2. Nonessential activities performed.
  a. Reports are issued but not used.
  b. Statistical summaries are maintained but not reported.
 3. Handling of exceptions.
  If exceptions are processed along with the routine work, delays result that affect service, and variance is automatically injected into processing a given quantity of work. The latter makes it difficult to evaluate performance and provides the clerk with a ready explanation for poor performance.

B. Transcription and Copying

 1. Question transcription (copying) of information.
  a. Many techniques are available to avoid copying.
  b. Copying is extra work
   (1) in itself.
   (2) in proofreading.
  c. Greater error possibility.
  d. Includes typing of statements and reports from handwritten drafts.
 2. Question need for extra copies of documents, forms, and reports.
  a. What use is made of the extra copies?
  b. Possible use of one copy for two or more purposes; may require slight rearrangement of data.
 3. Often find that hand entry is the best and cheapest method, e.g.,
  a. insertion of handwritten figures on multilith master forms instead of typing.
  b. manual extension and footing of invoices often saves unnecessary typing (copying) of the same information.
 4. In posting operations, review to ensure that source documents information is in the same sequence as the records to which they are posted.

C. Accounts Receivable

 1. Use of open-invoice (copy of invoice filed in place of ledger card posting); often more economical than posted ledger systems.
 2. Aging
  a. Only past-due accounts in detail—adding machine tape for current accounts.

b. Minimize frequency
c. Where volume of receivable accounts is great enough to warrant subcontrols in support of ledger account, cycle the balancing and aging of accounts to avoid unnecessary peak work loads.
3. Use form letters for handling routine collections and other correspondence to clients.
4. Balance receivables during the month instead of at the end of the month and save time in peak periods.

D. Purchasing, Receiving, Accounts Payable, and Cash Disbursements

1. Initiate longhand; direct purchase orders under specified amount.
2. Simplify and improve accuracy of receiving ticket and posting operations.
   a. Use carbon copies of purchase orders for receiving tickets.
   b. Use a copy of a reproducible master (spirit, etc.) of purchase orders for receiving tickets.
      (1) Provides complete order history for use of accounts payable, purchasing follow-up files, etc.
      (2) Use where large volume of partial shipments and/or backorders is the rule. Also for blanket orders.
3. Use copy of purchase order filed numerically to replace written purchase order log.
4. Prepare purchase order form in longhand for any orders placed by phone.
   a. Delivery date
   b. Shipping instruction
   c. Terms
5. Pay on specific invoice rather than statement basis to simplify accounts payable processing.
6. Eliminate accounts payable ledger and/or voucher register, and/or detail posted cash disbursements register.
7. Requisition
   a. Use bill of material as a requisition when possible. Sometimes master order schedules can be used for certain requisitions.
   b. See if the requisition has all standard information preprinted.
   c. Look for several approval steps in requisitioning and eliminate where possible.
8. Eliminate duplication or excessive work in checking vendors' invoices for clerical accuracy.
   a. When purchasing and accounts payable sections do the same checking.

    b. On invoices less than a predetermined amount.

    c. Conduct random sample and check only those vendors who usually make errors on invoices.

    d. Consolidate checking operations to reduce desk-to-desk movement of paper.

E. Payroll

1. Use nonmechanized methods to simultaneously prepare payroll register, earnings records, and checks—"one-write" system.
2. Use data collection systems to mechanically record payroll on punched cards or tape.
3. Use tables for deductions (and sometimes for elements of gross pay), except for punched card systems.
4. Development of labor efficiency reports—daily or weekly.
5. Preparation of overtime and absence reports in terms of "equivalent employees." Valuable information where fringe benefit costs are high.
6. Use a combination time card–distribution card for weekly distribution, where possible.
7. See if daily, weekly, or semimonthly distribution is the best.

F. Property

1. Eliminate manual and repetitive calculations of depreciation charges.
    a. Use estimates for monthly closings.
    b. Use lapsing schedules.
2. Eliminate duplicate property records.
    a. Combine records duplicated between the accounting and maintenance departments.
    b. Combine property records maintained on both a book basis and a tax basis.

G. Reports and Statements

1. Eliminate recurring reports that are infrequently used.
    a. Prepare special analysis as required to provide the same information.
    b. Change frequency of reports, e.g., from daily to weekly, from semimonthly to monthly.
2. Eliminate unnecessary detail in figures; e.g., pennies, tenths of hours, etc.

3. Combine two or more similar reports.
4. Use preprinted masters (ditto, multilith, ozalid, etc.) and enter figures manually instead of typing.
   a. To save typing, proofreading, and frequent footing.
   b. To speed up issuance of reports.
   c. Sometimes permits decentralized preparation of reports that can be assembled by a smaller group in home office and thereby speed up issuance.
   d. Manually insert only current figures, increases, decreases, etc. Prior month columns, etc., can be reproduced.
5. Prepare summary reports for top management and detail reports for lower management ("responsibility reporting").
6. Use of "flash" reports.
   a. To convey pertinent data to management during and immediately after end of month.
   b. Not necessary to wait for normal accounting closing.
   c. Report significant selected figures only and round to the nearest thousand dollars, hundred tons, etc.

CASH RECEIPTS

1. Cash receiving activities are centralized in as few hands as possible.
2. The receipt of cash is provable by other records.
3. Persons receiving cash have no access to accounting records. Incoming receipts are controlled by other than those having access to cash or the accounting records.
4. The bank has been instructed not to cash checks payable to the company.
5. All cash receipts are deposited intact.

CASH DISBURSEMENTS

1. All disbursements (other than petty cash) are made by check.
2. All checks are countersigned.
3. No checks are made payable to cash.
4. All checks are prenumbered.
5. No counter checks are permitted.
6. All disbursements are properly substantiated. Supporting documents include evidence of receipt and approval.
7. All such supporting documents are canceled in such a manner as to preclude their use a second time.

8. Monthly bank reconciliations are made by someone other than the person writing the checks or recording disbursements.
9. All checks are protectographed.
10. Petty cash funds are maintained on an imprest basis with the same standard of developing documentary evidence as for other disbursements.

ACCOUNTS RECEIVABLE

1. Each entry to the accounts receivable ledger is supported by documentary evidence.
2. All noncash credits, such as credit memos, allowances, bad debts, etc., are properly authorized.
3. Subsidiary ledgers are balanced regularly.
4. Postings are made by other than those having access to incoming receipts.
5. Statements are mailed monthly by someone other than the bookkeeper or cashier.

NOTES RECEIVABLE AND INVESTMENTS

1. Notes and other investments on hand are checked regularly with the controlling account.
2. This checking is done by someone other than the person receiving cash or recording the transaction.
3. Partial payments are endorsed on back of notes.
4. Note renewals are properly authorized.
5. Discounted notes are credited to a note receivable–discount account.

ACCOUNTS PAYABLE AND PURCHASES

1. Prenumbered purchase orders are used for all purchases.
2. The responsibility for receiving incoming merchandise is established with one individual.
3. Prenumbered receiving tickets are prepared for all incoming merchandise.
4. A numerical file of receiving tickets (or a comparable record) is maintained.
5. Persons responsible for purchasing and receiving merchandise do not approve invoices for payment or handle disbursements.

6. Invoice prices, extensions, additions, and freight charges are checked.
7. Invoices are compared with purchase orders and receiving tickets prior to payment.
8. An approved list of vendors is maintained.
9. A voucher or purchase register and an accounts payable subsidiary ledger are maintained.
10. Suppliers' monthly statements are regularly compared with record liabilities.
11. Distributions to purchase and expense accounts are established by responsible employees.
12. Periodic physical checks of the inventory records are conducted by persons other than those keeping the inventory records.
13. The inventory is taken under the supervision of responsible officials.

NOTES PAYABLE AND CAPITAL

1. Proper detail subsidiary records are maintained and checked periodically against the various general ledger control accounts.
2. This checking is performed by a person having no access to receiving cash or recording any related transactions.
3. All transactions are approved or otherwise authorized by responsible officials.
4. Canceled instruments are effectively marked to prevent misuse and are properly retained and filed.

PAYROLL

1. Written authorizations are on file for all employees appearing on payrolls and for all salary and wage rate changes.
2. All salary and wage payments are made by checks signed and distributed by persons other than the ones preparing the payroll.
3. All payroll computations are independently checked and the payroll bank account is reconciled by someone other than the person preparing the payroll or signing payroll checks.

FIXED ASSETS

1. Detailed subsidiary records of fixed assets and reserves for depreciation are maintained.

2. These records are periodically compared with fixed assets on hand.
3. All capital expenditures are authorized by responsible officers.
4. The accounting personnel is capable of distinguishing between capital expenditures and maintenance and repair items.
5. Retirements are under satisfactory accounting control.

7: Financial Accounting Applications

INTRODUCTION

There is probably no firm that needs sound financial accounting practices more than the construction firm. The success of the construction firm is often dependent on the firm's ability to keep its financial house in order.

Unfortunately, the construction firm is often characterized as a firm that has weak financial accounting practices. The firm's financial records are often difficult to reconstruct by a CPA auditor, the records may not "tie," some financial transactions may go unrecorded; and lacking good financial records, the firm may not make favorable financial decisions that might have been made otherwise.

Because of inefficient and inaccurate financial accounting practices, the construction firm may lose potential profit or incur additional unnecessary expense relative to its accounts payable or accounts receivable functions. Equally important is the fact that owing to poor financial accounting internal controls, the firm may incur unnecessary expense relative to its payroll function and may in fact lose or incur added expense relative to its fixed assets, including its construction equipment.

There are likely several somewhat independent reasons why some construction firms have weak financial accounting practices and systems. Some of these are as follows:

1. The uniqueness of the construction industry's product, including its mobility and flexibility of design, and the firm's dependence on many "cost objects or centers" (i.e., numerous labor crafts and

workers, numerous types of material, etc.) makes the construction firm's accounting task very tedious, complex, and time consuming. The construction firm's financial accounting function is characterized by the firm's need to handle numerous financial transactions each and every day.

2. The construction firm is often a small closely held company and may be understaffed relative to performing each of the business functions of marketing (sales), production, and control (accounting). Given the time pressures placed on the firm, and given the fact that most construction firms have been started and owned by a former craftsman, skilled in the production function, the firm may have a tendency to overlook the importance of the accounting function. Perhaps the firm has placed a higher priority on the marketing and production functions and slighted the financial accounting function.

These reasons are especially relevant to the possibility of using a computer to assist the firm in its financial accounting functions. The computer, given its attributes of speed, accuracy, and large memory storage, can greatly reduce the construction firm's past difficulties relevant to implementing sound financial accounting practices. In particular, the use of a computer for financial accounting can greatly reduce the firm's clerical time required to process the many financial transactions that occur in the life of the firm daily. Equally important, the potential for improved accuracy in handling the transactions and controls to ensure that the records "tie" together are improved by computer usage.

Not to be overlooked as an advantage of the computer is the fact that the use of a computer may enable the contractor to speed up his financial accounting (and therefore obtain more timely and useful financial records) by enabling data input directly at the firm's job sites. Via computer terminals, it becomes possible for the construction firm to have the on-site project management team access the firm's main computer data base at the firm's central office. Equally important, this enables the firm to "send" more timely reports back to the job site; i.e., data and reports can be sent almost instantaneously to the job sites via computer terminals. In effect, this has the effect of enabling the firm to place its entire accounting system and records at each of its decentralized job sites.

In summary, computers should have a major role in improving the financial accounting practices that characterize the construction firm. Many construction firms will and should implement a computer system based on the financial accounting function alone.

UNDERSTANDING THE FINANCIAL ACCOUNTING PROCESS

Financial accounting's objective is, in great part, the preparation of financial statements, including the firm's balance sheet (also referred to as its statement of financial position) and its income statement (also referred to as the firm's profit and loss statement). While this is the major objective of financial accounting, accounting actually consists of the following somewhat separate tasks:

- General ledger accounting
- Accounts payable
- Accounts receivable
- Payroll
- Job costing

Each of these accounting functions/tasks can be viewed as a by-product of the financial accounting system. While one might believe that the financial accounting system/process is complex and unique to each firm, in reality the process is relatively simple and in fact is essentially the same for each firm, independent of its size or type of work performed. To illustrate just how simple the process is and also to enable the reader to understand how one might computerize the financial accounting function, we will now attempt to describe, in layman's language, the financial accounting process.

Accounting Fundamentals

Regardless of the type of accounting model or system used, or who actually uses the accounting model, it has certain characteristic fundamentals. The accounting model is based on an equation relating the data that pertains to a company's financial state of existence. These data are separated into one of five categories: assets, liabilities, net worth, revenue, or expense. A company's assets may be conceived as all the things that add to the value of the company. The liabilities of a company refer to the company's debts, or all the things the company owes. The net worth represents the amount of money invested in the company. Revenue represents the amount of money taken in by the company. A company's expense is the money spent for things that do not add directly to the company's assets. For example, payment of a utility bill would be an expense. The payment of the bill does not add directly to the company's assets. A company's assets, liabilities, net worth, revenue, and expense are related by the following equation.

Assets = liabilities + net worth + revenue − expense

Let us view this financial equation in terms of the formation of a particular construction company. Let us suppose we invest $60,000 in the formation of a construction company. We have then created assets of $60,000 for our company. We, as the investors, also have a net worth of $60,000 in the company. Our financial equation of balance is as follows.

Assets = net worth
$60,000 = $60,000

Let us now assume that we buy $20,000 worth of new construction equipment for our company. Rather than pay cash for the equipment, we buy it on credit. We have now increased the assets of our company by $20,000. However, we have created a company liability of $20,000, i.e., we eventually will have to pay for the equipment. Our financial equation of balance is as follows.

Assets = net worth + liabilities
$80,000 = $60,000 + $20,000

Let us assume that our newly formed construction company receives a contract to build a construction project. While building the project we have to pay our employees. Let us assume that at the end of a particular week we pay them a total of $2000. Let us assume that we pay them cash, reducing our company assets by $2000. We have incurred an expense of $2000, which has not directly increased our company's assets. Our financial equation of balance is as follows.

Assets = net worth + liabilities − expense
$78,000 = $60,000 + $20,000 − $2,000

At the end of the month, the project owner pays us $5000 for the work we have completed. This $5000 worth of cash increases our company's assets by $5000. Likewise, we have had a company revenue of $5000. Our financial equation of balance now becomes the following.

Assets = net worth + liabilities + revenue − expense
$83,000 = $60,000 + $20,000 + $5,000 − $2,000

The financial equation for our company is now complete. Obviously, a real company would have many more entries during its operation. Each entry would affect the derived equation. However, at all times the equation would remain in equilibrium. That is, assets would always be equal to liabilities plus net worth plus revenue minus expenses. In the derived accounting equation or model, the difference between the revenue and expense terms is often referred to as net income.

Tradition has established a procedure of keeping the derived accounting equation in balance by means of terms referred to as *debits* and *credits*. When an entry is made in one of the terms (e.g., assets or liabilities) of the accounting equation, it is identified as being either a debit or credit. Thus, each term of the accounting equation is divided in debits and credits.

The reader should be cautioned against attempting to relate any real significance to the words *debit* and *credit*. Their significance is limited to the accounting model. There are two fundamental definitions that are part of the accounting model. An entry that increases the assets of the company is defined as a debit and is assigned a positive value. The second fundamental definition is that for every debit entry in the accounting model there must also be a corresponding credit entry.

As previously stated, the financial equation of balance or accounting equation, relating a company's assets, liabilities, net worth, revenue, and expenses, must balance after every financial entry. As defined, an asset debit is positive. For the financial equation to balance, and for consistency with the asset debit definition and the "equal debit–equal credit" definition, a debit is considered negative and a credit is considered positive if the entry is a liability, a net worth, or revenue. If an entry is an expense, it is positive if it is a debit, and negative if it is a credit. Similarly, an asset credit is negative. The described convention of assigning positive or negative values to the various debits and credits in the accounting equation is summarized in Figure 7.1.

Having included debits and credits in the accounting model, let us now view the model with respect to the formation of our previously discussed construction company. Originally, we invested $60,000 in the formation of the company. The $60,000 increased our company's assets. Thus, the $60,000 is entered as a debit in the asset term of the accounting model. We, as the investors, have created a net worth of $60,000. Consistent with the accounting model definitions, this becomes a credit entry in the net worth term of the accounting model.

Assets		Net Worth	
Debit (+)	Credit (−)	Debit (−)	Credit (+)
60,000			60,000

The financial equation of balance is in fact in balance in that plus $60,000 equals plus $60,000.

Assets		=	Liabilities		+	NetWorth		+	Revenue		−	Expense	
Debit	Credit		Debit	Credit		Debit	Credit		Debit	Credit		Debit	Credit
+	−		−	+		−	+		−	+		+	−

Figure 7.1   The financial equation of state.

Having created the company, we purchased on credit $20,000 worth of new construction equipment. The new construction equipment increased our assets by $20,000. Thus, it is entered as a debit in the asset term of the accounting model. The $20,000 we owe to the seller of the equipment is a liability. Since the equipment was assigned to "debit" in the asset term of the accounting model, the newly created liability is a credit. Once again, the financial equation of balance is in equilibrium. The accounting model is now as follows.

Assets		+	Liabilities		+	Net Worth
Debit (+)	Credit (−)		Credit (+)	Debit (−)		Credit (+)
60,000			20,000			60,000
20,000						

We then performed part of the work on a construction project, and payed our workers a sum of $2000. The payment of the $2000 decreased our cash and, therefore, our assets. Thus, the $2000 is a credit in the asset term of the accounting model. The $2000 was a project expense. Consistent with the fact that the $2000 was a credit in the asset term in the accounting model, it is a debit in the expense term. The accounting model is now as follows.

Assets		=	Liabilities		+	Net Worth		−	Expenses	
D(+)	C(−)		D(−)	C(+)		D(−)	C(+)		D(+)	C(−)
60,000	2,000			20,000			60,000		2,000	
20,000										

Once again the financial equation remains in balance.

Finally, we received $5000 revenue from the construction project owner. The $5000 increased our company assets by $5000. Thus, it is a debit. Similarly, the $5000 is identified as revenue since it was received as a result of our project performance. Owing to the fact that the $5000 was an asset debit, the $5000 is a credit in the revenue term of the accounting model. The accounting model is now complete and is as follows.

Assets		= Liabilities	+	Net Worth	+	Revenue	−	Expenses	
D(+)	C(−)	D(−) C(+)		D(+) C(+)		D(−) C(+)		D(+)	C(−)
60,000	2,000	20,000		60,000		5,000		2,000	
20,000									
5,000									

The equation remains in balance.

Other financial transactions could be entered into the accounting model now that is it complete. In actuality, the user of the accounting model does not enter his transactions into the described financial equation of balance. The accounting system consists of journals, ledgers, and worksheets. However, the entire accounting system is based on the described financial equation. Thus, assets, liabilities, net worth, revenue, expense, debits, and credits are fundamental to the accounting model or system.

A defined set of accounts within an accounting system partly depends on the type of work the accounting system user performs. The construction contractor's accounting system usually contains numerous accounts. The purpose of the individual accounts is to separate and keep track of the different types of company transactions. These transactions include the purchase of equipment, the payment of utility bills, the payment of interest on debts, etc. It is left to the particular construction contractor to define his accounts. He may define concrete as an account; or he may define slab concrete, footing concrete, and wall concrete as separate accounts. In other words it is the individual contractor's responsibility to define the degree of his accounts. The degree to which he defines the various accounts depends on his purpose in keeping an accounting system. He may be keeping accounts merely to produce required financial statements. On the other hand he may be using his accounting system as a means of cost control or as an integral part of a planning, estimating, payroll, and cost control system. His various purposes will require different degrees of definition for individual accounts. Consistent with the cost control objective of the chapter, we will assume that the accounting system can aid in the cost control task. Every defined account will be either an asset, a liability, a net worth, a revenue, or an expense account in the accounting system. A list of some typical construction accounts is shown in Figure 7.2. The accounts are classified as to whether they are assets, liabilities, net worths, revenue, or expense accounts.

	ASSETS			NET WORTH	
REF.	ITEM		REF.	ITEM	
11.1	General Bank Account		50.0	Capital Stock	
11.2	Payroll Bank Account		51.0	Retained Earnings	
12.3	Notes Receivable			*REVENUE*	
14.3	Motor Vehicles		REF.	ITEM	
14.620	Electric Drills		70.101	Project Revenue	
14.90	Office Equipment		70.4	Equipment Rental	
18.10	Returnable Plan Deposit		70.5	Interest Revenue	
19.1	Prepaid Insurance			*EXPENSE*	
	LIABILITIES		REF.	ITEM	
REF.	ITEM		80.10	Project Work Accounts	
40.0	Accounts Payable		81.1	Office Salaries	
45.0	Taxes Payable		85.1	Equipment Depreciation	
46.1	Wages and Salaries				

Figure 7.2   Example chart of accounts.

An identification account number is also shown for each of the accounts listed in Figure 7.2. It is common practice to assign such account numbers to the defined accounts. Rather than having to write out the entire account name, the account in question may be referred to by its account number. In addition to being useful in terms of addressing the various accounts, the account number may be used to aid in grouping the different types of accounts. For example, a typical accounting system may reference asset accounts by means of account numbers between 10 and 39. Similarly, liability accounts may be referenced by account numbers 40 to 49, net worth accounts by account numbers 50 to 69, revenue accounts by account numbers 70 to 79, and expenses by account numbers 80 to 89. The account numbers shown in Figure 7.2 are consistent with this numbering system. Having implemented such a numbering system into his accounting system, the contractor has a means of addressing accounts of a similar type.

Handling Financial Transactions

The types of accounts that are part of a contractor's accounting system vary considerably from the types of accounts that would be part of a retail store, manufacturing, or government service accounting system. However, the actual procedure by which the financial transactions affecting the accounts are handled remains very much the same. Such a procedure for handling financial transactions is shown in Figure 7.3.

The accounting procedure is initiated when the company has a financial transaction. A financial transaction is anything that affects the company's financial condition. When a financial transaction occurs, it is recorded in the company's journal. The journal may be viewed as a notebook used for recording the various financial transactions of the company.

A construction contractor's accounting system will often have both company and project journals. Rather than enter all of the financial transactions that occur on a single project into the company journal, the project transactions are entered into a project journal. A project journal may be kept for each project the contractor builds. At some convenient point in time (e.g., when financial documents are generated), the project journal accounts are summarized and entered into the company journal. Company financial transactions not directly associated with a single project are entered directly into the company journal.

Although the contractor may use a company journal and project journals, the overall purpose of each remains the same. They furnish the contractor the means of recording his financial transactions. In the remainder of this chapter, the project journal will be considered part of the company journal. The reader should remember that a given transaction may actually be entered into a project journal and later accounted for in the company journal.

For every company transaction there will be two or more entries made in the journal. A transaction implies an exchange. For example, a contractor may exchange cash for construction equipment. The financial transaction must be recorded as both a cash exchange and an equipment exchange.

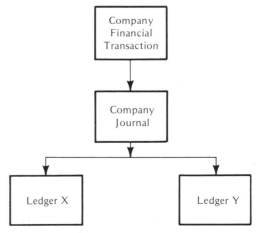

Figure 7.3 Entering financial transactions.

Thus, the transaction must be entered twice in the journal—once as a cash entry and once as an equipment entry.

A page from a typical company journal is shown in Figure 7.4. The typical journal form shown in the figure contains five columns. The date of the particular transaction is placed in column 1. The second column lists the description of the entries involved in the transaction. This entry description may or may not be merely the name of an account. Since the next column is used for identifying the account in question, the contractor may choose to give a more detailed description of the entry in the second

| | Company ABC | Company Journal | | Page J1 |
Date	Description	Account	Debit	Credit
11/1/85	Cash (Formation)	10.10	60,000	
11/1/85	Joe Smith—Stock	50.01		60,000
11/2/85	Pile Driver	11.1	20,000	
11/2/85	Pile Driving Corp.	40.1		20,000
11/26/85	101—Labor wages	81.0	2,000	
11/26/85	Cash (Wages 101)	10.10		2,000
11/30/85	Cash (Revenue 101)	10.10	5,000	
11/30/85	Revenue 101	71.0		5,000
12/2/85	Rent Eq.—101	81.1	1,000	
12/2/85	Cash (Eq. Rent)	10.10		1,000
12/6/85	Depreciate Eq.—101	81.2	2,000	
12/6/85	Pile Driver (Accu. Depr.)	11.1		2,000
12/14/85	Cash (Revenue 101)	10.10	4,000	
12/14/85	Revenue 101	71.0		4,000
12/15/85	101—Labor Wages	81.0	2,000	
12/15/85	Cash (Wages 101)	10.10		2,000
12/16/85	Office Eq.	15.0	500	
12/16/85	A-1 Office Eq.	41.0		500
12/18/85	Cash	10.10	200	
12/18/85	Eq. Rental Corp.	85.0		200
12/23/85	Dump Trucks	12.0	2,000	
12/23/85	Cash	10.10		2,000
12/23/85	Utilities—Job 101	82.0	20	
12/23/85	Cash	10.10		20
12/24/85	Labor Wages—101	81.0	1,000	
12/24/85	Cash	10.10		1,000
12/28/85	Cash	10.10	3,000	
12/28/85	Revenue—101	81.0		3,000

Figure 7.4 Journal entries.

column. Such a detailed description may be useful in using the information for other contracting tasks, such as estimating or project control. The account number associated with a particular entry is listed in column 3 of the typical journal form. This number refers to the account to which the entry will be assigned in the accounting system. Columns 4 and 5 are labeled debit and credit, respectively. As discussed in the previous section, for every transaction there will be both a debit and a credit entry in the journal. By definition, an entry that increases the company's assets is identified as a debit. Given the fact that there is both a debit and a credit entry for a transaction, and that an increase in assets is a debit, each entry into the journal may be identified as a debit or a credit.

Let us now consider some of the financial transactions a contractor may have and observe how they would be entered into the journal. Let us assume that Joe Smith invests $60,000 in the formation of a construction company (company ABC). This investment occurs on November 1, 19XX. Let us define two initial accounts. "Cash" will be considered an account and will be referenced with an account number of 10.10. Another account will be "Joe Smith's Stock Value" and will be referenced as 50.01. The transaction is recorded in company ABC's journal as shown in Figure 7.4. The "Cash" entry is debited $60,000 and the "Joe Smith's Stock Value" account is credited $60,000.

Let us now assume that company ABC (Joe Smith being the owner) purchases a $20,000 pile driving piece of construction equipment from a company named Pile Driving Corporation. This is purchased on November 2, 19XX. Rather than pay cash for the equipment, company ABC buys the equipment on credit. Thus, the company owes Pile Driving Corporation $20,000. The transaction is recorded in the company's journal as shown in Figure 7.4. An account labeled "Heavy Equipment" is debited $20,000. Construction equipment is a company asset, therefore, "Heavy Equipment" is referenced with an asset account number. Another entry called "Pile Driving Corporation" is credited $20,000. This implies that the company has created a $20,000 liability.

Let us assume that company ABC receives a contract for driving piles on a project referred to as project 101. At the end of a two-week period (November 26, 19XX), company ABC is required to pay its laborers a total of $2000. An entry labeled "Cash" is credited $2000 in the company's journal. An entry labeled "Wages and Salaries—Project 101" is debited $2000. "Wages and Salaries—Project 101" is a company expense, therefore, it is referenced with an expense account number. The two entries in the company's journal are shown in Figure 7.4.

Let us assume that at the end of the month (November 30, 19XX), company ABC is paid in part for its services on project 101. The owner of project 101 pays $5000 in cash to company ABC. "Cash" is debited $5000 in company ABC journal. Another entry described as "Revenue—Job 101" is credited $5000. "Revenue—Job 101" is referenced as a company revenue. The entries for this transaction are shown in the company's journal shown in Figure 7.4.

As company ABC continued to do business, it would have many more financial transactions. Probably, company ABC would buy more equipment, depreciate existing equipment, purchase a central office, pay office overhead costs, and have revenues and costs associated with undertaking new projects. Many of the transactions would require company ABC to define new accounts for its accounting system. Each financial transaction of the company would be entered into its accounting system in a manner similar to that for the described transactions. In addition to the previously discussed transactions, several other transactions of company ABC are shown in Figure 7.4.

An individual sheet of paper, a notebook, or a computer file, used to group or store information about a particular account in a company's accounting system, is referred to as a ledger. For every defined account within a company's accounting system there should be a ledger. For every company transaction placed in the company journal there will be ledger entries.

A typical form of a ledger is shown in Figure 7.5. The ledger is identified by its account description and its account number. The entries in a ledger are transferred from the journal. Column 1 of the ledger form shown refers to the date of transaction, which corresponds to the entry in the journal. Column 2 is for a description of the entry. If desired, this column may be omitted. However, it may be desirable to have a detailed description of the individual entries of a ledger. Column 3, labeled "Reference," is for referencing the ledger entry to the journal entry. One might simply list the journal page number from which the entry was taken. If a mistake is judged to have taken place when summing ledger entries, it is convenient to be able to reference them back to the journal to determine the origin of the mistake. Columns 4 and 5 of the ledger form shown are for recording the entry as a debit or credit, respectively.

The ledger shown in Figure 7.5 is the "Cash" ledger for the previously discussed company ABC. The ledger is complete for all the entries shown in company ABC's journal, shown in Figure 7.4. Thus, all of the "Cash" account entries in the journal shown in Figure 7.4 are transferred to the

Cash

Ledger No. 10.10				
Date	*Description*	*Reference*	*Debit*	*Credit*
11/1/85	Company Formation	J1	60,000	
11/26/85	Wages—101	J1		2,000
11/30/85	Revenue—101	J1	5,000	
12/2/85	Equip—101	J1		1,000
12/14/85	Revenue—101	J1	4,000	
12/15/85	Wages—101	J1		2,000
12/18/85	Equip. Rental	J1	200	
12/23/85	Dump Truck	J1		2,000
12/23/85	Utilities—101	J1		20
12/24/85	Wages—101	J1		1,000
12/28/85	Revenue—101	J1	3,000	

Figure 7.5   Example ledger accounts.

ledger shown in Figure 7.5. Similarly, ledgers for each of the other accounts in company ABC's journal may be produced.

The ledgers of the accounting system serve several purposes. Each ledger groups all of the entries of a particular account. Thus, they enable the contractor to identify his different types of revenues and costs. The ability to identify the amount and the timing of his revenues and costs is fundamental to his project control and company control tasks. For example, if the contractor, by means of his accounting system, can determine that his labor costs for a particular construction project operation are exceeding his estimated costs, he may be able to eliminate any future unexpected costs for the operation by analyzing the construction method used and determine a more productive method. It is his accounting system that may bring to his attention the less-than-optimal construction method.

In addition to aiding in the identification of the status of various accounts for purposes of control, the ledgers provide the means by which the company transactions are grouped for producing required financial statements, such as a balance sheet or a profit and loss statement. The production of such financial statements is discussed in the next section.

To evaluate the financial status of his company versus that of his competitors, the contractor must be able to sum the value of his various types of accounts. It is the ledgers of the accounting system that sum the various entries into a single account dollar value.

Cost Control and the Accounting Model

If the contractor's accounting model is to aid in the company cost task, certainly it should ensure that the company's financial transactions are accurately entered into the system. The accounting system should also ensure that financial transaction information is made available to the contractor as quickly as possible. If the financial transaction information is to aid in limiting and controlling the contractor's costs, the information must be made available to the contractor in time for him to implement any of the decisions resulting from the study of the information. If the information is quickly made available to the contractor, he is better able to implement a cost control program based in part on the information.

The contractor's use of his accounting system as an aid to the cost control task is also influenced by economics. Accuracy and the speed of availability of accounting information are not the only variables in question. If they were, the contractor would do well to employ many people to serve as on-site accountants and several more people to serve as overseeing company accountants. Obviously, the contractor cannot afford such an expensive (many employees) accounting and cost control program. The cost of such a program would almost certainly outweigh the benefits. Therefore, economics is an important consideration in evaluating the benefits of using an accounting model for cost control.

Thus, the contractor should seek an accurate, rapid, and economic means of implementing his accounting model or system for his company control tasks. The use of project forms for recording project labor, equipment, and material costs is consistent with this objective. These costs are then transferred directly to the accounting system. These implement similar forms for gathering other company financial transactions. The use of such forms provides an accurate, rapid, and economic means of gathering company financial transaction information. At the project level, the implementation of these forms is often the responsibility of the project superintendent. Similarly, the contractor may assign various individuals the task of implementing the use of similar forms for gathering nonproject company financial transaction information.

As a contractor's company grows in size, the number and types of financial transactions increase. His tasks of gathering financial transaction information and using the information via his accounting model soon become very complex and costly. No longer are a few people within his company capable of handling the vast amount of financial transaction information. To help alleviate this tremendous bookkeeping problem, companies (including contractors) are turning to computers. Computers are especially useful for storing and structuring information. They offer the contractor a means of accurately, rapidly, and economically (assuming much information is to be handled) storing and structuring financial transaction information. By means of a keypunch or a teletypewriter, a typist can enter the contractor's financial transaction information into a computerized accounting system. Such a computer system can eliminate recording entries into ledgers since it may be programmed to group various types of financial transactions. When this is the case, computer files correspond to the ledgers of the accounting system.

The use of a computerized accounting system can facilitate the development of a central information system that can be used to integrate several contracting tasks, e.g., the company cost control task and the contractor's payroll task (the actual determination of wages and their payment).

Financial Statements

A company may be required by law to produce certain financial statements regarding its operations. The construction contractor is no exception to this. At certain intervals of time he must produce financial statements, e.g., a balance sheet and an income statement.

Summing the various company ledgers enables the contractor to generate financial statements. When the contractor desires to produce a financial statement, the ledgers are totaled to yield a single value for each ledger.

When a financial statement is to be produced, it is often useful to produce a worksheet. This is used to summarize the debits and credits of all current company ledgers. The debits and credits of every company ledger that affect the desired financial statements are totaled. The account name of each ledger and its total debit and credit value are entered on the worksheet. It is advisable to group the worksheet ledger entries as to asset accounts, liability accounts, net worth accounts, etc. A sample worksheet is shown in Figure 7.6. The entries in the worksheet shown correspond to the journal transactions for company ABC shown in Figure 7.4. Thus, the worksheet is for a two-month period of time, November and December, 19XX. In actuality, the contractor may construct a worksheet for any period of time. For example, if company ABC was interested in producing an income statement for the month of November, 19XX, it could generate a worksheet for the November company transactions.

The worksheet shown in Figure 7.6 is constructed so that it facilitates the production of both a company balance sheet and an income statement.

Sample Worksheet

Description	Trial Balance Debit	Trial Balance Credit	Adjustments Debit	Adjustments Credit	Adjusted Trial Balance Debit	Adjusted Trial Balance Credit
Cash	72,200	8,020		200	72,200	8,220
Heavy Equip.	20,000	2,000			20,000	2,000
Trucks	2,000				2,000	
Office Equip.	500				500	
Pile Driving Corp.		20,000				20,000
A-1 Office Equip.		500				500
Joe Smith's Stock		60,000				60,000
Equip. Rental Revenue		200				200
Job 101—Revenue		12,000				12,000
Job 101—Utilities	20				20	
Job 101—Equip. Rental	1,000				1,000	
Job 101—Equip. Depr.	2,000				2,000	
Wages—Job 101	5,000		200		5,200	
Totals	102,720	102,720	200	200	102,920	102,920

Figure 7.6 Example trial balance worksheet.

If only one of these documents is to be produced, only part of the worksheet shown has to be constructed. For example, if only an income statement is to be produced, only revenue and expense accounts have to be considered in the construction of the worksheet. On the other hand, if only a balance sheet is to be produced, the worksheet should list asset, liability, and net worth accounts.

In the worksheet shown in Figure 7.6, the various accounts are listed in column 1. In columns 2 and 3 the debit and credit amounts of the various accounts are listed. These two columns are labeled the "Trial Balance Columns." The debits and credits, as summed from the company ledgers, are totaled in these trial balance columns. Unless there has been a mistake made, the total of the debit column of the worksheet should equal the total of the credit column. This is because there is an equal debit and credit entered into the company journal for every company transaction. Columns

4 and 5 in the worksheet shown in Figure 7.6 are labeled as "adjustment" columns. These columns are not corrections owing to mathematical errors but for additions or subtractions, which are required to state the company's actual financial condition.

For example, a contractor may pay his workers every two weeks. At the time the worksheet is constructed, the contractor may actually owe his workers one week's pay. Thus, although the workers are not to be paid until the end of the following week, the contractor has actually incurred a cost. This, it may be desirable to adjust the worksheet entries to represent the true financial state of the contractor.

Finally, columns 6 and 7 in the worksheet shown in Figure 7.6 are for calculating the adjusted trial balance. The adjusted values in columns 4 and 5 are added or subtracted to the trial balance figures in columns 2 and 3 to yield the adjusted trial balance figures. Once again, the sum of the debits should equal the sum of the credits.

In addition to grouping the company accounts so that the contractor may easily produce financial statements, the worksheet enables the contractor to check the balancing characteristics of his accounting system. If for some reason the accounts did not balance, this fact would clearly be shown in the comparison of the sum of the debits and credits of the worksheet. If the debits and credits do not balance, the error may merely be a mathematical mistake, in which case it must be traced and corrected. However, the fact that the debits and credits do not balance may also be caused by an erroneous entry of a company transaction. If this is the case, the contractor must retrace his accounting documents to find the original error. The reference and description columns of the ledgers and journals greatly facilitate the task of searching for an erroneous transaction entry.

Income Statement

One of the more frequently produced company financial statements is the income statement. The income statement is sometimes referred to as a profit and loss statement. This statement shows the change in the financial condition of the company resulting from the performance of business. The income statement compares a company's revenues and expenses for a stated period of time, and may be produced for any stated period of time. Companies, including construction contractors, often produce quarterly (every 3 months) or even monthly income statements.

The revenue and expense accounts are transferred from the worksheet (developed for the period of time in question) to the income statement. However, before doing this, each of the account's debits and credits, as shown on the worksheet, is compared, and a single positive or negative value is obtained for each. In the case of revenue accounts, an account's debit is subtracted from its credit. If the resulting number is positive, the account is considered positive. Obviously, if the result is negative, the account value is negative. In the case of expense accounts, an account's credit is subtracted from its debit. If the resulting number is positive, then there is a positive expense. Similarly, if the result is negative, the expense account has a negative value.

The revenue accounts and their values (either positive or negative) and the expense accounts and their values (either positive or negative) are each listed on the income statement in separate columns, as shown in Figure 7.7. The account entries used in determining the status of each account occur in the time period for which the income statement is constructed. The entries shown in Figure 7.7 correspond to the transactions of company ABC in the months of November and December, 19XX, as shown in Figure 7.4.

The net income row shown in Figure 7.7 is for calculating the company's profit or loss for the period of time in question. To calculate this value, the revenue entries' values are summed (negative values are subtracted) and the expense entries' values are summed (negative values are subtracted). If the sum of the revenue entries' values exceeds the sum of the expense entries' values, the difference between the two sums corresponds to company profit. Similarly, if the sum of the expense entries' values exceeds the sum of the revenue entries' values, the difference between the two sums corresponds to company loss.

Income Statement

November 1–December 31

Account	Debit	Credit
Equip. Rental Revenue		200
Job 101—Revenue		12,000
Job 101—Utilities	20	
Job 101—Equip. Rental	1,000	
Job 101—Equip. Depr.	2,000	
Wages—Job 101	5,200	
Totals	8,220	12,200
Net Income	3,980	

Figure 7.7   Example income statement.

The value of the calculated net income represents the change in the financial condition of the company, as a result of performing its business in the period of time in question. This change is often reflected in the net worth of the company. If the company made a profit, its net worth is increased; if it lost money, the company's net worth is decreased. However, the net worth will remain unchanged if all profits are paid out in the form of dividends.

Balance Sheet

Unlike the income statement, the company balance sheet shows the financial condition of the company at a point in time. It is common to produce such a statement at the end of the year, or even quarterly. The balance sheet is actually a representation of the financial equation of balance relating assets, liabilities, net worth, revenues, and expenses.

The company's asset, liability, and net worth accounts, and their values, are listed on the balance sheet. As in the income statement, their values (usually changed to positive or negative values rather than debit or credit values) may be obtained from the worksheet.

An account referred to as "retained earnings" is included in the net worth entries in the balance sheet. This retained earnings represents the difference between the company's income and expenses, as determined by the income statement (assuming no dividends). Thus, the net income, as shown on an income statement is often referred to as retained earnings. The net income (either positive or negative) is integrated into the company's balance sheet by means of the net worth account called "retained earnings."

A company may choose to pay out dividends from some of its earned profits. If this is the case, its net income is actually divided into dividends and retained earnings. In either case they are recognized in the balance sheet for the company.

Only the asset, liability, and net worth accounts are listed in the balance sheet. However, the net worth recognizes the company's revenues and expenses. Thus, the financial equation of balance may be expressed in terms of asset, liability, and net worth accounts. The company's assets should therefore equal the company's liabilities plus its net worth.

A typical balance sheet form is shown in Figure 7.8. It is a balance sheet for the previously discussed company ABC, as of December 31, 19XX. It is common to list the asset accounts in one column or page and the liability and net worth accounts in a second column or page. Obviously, the sum of the entries of each column (or page) must be equal.

January 1	Balance Sheet
Assets	63,980
Cash	18,000
Heavy Equip.	2,000
Trucks	500
Office Equip.	84,480
Liabilities	20,000
Piling Driving Corp.	500
A-1 Office Equip.	
Net Worth	60,000
Joe Smith Stock	3,980
Retained Earnings	84,480

Figure 7.8 Example balance sheet.

EXAMPLE GENERAL LEDGER COMPUTER PROGRAM

To illustrate computer software programs that perform the entire financial accounting functions for a construction firm would likely require an entire book on just this topic. Software programs would need to perform general ledger functions, accounts receivable, accounts payable, payroll, and job costing. A computer program to do any one of these functions would in itself be long and complex.

While we will not illustrate programs that do each of the above-noted financial accounting functions, in Figure 7.9 we list a program written in BASIC that performs the general ledger functions. The program enables the user to set up general ledger accounts, enter financial transactions for the accounts, and print a trial balance or balance sheet. Example output from the program is illustrated in Figure 7.10.

In the interest of presenting a relatively simple program that the reader can follow and understand, we have not concerned ourself with error routines or preferred instructions to the user that would normally be included in an off-the-shelf program.

While we will not discuss every line of the program illustrated in Figure 7.9, we will now discuss several of the unique and more important parts of the program. Perhaps the one unique aspect of the general ledger program listed in Figure 7.9 (relative to the other illustrated programs in this book), is the use of many subroutines. A subroutine is used by a programmer if a certain routine (the instructions in the subroutine) occur in several places in the overall program. Rather than repeat the routines several times, the programmer has the program "branch" to the subroutine when the program wants to execute the instructions. The subroutine is *called* by a GOSUB instruction.

```
10 CLS
20 INPUT "ENTER COMPANY NAME= ";NA$
30 INPUT "ENTER DATE= ";DA$
34 INPUT "ENTER C TO CONTINUE ";C$
35 CLS
40 GOSUB 200
50 GOSUB 400
60 CLS
70 PRINT "ENTER D: TO DISPLAY AN ACCOUNT"
80 PRINT "ENTER E: TO ENTER A FINANCIAL TRANSACTION"
90 PRINT "ENTER T: TO PRINT A WORKING TRIAL BALANCE"
100 PRINT "ENTER B: TO PRINT A BALANCE SHEET"
110 PRINT "ENTER S: TO STOP/TERMINATE THE PROGRAM"
120 INPUT CH$
130 IF (CH$="D") THEN GOSUB 600
140 IF (CH$="E") THEN GOSUB 800
150 IF (CH$="T") THEN GOSUB 1000
160 IF (CH$="B") THEN GOSUB 1200
170 IF (CH$="S") THEN 2000
180 CLS
190 GOTO 60
200 CLS
205 INPUT "ENTER NO. OF GENERAL LEDGER ACCOUNTS= ";N
210 INPUT "ENTER NO. OF ASSET ACCOUNTS= ";A
215 INPUT "ENTER NO. OF LIABILITY ACCOUNTS= ";L
220 INPUT "ENTER NO. OF EQUITY ACCOUNTS= ";Q
230 FOR J=1 TO N
235 CLS
240 PRINT "ENTER ACCOUNT NO. ";J;
245 INPUT N$(J)
250 PRINT "ENTER D IF DEBIT ACCOUNT OR C IF CREDIT ACCOUNT";
255 INPUT T$(J)
260 NEXT J
265 TA$="DEBIT"
270 TB$="CREDIT"
275 FA$="$$###,####.##"
280 FB$="$$###,####.##   $$###,####.##   $$###,####.##"
285 FC$="$$###,####.##   $$###,####.##"
290 FD$="-----------------------------------------------"
300 RETURN
400 CLS
402 D=0
405 PRINT "ACCOUNT BALANCES BEING INITIALIZED"
410 PRINT "YOU WILL NOW INPUT ACCOUNT BALANCES FROM END OF PREVIOUS YEAR"
411 INPUT "ENTER C TO CONTINUE ";C$
412 CLS
415 DIM AA(100,2)
416 DIM AB(100,2)
420 FOR K=1 TO N
425 CLS
430 PRINT N$(K);
```

Figure 7.9 Example computer program written in BASIC for general ledger accounting.

```
435 IF (T$(K)="C") THEN 455
440 PRINT " ACCOUNT TYPE= ";TA$
445 INPUT "ENTER ACCOUNT BALANCE= ";AA(K,1)
447 AA(K,2)=0
450 GOTO 465
455 PRINT "ACCOUNT TYPE= ";TB$
460 INPUT "ENTER ACCOUNT BALANCE= ";AA(K,2)
462 AA(K,1)=0
465 NEXT K
470 PRINT "THE PROGRAM WILL NOW CHECK TO SEE IF THE DEBITS EQUAL THE CREDITS
472 INPUT "ENTER C TO CONTINUE ";C$
473 CLS
475 GOSUB 1500
478 IF (D=1) THEN 400
485 PRINT "THE PROGRAM WILL NOW CHECK TO SEE IF ASSETS=LIABILITIES PLUS NET WORT
H
486 INPUT "ENTER C TO CONTINUE ";C$
487 CLS
490 GOSUB 1600
495 IF (D=2) THEN 400
498 RETURN
600 CLS
605 GOSUB 700
608 GOSUB 1700
610 PRINT "DO YOU WANT TO PRINT MORE ACCOUNT NAMES?"
615 INPUT "ENTER Y OR N";CB$
620 IF (CB$="Y") THEN 600
625 RETURN
700 CLS
705 INPUT "ENTER NO. OF ACCOUNTS YOU WANT TO VIEW= ";NT
710 FOR R=1 TO NT
715 PRINT "NO.";R;"   ";N$(R)
720 NEXT R
725 INPUT "ENTER ACCOUNT NUMBER= ";ACC
730 RETURN
800 CLS
805 GOSUB 700
810 INPUT "ENTER D FOR DEBIT OR C FOR CREDIT ";CT$
815 INPUT "ENTER AMOUNT= ";AMT
820 IF (CT$="D") THEN AA(ACC,1)=AA(ACC,1)+AMT
825 IF (CT$="C") THEN AA(ACC,2)=AA(ACC,2)+AMT
830 INPUT "ENTER C TO INPUT OFFSETTING ACCOUNT ";C$
835 GOSUB 700
840 IF (CT$="D") THEN AA(ACC,2)=AA(ACC,2)+AMT
845 IF (CT$="C") THEN AA(ACC,1)=AA(ACC,1)+AMT
850 GOSUB 1500
852 INPUT "ENTER C TO CONTINUE ";C$
855 GOSUB 1600
860 RETURN
1000 CLS
1005 PRINT "TRIAL BALANCE"
1010 PRINT TAB(20);FD$
1015 PRINT "ACCOUNT";TAB(30);TA$;TAB(53);TB$
1020 T1=0
1025 T2=0
1030 FOR S=1 TO N
1035 IF AA(S,2)>AA(S,1) GOTO 1070
1040 PRINT N$(S);TAB(25);
1045 PRINT USING FC$;AA(S,1)-AA(S,2),0
```

Figure 7.9 *Continued*

```
1055 T1=AA(S,1)-AA(S,2)+T1
1060 GOTO 1090
1070 PRINT N$(S);TAB(25);
1075 PRINT USING FC$;0,AA(S,2)-AA(S,1)
1080 T2=AA(S,2)-AA(S,1)+T2
1090 NEXT S
1095 PRINT TAB(10);"TOTALS";TAB(25);
1100 PRINT USING FC$;T1,T2
1105 INPUT "ENTER C TO CONTINUE ";C$
1110 RETURN
1200 CLS
1205 PRINT "BALANCE SHEET"
1210 FOR I=1 TO N
1215 AB(I,1)=AA(I,1)
1220 AB(I,2)=AA(I,2)
1225 M$(I)=N$(I)
1230 NEXT I
1235 CLS
1240 PRINT TAB(15);NA$
1245 PRINT TAB(15);"BALANCE SHEET"
1250 PRINT TAB(15);DA$
1255 PRINT " ASSETS"
1260 AF=0
1265 FOR I=1 TO A
1270 PRINT M$(I);TAB(25)
1275 PRINT USING FA$;AB(I,1)-AB(I,2)
1280 AF=AF+AB(I,1)-AB(I,2)
1285 NEXT I
1290 PRINT "   TOTAL ASSETS ";TAB(35);
1295 PRINT USING FA$;AF
1300 PRINT "  LIABILITIES "
1305 LF=0
1308 R=A +L
1310 FOR I=(1 + A) TO R
1315 PRINT M$(I);TAB(25);
1320 PRINT USING FA$;AB(I,2)-AB(I,1)
1325 LF=LF + AB(I,2)-AB(I,1)
1330 NEXT I
1335 PRINT "  TOTAL LIABILITIES ";TAB(35);
1340 PRINT USING FA$;LF
1345 PRINT ""
1350 PRINT " OWNER'S EQUITY"
1355 EQ=0
1360 FOR I=A+L+1 TO N
1365 PRINT M$(I);TAB(25);
1370 PRINT USING FA$;AB(I,2)-AB(I,1)
1375 EQ=EQ+AB(I,2)-AB(I,1)
1380 NEXT I
1385 PRINT "  TOTAL OWNER'S EQUITY ";TAB(35);
1390 PRINT USING FA$;EQ
1395 PRINT ""
1400 PRINT "TOTAL LIABILITIES + OWNER'S EQUITY= ";TAB(50)
1405 PRINT USING FA$;LF +EQ
1410 INPUT "ENTER C TO CONTINUE ";C$
1420 RETURN
1500 T1=0
1505 T2=0
```

Figure 7.9 *Continued*

```
1510 FOR LA=1 TO N
1515 T1=T1+AA(LA,1)
1520 T2=T2+AA(LA,2)
1525 NEXT LA
1530 PRINT "DEBITS= ";
1535 PRINT USING FA$;T1
1540 PRINT "CREDITS= ";
1545 PRINT USING FA$;T2
1550 IF (T1=T2) THEN RETURN
1555 PRINT ""
1560 PRINT "DEBITS TO NOT EQUAL CREDITS"
1565 INPUT "ENTER C TO REENTER ACCOUNT BALANCES ";C$
1570 D=1
1575 RETURN



1600 AS=0
1605 FOR M= 1 TO A
1610 AS=AS +(AA(M,1)-AA(M,2))
1615 NEXT M
1620 LI=0
1625 FOR M=1+A TO A+L
1630 LI=LI+ (AA(M,2)-AA(M,1))
1635 NEXT M
1640 OQ=0
1645 FOR M=1+A+L TO N
1650 OQ=OQ+(AA(M,2)-AA(M,1))
1655 NEXT M
1660 PRINT "      ASSETS      LIABILITIES      OWNER'S EQUITY
1665 PRINT USING FB$;AS,LI,OQ
1667 INPUT "ENTER C TO CONTINUE ";C$
1670 IF (AS=LI+OQ) THEN RETURN
1675 PRINT "ASSETS ARE NOT EQUAL TO LIABILITIES PLUS OWNER'S EQUITY
1680 D=2
1685 INPUT "ENTER C TO REENTER ACCOUNT BALANCES
1690 RETURN
1700 CLS
1705 PRINT N$(ACC)
1710 PRINT TAB(7);FD$
1720 PRINT TAB(10);TA$;TAB(31);TB$
1725 PRINT TAB(7);FD$
1730 PRINT USING FC$;AA(ACC,1),AA(ACC,2)
1735 PRINT TAB(7);FD$
1740 PRINT "BALANCE= ";
1745 PRINT USING FC$;ABS(AA(ACC,1)-AA(ACC,2))
1750 PRINT " ";
1755 IF (AA(ACC,1)>AA(ACC,2)) THEN PRINT TA$
1760 IF (AA(ACC,2)>AA(ACC,1)) THEN PRINT TB$
1770 RETURN
2000 CLS
2005 PRINT "THIS IS THE END OF THE PROGRAM"
```

Figure 7.9 *Continued*

```
TRIAL BALANCE
                        ----------------------------------------------
ACCOUNT                      DEBIT                     CREDIT
CASH                      $9,000.00                  $0.00
ACC. REC                  $5,000.00                  $0.00
EQUIPMENT                 $2,000.00                  $0.00
ACC. PAYABLE                  $0.00              $3,000.00
NOTE REC.                     $0.00              $2,000.00
LOAN DUE                      $0.00              $6,000.00
RET. EARNINGS                 $0.00              $5,000.00
          TOTALS         $16,000.00             $16,000.00
ENTER C TO CONTINUE ?


                    GOODWORK CONSTRUCTION
                    BALANCE SHEET
                    4-24-1984
     ASSETS
CASH                          $9,000.00
ACC. REC                      $5,000.00
EQUIPMENT                     $2,000.00
   TOTAL ASSETS                            $16,000.00
     LIABILITIES
ACC. PAYABLE                  $3,000.00
NOTE REC.                     $2,000.00
LOAN DUE                      $6,000.00
   TOTAL LIABILITIES                       $11,000.00

  OWNER'S EQUITY
RET. EARNINGS                 $5,000.00
   TOTAL OWNER'S EQUITY                     $5,000.00

TOTAL LIABILITIES + OWNER'S EQUITY=                   $16,000.00
ENTER C TO CONTINUE ?
```

Figure 7.10 Example reports from general ledger program.

Let us now describe how the overall program works. After having the program user input the project name and date in lines 20 and 30, the program branches to subroutines 200 and 400. In subroutine 200 (lines 200 through 300) the user informs the program about the number of accounts, if they are primarily debit or credit balance accounts, and with the use of the loop in lines 230 through 260 inputs the general ledger account names. Various variables that will subsequently be used to format output are also initialized in subroutine 200.

Subroutine 400 enables the user to input account balances for each of the previously defined account names. The account balances would be entered as zeros in the initial run. After the initial run, the account balances received as output from the last run would be input.

The reader should note that the program illustrated is intentionally simple such that we can easily follow it. To be an effective program for general ledger accounting, several modifications would be needed. For example, as it now stands, the user would have to redefine the general ledger accounts each time he runs the program.

To be more effective as a program, we would want to use data file programming to "store" the setup account names on a data disk. After the first run of the program we would then have the program read the data disk (on which would be the account names). This would eliminate our need to enter them each time. The same type of programming would be done in regard to the account balances. By storing the account balances on a data disk, we would not have to reenter them each time we ran the program. While we will not discuss the storing of data on a data disk in this chapter, it will be illustrated in another example program in a later chapter.

Once the user enters the account balances in subroutine 400, the program branches to subroutines 1500 and 1600. In subroutine 1500 the program checks to determine that the sum total of all inputted debit amounts equals the sum total of all inputted credit amounts. Similarly, in subroutine 1600, the program checks that the sum of the financial entries for the asset accounts equal the liability plus the owner's equity accounts. Assuming that both of these subroutines find that entries "do balance," the program execution is returned to subroutine 400, which in turn returns to line 60.

The user is then given an option menu of displaying accounts, entering financial transactions, printing a working trial balance, or printing a balance sheet. Let us now describe the purpose of each of these program options.

If the user selects to display an account, the program branches to subroutine 600. Subroutine 600 in turn branches to subroutine 700 and 1700. In subroutine 700 the user is given an opportunity to view the previously entered general ledger account names. He also selects the account number for which he wants a display.

The program then branches to subroutine 1700. This subroutine prints the debit and credit balances for the selected account and also prints the net balance amount. After completing this, the program returns to subroutine 600, which in turn returns the user to the option menu.

If the user selects to enter financial transactions, the program branches to subroutine 800. This subroutine in turn first branches to subroutine 700, which again enables the user to identify the account name for which he wants to enter a transaction. After identifying the account, the program returns to subroutine 800. This subroutine then requests the user to enter the financial transaction. The reader should note that after inputting the transaction, subroutine 800, by branching back to subroutine 700, requests the name of the offsetting account. The reader will note that for every debit entry for an account there must also be an account credited. After a transaction is entered, subroutine 800 branches to subroutines 1500 and 1600 again to check that debits equal credits, and assets equal liabilities plus owner's equity. Subroutine 800 then returns the user to the option menu.

If the user selects to print a trial balance, the program branches to subroutine 1000. This subroutine accesses no other subroutines. Instead, via the program loop in lines 1030 to 1090, the program prints the account balances for each general ledger account. The totals are also printed and the user is returned to the options menu.

If the user selects to print a balance sheet, the program branches to subroutine 1200. Subroutine 1200 also executes without accessing another subroutine. Three program loops (lines 1265–1285, lines 1310–1330, and lines 1360–1380) print the name and account balances for the assets, liabilities, and owner's equity accounts. The subroutine then returns to the options menu. The user can select to stop/terminate the program from the options menu.

The program listed in Figure 7.9 is designed to print/display all reports on the computer menu. Modifications would be necessary to yield hard-copy printer reports such as the reports illustrated in Figure 7.10.

8: Conceptual Estimating Applications

INTRODUCTION

One of the first, if not the first, estimate prepared for a proposed project is the feasibility estimate or pro forma estimate. This estimate calculates the rate of return the proposed project is to yield the project owner. The project owner uses the prepared feasibility estimate as a basis for his decision as to whether or not to construct the project.

The analysis included in a feasibility estimate covers several years. For example, assuming a project owner is planning to construct and own an office building for seven years, the analysis would include an estimation of revenue and costs for the seven-year period. Given the need to include estimates of uncertain numbers for several future years, one might argue that at best the results of the feasibility estimate are approximate and should be used with a degree of skepticism.

In spite of the fact that each and every feasibility estimate includes an estimate of many uncertain factors, the fact that the preparer of the feasibility estimate places a fancy folder/jacket cover over the calculated results often leads the reader of the feasibility estimate to accept the calculated results as deterministic and to view the results as being 100 percent accurate. In reality, the fancy cover does little to add to the accuracy of the results.

The problem of accuracy owing to uncertain variables that one includes in the feasibility estimate could partly be solved if the preparer would produce several feasibility estimates, each based on different assumptions regarding the value of the variables. The reader of the multiple prepared estimates could then study the various calculated rate of returns and base his decision to proceed or not proceed on the various estimates.

While such an approach would be advantageous relative to basing a decision on a single feasibility estimate (based on a single set of assumed values on the variables), the approach would likely prove impractical if the estimates were prepared manually.

Given the numerous mathematical calculations that are part of the preparation of a feasibility estimate, the preparation of the numerous feasibility estimates that would need to be prepared would result in literally several man-days if not man-months to prepare. Even then one might argue that the results would be questionable.

A computer can perform mathematical calculations in a matter of fractions of a second. A series of mathematical calculations can be performed via the computer microprocessor faster than a program user can input them via a keyboard. The end result is that via the use of a feasibility estimate computer software program the user can create an endless number of feasibility estimates for a proposed project, each one for a different set of values of the input variables. The only limitation becomes one of the time the program takes to input the value of the variables via the computer keyboard.

The end result is that the use of a computer enables the project owner (or his representative, the project designer) to play "what if" situations and measure the sensitivity of the calculated rate of return to changes in one or more of the risk variables. The computer becomes a tool to evaluate risk and uncertainty.

Before illustrating a feasibility estimate software program, we will first present the manual calculations for an example feasibility estimate. This will enhance our understanding of the benefits of the computerized approach.

Once a feasibility estimate is made for a project and the project receives the go ahead to proceed, other design estimates are prepared. These design phase estimates are also referred to as conceptual estimates. One such design estimate is referred to as a parameter estimate. In this chapter we will also present the concept of parameter estimating along with an example BASIC program to perform parameter estimating calculations. The parameter estimating program will give us our first introduction to data file programming.

FEASIBILITY ESTIMATE FOR AN OFFICE BUILDING

This section illustrates a feasibility estimate. The relevant factors and terminology that are part of a feasibility estimate are somewhat a function of the type of project being considered; thus, it is impossible to present a single example that encompasses all factors and terminology. However, the procedure and objectives of the feasibility study are essentially the same regardless of the project's type or size, so the techniques illustrated here should prove applicable to numerous types of projects.

Let us assume that an individual or firm is considering constructing an office building with the intention of leasing office space. Based on his available budget, the lot size, and his familiarity with similar projects, the potential investor has decided on a three-story building with approximately 12,500 square feet. At the time of the feasibility estimate, little has been determined about building quality other than that a brick building is preferred. The project is to be conventionally financed and is to be built in a metropolitan area.

The initial cost of the project can be approximated by using office building data published in cost books. On the basis of the square footage desired, at $80 per square foot, initial cost for the improvements on the land would be approximately $1 million. To this must be added the land cost. This cost is usually easier to calculate than the improvement costs because it can be determined by means of an option contract with the landowner. Such a contract gives the potential investor a right to purchase the land in question for a specific amount of money within a given time period—say two months. For this right the investor gives the landowner an amount of money that will be forfeited if the investor fails to exercise his purchase right. If he purchases the land, the option money usually is credited to his purchase price. For purposes of our example, let us assume that the investor has a right to purchase the required land for $100,000. Thus, the initial office building costs are approximated as follows.

Land	$ 100,000
Improvements	1,000,000
Initial Costs	$1,100,000

Project Owner's Estimate

Let us assume that the cost of money is such that it will be possible for the investor to secure an 80 percent conventional financing loan at 15 percent interest per annum payable over 20 years. The other 20 percent of the initial costs are to be financed by means of equity capital of the investor. Thus, the investor would obtain a loan for 80 percent of the $1.1 million, or $880,000.

By using interest formuli tables, it is possible to calculate the equal monthly or yearly payment that retires the loan and reflects the interest charged by the lender. In a feasibility estimate this monthly or yearly payment is commonly referred to as the debt service. Using interest tables, an annual debt service of $140,588.80 can be determined as the annual payment required by the company to repay the $880,000 and the 15 percent interest.

The operating expense component of the project is commonly expressed as a percentage of the construction costs of erecting the building. Operating expenses normally range from 6 to 30 percent of construction cost, depending on the type of building being erected.

Let us assume that the initial operating expense (maintenance and repair) for the office building is expected to be 10 percent of the construction costs. Based on anticipated construction costs of $1 million, the initial operating expenses are estimated to be $100,000.

A market analysis must be made of the immediate project vicinity in order to establish an estimate of the rental area. A primary part of the market analysis consists of a comparison of rental or leasing rates of comparable types of buildings in the surrounding geographic area. Let us assume that the market analysis for our example yields an anticipated leasing rate of $2.50 per square foot per month.

Although the gross square footage of the proposed office building is 12,500, interior walls, doorways, columns, etc., will reduce the leasable space. The rule of thumb for office buildings is that a building is efficiently designed if the leasable area approaches 80 percent of the gross area.

Assuming 80 percent leasable space, a 7 percent vacancy allowance, and an expected leasing rate of $2.50, the gross possible income is calculated as follows:

$$
\begin{aligned}
\text{Gross area} \; &= \; 12{,}500 \text{ square feet} \times .80 \text{ leasable} \\
&= \; 10{,}000 \text{ square feet} - .12 \text{ vacancy allowance} \\
&= \; 9{,}300 \text{ square feet} \times \$2.50 \text{ per square foot} \\
&= \; \$23{,}250 \text{ per month} \times 12 \text{ months} \\
&= \; \$279{,}000
\end{aligned}
$$

As noted earlier, operating expenses will be assumed as $100,000 for the first year. Naturally, the operating expenses will increase from one year to the next. However, they will be compensated by equal relative increases in leasing rates.

For an accurate rate-of-return calculation, one must have sufficient information. For example, for our office building project, analysis must include such factors as the owner's decision to sell the project after a number of years, the investor's tax rate, and the particular depreciation method to be used.

Let us assume that the office building investor is in the 40 percent tax bracket, that he is planning to sell the project after seven years, and that he would like to utilize the straight-line depreciation method. The fact that the owner plans to sell the project before it has no value means that the selling price must be estimated. The estimated future value of a building is often determined by assuming a constant appreciation (or depreciation) rate for the building. This rate is probably unrelated to the depreciation rate used to reduce the value of the building for tax purposes. For our example we will assume an annual appreciation rate of 1 percent.

We will now proceed to determine the annual cash inflow or outflow for each of the years of the analysis. As indicated earlier, the gross possible income (i.e., the rental income) and the operating expense will likely vary from year to year. However, the investor will probably increase rental rates to reflect increased operating expenses. Thus, it is the net of the rental income and operating expenses that is of concern to us here; this amount can be assumed constant throughout the relevant time period.

Initially (i.e., at time period 0), the investor in the office building has an outflow of $220,000. This represents the invested equity in the project. The annual cash inflows from owning and operating the office building for the first year is illustrated in Figure 8.1. The cash flow calculation is initiated by first listing the gross possible income (i.e., the lease income). The $279,000 is shown as the net of the vacancy allowance.

The operating expenses shown include annual utilities, maintenance and repairs, insurance, real estate taxes, advertising, legal and accounting costs, and caretaker/manager fees. On the basis of the previous assumed operating expense amount of 10 percent times initial construction costs, $100,000 is indicated in Figure 8.1 as the first-year operating expense. The $100,000 difference between the gross possible income and the operating expense is shown as the net operating cash income. It is the cash inflow to the investor before consideration of the debt service, depreciation, and tax effects.

The debt service amount of $140,588.80 is subtracted from the net operating cash income. The constant of .15976 used to determine the debt service is a factor that equates to 15 percent interest rate and a payback period of 20 years. Subtracting the $140,588.80 from the $179,000.00 leaves a net cash flow of $38,411.20. This amount does not, however, reflect depreciation, interest, or tax effects.

Part F of Figure 8.1 reflects the effect of depreciation, interest, and taxes. The calculation starts with a restatement of the gross possible income; i.e., the $279,000 is the previously determined inflow from rental receipts. In order to calculate the actual operating gain or loss for purposes of taxes,

Pro Forma
Annual Cash Results for Office Building

A. Gross Possible Income (including vacancy allowance)		$279,000.00
B. Operating Expenses		−100,000.00
C. Net Operating Cash Income		179,000.00
D. Less Mortgage of $880,000 times Debit Service Constant of .15976		−140,588.80
E. Net Cash Flow		$ 38,411.20
F. Depreciation, Interest, and Tax Effects		
1. Gross Possible Income	$279,000.00	
2. Operating Expenses	−100,000.00	
3. Depreciation–Construction costs of $1 million at 150% straight-line depreciation with life of 15 years	− 66,666.67	
4. Interest Cost (i.e., part of the debt service)	−132,000.00	
Net Operating Gain	$−19,666.67	
Tax Liability (40% bracket) ($19,667.67)		+ 7,866.07
G. Total Cash Inflow After Taxes		$ 46,277.27

Figure 8.1 First-year cash inflow.

the operating expenses, depreciation, and interest effects must be subtracted from the gross possible income. (The operating expense, previously calculated as $100,000, is shown in line 2.)

Depreciation is an expense that is allowable for purposes of taxes; however, it is not a cash expense in regard to the firm. Depreciation provides the potential investor a benefit in that while not expending cash, the depreciation expense has the effect of reducing tax liability. Earlier it was stated that the office building investor wanted to use the straight-line depreciation method. Current tax laws also dictate the minimum number of years over which an asset can be depreciated. Current tax laws permit many buildings to be depreciated in 15 years. A 15-year depreciation period is assumed in the example. Thus, the calculation of depreciation for the office building illustrated in Figure 8.1 uses straight-line depreciation over a 15-year life. Given these assumptions, the calculated depreciation for the first year of the office building is $66,666.67.

We previously calculated an annual debt service of $140,588.80 to pay back the mortgage that was taken on the office building. This debt service was made up of a payback of principal and interest. Only the interest cost or expense is a deductible expense for purposes of calculating taxable income. Therefore, the interest cost must be broken out of the debt service so we can calculate the effect of interest on cash flow. In early years the interest expense is large, while the payback on the principal is small. In particular, the interest cost for the first year is 15 percent times the mortgage. This yields an interest expense of $132,000 for the first year.

When we subtract the operating expense, depreciation, and interest expense from the gross possible income, we achieve a calculated net operating tax loss of $19,667.67. The effect of the depreciation and interest expense results in a net operating tax loss. This is in fact desirable because it results in a reduction of taxes to the point at which the tax effect actually adds to the net cash flow for the investor. In our example the effect of depreciation and interest does reduce the net operating income to a negative number. The depreciation and interest expenses have the effect of reducing the tax liability.

Earlier it was indicated that the investor was in the 40 percent income tax bracket. His tax liability (gain) is calculated by multiplying 40 percent times the net operating loss of $19,666.67; this results in a tax gain of $7866.07. This tax gain is added to the net cash flow in order to calculate the total cash inflow after taxes. As is shown in Figure 8.1, this results in a total cash inflow after taxes of $47,277.27. This is the total cash inflow at the end of the first year for the office building. This cash inflow will change in following years because the depreciation and interest expense for following years will also change. Thus, the tax liability will change also, so that total cash inflow decreases over the years.

In order to calculate the total cash inflow for years 2 through 7, we must be able to determine the actual amount of depreciation and the actual interest expense for each of these years. These calculations are shown in Figures 8.2 and 8.3, respectively. In Figure 8.2 the depreciation charge for any one year is determined as $66,666.67 because the straight-line depreciation method is used.

The calculation of the interest payment is shown in Figure 8.3. The debt service charge for each year is constant. This payment is $140,588.80, as shown in the figure. Note that this debt service includes an interest

End of Year	Depreciation Charge	Book Value
0	$66,666.67	$1,000,000.00
1	66,666.67	933,333.33
2	66,666.67	866,666.66
3	66,666.67	799,999.99
4	66,666.67	733,333.32
5	66,666.67	666,666.65
6	66,666.67	599,999.98
7	66,666.67	533,333.31

Figure 8.2   Depreciation charge and book value for improvements.

End of Year	Debit Service	Interest Payment	Principal Payment	Mortgage
0				$880,000.00
1	$140,588.80	$132,000.00	$ 8,588.80	871,411.20
2	140,588.80	130,711.68	9,877.12	861,534.08
3	140,588.80	129,230.11	11,358.69	850,175.39
4	140,588.80	127,526.30	13,062.50	837,112.89
5	140,588.80	125,566.93	15,021.87	822,091.02
6	140,588.80	123,313.65	17,275.15	804,815.87
7	140,588.80	120,722.33	19,866.47	784,949.40

Figure 8.3   Debt service breakdown.

payment and a principal payment. The interest payment is calculated by multiplying the interest rate of 15 percent times the mortgage at the end of the previous year. The remainder after subtracting the interest payment from the debt service is the principal payment. As can be seen in Figure 8.3, the interest payment decreases each year, while the principal payment increases yearly.

Having calculated the depreciation expense and interest expense for each of the years 1 through 7, we can now calculate the total cash inflow for each of these years. Previously, we determined the total cash inflow at the end of year 1. Note that the depreciation expense and the interest expense have the effect of changing the tax liability for each of the years. The operating expense and the gross possible income or rental income will

End of Year	Operating Expense	Depreciation	Interest	Net Operating Loss	Tax	Total Cash Inflow
1	$100,000.00	$66,666.67	$132,000.00	$19,666.67	$7,866.67	$46,277.27
2	100,000.00	66,666.67	130,711.68	18,378.35	7,351.34	45,762.54
3	100,000.00	66,666.67	129,230.11	16,896.76	6,758.70	45,169.90
4	100,000.00	66,666.67	127,526.30	15,192.97	6,077.19	44,488.39
5	100,000.00	66,666.67	125,566.93	13,233.60	5,293.44	43,704.33
6	100,000.00	66,666.67	123,313.65	10,980.32	4,392.13	42,803.33
7	100,000.00	66,666.67	120,722.38	8,389.05	3,355.62	41,766.82

Figure 8.4 Cash inflows for years 1 to 7.

be assumed constant because the net of these two amounts will remain unchanged throughout the year. The net operating loss for each of the years shown in Figure 8.4 has been calculated by subtracting the operating expense and depreciation expense from the gross possible income for each of these years. The tax cash gain shown in Figure 8.4 was determined by multiplying 40 percent by the indicated net operating loss for that year. Finally, the total cash inflow is calculated by adding the tax cash gain shown to the net cash flow previously calculated as $38,411.20.

An additional net cash inflow occurs at the end of the seventh year owing to the planned sale of the office building at that point in time. This calculation is shown in Figure 8.5.

The calculation starts with the listing of sale price. The anticipated sale price is determined from our previous assumption of a 1 percent appreciation rate per year for the land and the improvements; it results in an anticipated sales price of $1,179,348.80. It is anticipated that the owner of the office building complex will incur a 5 percent commission cost in order to sell the building. When this figure is subtracted from the anticipated sales price, we arrive at the gross amount of $1,120,381.40. The mortgage balance at the end of the seventh year for the loan is calculated in Figure 8.3 as $784,949.40. When the office building is sold, this mortgage balance will have to be paid to the lending institution. After paying this mortgage balance, the adjusted cash flow to the investor is $335,432, as shown in Figure 8.5.

Because taxes must be paid on the gain from the sale of the office building, the adjusted cash income will be reduced. The calculation of the tax liability is shown in Figure 8.5. The calculation is made by subtracting

A.	Cash for Sale		
	1.	Sales price (1% appreciation)	$1,179,348.80
	2.	Less 5% commission	58,967.40
	3.	Gross cash	$1,120,381.40
	4.	Less mortgage balance	784,949.40
	5.	Adjusted cash income	$ 335,432.00
B.	Taxes to be Paid		
	1.	Gross cash	$1,120,381.40
	2.	Less book value	533,333.31
	3.	Taxable gain	$ 587,048.09
	4.	Total tax due	$ 117,409.61
C.	Net Cash from Sale		
	1.	Adjusted cash income	$ 335,432.00
	2.	Less taxes due	117,409.61
	3.	Net cash	$ 218,022.39

Figure 8.5 Cash flow from sale.

the book value at the end of the seventh year from the gross cash received from the sale of the office building at that time. The book value at the end of the seventh year was calculated in Figure 8.3. The result is a taxable gain of $587,048.09. This tax gain is assumed to be taxed as a capital gain. A capital gain has the advantage of being taxed at a reduced rate relative to an ordinary gain.

Let us assume a capital gain rate of 20 percent. The tax liability is determined by multiplying the taxable gain times the capital gain rate. Finally, the net cash flow to the investor from the sale of the office building at the end of the seventh year is determined by subtracting the tax liability from the adjusted cash income previously calculated. This calculation is shown in Figure 8.5.

We have now calculated the cash outflows and inflows for the period in which the investor is affected by the project. These cash outflows and inflows are best illustrated on a time scale, as shown in Figure 8.6. The

46,277.87	45,762.54	45,169.90	44,488.39	43,704.33	42,803.33	41,766.82	218,022.39
1	2	3	4	5	6	7	

220,000

Figure 8.6   Time scale of cash inflows and outflows.

number below the year indicates a cash outflow. For the example in question, there is only one net cash outflow resulting from the initial cash investment in the project. The numbers above the years represent net cash inflow to the office building investor. Note should be made of the fact that after the seventh year two numbers are shown, indicating two net cash inflows. They represent the cash inflow from operating the office complex in the seventh year and the cash inflow from the sale of the office building after the seventh year.

At this point in time, the analysis has yielded a net cash inflow or outflow for each year. This in itself provides the potential investor with a tool for evaluating the feasibility of the project. The rate of return for any one year can be determined by dividing the cash inflow for that year by the equity investment. For example, for the third year a net cash inflow was determined as $45,169.90. Thus, the rate of return for this third year is $45,169.90 divided by $220,000.00. This calculation yields a rate of return for the third year of approximately 20.53 percent. However, this is not the true rate of return.

The error in calculating the rate of return in this manner for any given year is that the time value of money is not taken into account. In particular, future net inflows of money are not worth as much as if the cash inflows were received at the present time. A true rate-of-return calculation should discount future net cash inflows to reflect the period of time at which they are received.

In order to discount future cash inflows or outflows in a rate-of-return calculation, the analysis must include the interest formulas discussed in a previous section. Essentially, the analysis consists of determining the interest rate at which future sums of money are discounted back to the present time to equal the initial investment. Figure 8.6 shows that there are cash inflows at the end of each of the years 1 through 7. If we can determine the interest rate, i, at which the discounted value of their sum equates to the initial investment of $220,000, then we will have found the true rate of return for this investment.

The analysis that follows is essentially a trial-and-error analysis. Initially, it consists of making a guess at the rate of return. The initial guess can be guided if one looks at the magnitude of the future cash inflows versus the initial investment. If one were to sum all of the future cash inflows, they would equal $527,995.57. This is considerably larger than the initial investment of $220,000. It follows that because the cash inflows are considerably in excess of the initial investment, a fairly large rate of return seems evident.

Let us start the analysis by assuming a rate of return as 20 percent. The cash inflows illustrated in Figure 8.7 are multiplied by interest factors that reflect the year in which the cash inflow is received. The discounted cash inflows from Figure 8.7 yield a sum of $222,345.54—this is considered the present worth of the future cash inflows. This value of $222,345.54 is in excess of the $220,000 initial investment. A comparison of these two numbers leads us to conclude that the true rate of return is in excess of 20 percent for the office building. This conclusion is determined by reasoning that if the investor in the office building contributed $222,345.54 in equity for the office building he would in fact have received the cash inflow illustrated in Figure 8.7. However, he did not have to invest $222,345.54 in order to receive the cash inflow; he only had to invest $220,000. So it follows that the rate of return is in excess of 20 percent.

We have now determined that the interest rate or rate of return is greater than 20 percent for the office building. However, the question remains, how much greater than 20 percent is the true rate of return? Again we require another guess. Let us assume an interest rate of 25 percent. By so doing, it is likely that we will bound a solution. That is, if we find that

Year	Cash Inflows	SPPW $i - 20\%$ $n = x$	Discounted Value
1	$ 46,277.87	0.8333	$ 38,563.35
2	45,762.54	0.6944	31,777.51
3	45,169.90	0.5787	26,139.82
4	44,488.39	0.4823	21,456.76
5	43,704.33	0.4019	17,564.77
6	42,807.33	0.3349	14,336.17
7	259,789.21	0.2791	72,507.17
			$222,345.54

Figure 8.7   Discounted cash inflows at $i = 20\%$.

Year	Cash Inflows	SPPW $i = 25\%$ $n = x$	Discounted Value
1	$ 46,277.87	0.8000	$ 37,022.30
2	45,762.54	0.6400	29,288.03
3	45,169.90	0.5120	23,126.99
4	44,488.39	0.4096	18,222.44
5	43,704.33	0.3277	14,321.91
6	42,807.33	0.2621	11,219.80
7	259,789.21	0.2097	54,477.80
			$187,679.27

Figure 8.8   Discounted cash inflows at $i = 25\%$.

an interest rate of 25 percent is too great, at least we will have established that the rate of return will be between 20 and 25 percent.

The discounted cash inflows at 25 percent are shown in Figure 8.8. The mathematics is the same as shown in Figure 8.7; the only difference is that the interest factors used now reflect an interest rate of 25 percent. As is shown in Figure 8.8, the sum of the present worth of the discounted cash inflows is equal to $187,679.27. This is less than the initial investment of $220,000. Had the owner invested in equity $187,679.27, he would have obtained the cash inflow shown in Figure 8.8. However, our office building owner had to invest more than this amount—in fact, he had to invest $220,000. This means that the true rate of return is less than 25 percent.

We have now bounded a solution. Naturally the next guess at a true rate of return should be between 20 and 25 percent. On the basis of the calculations shown in Figures 8.7 and 8.8, we will estimate an interest rate of 21 percent. Figure 8.9 shows an analysis for an interest rate of 21 percent; the sum or present worth of the discounted cash inflows discounted at 21 percent results in a sum of $214,641.01. This is close to the initial investment of $220,000. Thus, the true rate of return is approximately 20 to 21 percent. However, it is not necessary to carry the solution any closer at this point. Recognizing all the uncertainties of the various cash inflows, further analysis is not justified.

The discounted-cash-flow analysis of the office building project is now complete. The result of the analysis has been the determination of the rate of return the investor will receive from his equity investment in the project. This figure can be compared to alternative investments that may be avail-

Year	Cash Inflows	SPPW $i - 21\%$ $n = x$	Discounted Value
1	$ 46,277.87	0.8264	$ 38,244.03
2	45,762.54	0.6830	31,255.81
3	45,169.90	0.5645	25,498.41
4	44,488.39	0.4665	20,753.83
5	43,704.33	0.3855	16,848.02
6	42,807.33	0.3186	13,638.41
7	259,789.21	0.2633	68,402.50
			$214,641.01

Figure 8.9   Discounted cash inflows at $i = 21\%$.

able to him, including such things as interest or rate of return received from investment in stocks, treasury bills, bonds, and simple savings and loan passbook savings. Other investments might include business ventures such as investments in new products, new lines of business, or perhaps other types of construction projects. The analysis can also be used as a basis for evaluating design modifications. The point to be made is that the rate of return that has been calculated reflects all relevant financial considerations so that the calculated rate of return is in fact the true rate of return to the investor.

EXAMPLE FEASIBILITY ESTIMATE PROGRAM WRITTEN IN BASIC

An example computer program written in BASIC to perform feasibility estimate calculations and schedules similar to that described in the previous section is illustrated in Figure 8.10. The program is capable of printing a depreciation schedule, a loan amortization schedule, and a schedule of the cash flow for any specified year. Example reports for each of these schedules are illustrated in Figures 8.11 and 8.12.

We will now give an overview and describe some of the unique aspects of the program illustrated in Figure 8.10. It is not our intent here to describe each and every program line. It should also be noted that the program illustrated lacks the error routines and some program instructions and routines that would be necessary to have the program be such that it could be efficiently run by a noninformed user.

```
100 DEFDBL A,R,O,D,I,T,B,N,S
110 DIM RV(25)
120 DIM OP(25)
130 DIM A(20)
140 DIM IN(40)
150 DIM PR(40)
160 DIM DA(30)
170 DIM MB(40)
180 DIM BK(30)
190 CLS
200 D$="$$##,##############.##"
210 INPUT "ENTER PROJECT NAME ";A$
220 CLS
230 INPUT "ENTER THE LAND COST= ";A(1)
240 CLS
250 INPUT "ENTER THE BUILDING COST= ";A(2)
260 CLS
270 INPUT "ENTER THE EQUITY INVESTMENT= ";A(3)
280 CLS
290 PRINT "  LAND COST ";TAB(20);
300 PRINT USING D$;A(1)
310 PRINT "+ BUILDING COST ";TAB(20);
320 PRINT USING D$;A(2)
330 PRINT "- EQUITY PAYMENT";TAB(20);
340 PRINT USING D$;A(3)
350 PRINT TAB(20);"---------------------"
360 PRINT "= MORTGAGE";TAB(20);
370 A(4)=A(1)+A(2)-A(3)
380 PRINT USING D$;A(4)
390 INPUT "ENTER C TO CONTINUE ";C$
400 CLS
410 INPUT "ENTER THE LOAN LIFE IN YEARS= ";A(5)
420 CLS
430 INPUT "ENTER INTEREST RATE= ";A(6)
440 CLS
450 PRINT TAB(35);"ENTER S: FOR STRAIGHT LINE
460 PRINT TAB(35);"ENTER A: FOR ACCELERATED
470 PRINT ""
480 INPUT "ENTER S OR A FOR DEPRECIATION METHOD: ";AD$
490 IF (AD$="S") THEN 520
500 CH$="ACCELERATED"
510 GOTO 530
520 CH$="STRAIGHT LINE"
530 CLS
540 INPUT "ENTER THE DEPR. LIFE= ";A(7)
550 IF (AD$="S") THEN 590
560 PRINT ""
570 INPUT "ENTER THE DEPR. RATE (175=MAX.)= ";A(8)
580 PRINT ""
590 CLS
600 INPUT "ENTER INVESTOR'S TAX RATE= ";A(9)
620 PRINT "YOU CAN PERFORM AN ANALYSIS FOR ANY NUMBER OF YEARS FROM 1 TO 20
630 INPUT "ENTER THE NUMBER OF YEARS ";Y
640 CLS
650 INPUT "ENTER FIRST YEAR FORECASTED REVENUE= ";A(10)
660 INPUT "ENTER FIRST YEAR FORECASTED OPERATING COST= ";A(11)
670 CLS
680 PRINT "YOU HAVE COMPLETED THE DATA ENTRY FOR THE PROJECT NAMED:
690 INPUT "ENTER C TO CONTINUE ";C$
700 CLS
```

Figure 8.10 Example computer program written in BASIC to perform a feasibility estimate.

```
710 PRINT "                         THE FOLLOWING OPTIONS ARE AVAILABLE
720 PRINT ""
730 PRINT TAB(15);"ENTER A: TO EXECUTE A CASH FLOW ANALYSIS FOR A YEAR
740 PRINT TAB(15);"          YOU WILL SPECIFY"
750 PRINT ""
760 PRINT TAB(15);"ENTER D: TO PRINT A DEPRECIATION SCHEDULE FOR THE PROJECT
770 PRINT ""
780 PRINT TAB(15);"ENTER L: TO PRINT A LOAN AMORTIZATION FOR THE MORTGAGE
790 PRINT ""
800 PRINT TAB(15);"ENTER T: TO TERMINATE/EXIT THE PROGRAM-(CAUTION: THIS OPTION
WILL
810 PRINT TAB(15);"          RESULT IN THE LOSS OF THE INPUTED PROJECT DATA
820 INPUT FF$
830 IF (FF$="A") THEN 870
840 IF (FF$="D") THEN 1430
850 IF (FF$="L") THEN 1860
860 IF (FF$="T") THEN 2230
870 CLS
880 PRINT "YOU CAN OBTAIN A CASH FLOW ANALYSIS FOR ANY YEAR FROM 1 TO 15
890 PRINT ""
900 INPUT "ENTER THE YEAR FOR WHICH YOU WANT AN ANALYSIS-ENTER AS AN INTERGER ";
X
910 FOR P=1 TO 15
920 RV(P)=A(10)
930 OP(P)=A(11)
940 NEXT P
950 CLS
960 PRINT TAB(35);"PROJECT NAME ";A$
970 PRINT TAB(35);"CASH FLOW ANALYSIS"
980 PRINT TAB(39);"YEAR NO. ";X
990 PRINT ""
1000 GOSUB 1640
1010 GOSUB 2080
1020 YY$="$$##,##########.##"
1030 UU$="##,##########.##"
1040 PRINT "PROJECTED REVENUE";TAB(56);
1050 PRINT USING YY$;RV(X)
1060 PRINT "-FORECASTED OPERATING COST";TAB(58);
1070 PRINT USING UU$;OP(X)
1080 RO=RV(X)-OP(X)
1090 PRINT TAB(58);"----------------------"
1100 PRINT "REVENUE-OPERATING COST ";TAB(56);
1110 PRINT USING YY$;RO
1120 PRINT "-DEBT SERVICE PAYMENT ";TAB(58);
1130 PRINT USING UU$;AN
1140 RP=RO-AN
1150 PRINT TAB(58);"----------------------"
1160 PRINT "BEFORE TAX CASH FLOW";TAB(56);
1170 PRINT USING YY$;RP
1180 PRINT "TAX CALCULATION"
1190 PRINT "REVENUE";TAB(36);
1200 PRINT USING YY$;RV(X)
1210 PRINT "-OPERATING COST";TAB(38);
1220 PRINT USING UU$;OP(X)
1230 PRINT "-DEPRECIATION";TAB(38);
1240 PRINT USING UU$;DA(X)
1250 PRINT "-INTEREST EXPENSE";TAB(38);
1260 PRINT USING UU$;IN(X)
1270 PRINT TAB(38);"-------------------"
1280 TX=RV(X)-OP(X)-DA(X)-IN(X)
```

Figure 8.10 *Continued*

```
1290 PRINT "TAX GAIN OR LOSS";TAB(36);
1300 PRINT USING YY$;TX
1310 TL=TX *A(9) / 100
1320 PRINT "TAX LIABILITY";TAB(58);
1330 TH=-TL
1340 PRINT USING UU$;TH
1350 PRINT TAB(58);"---------------------"
1360 NC=RP-TL
1370 PRINT "NET CASH FLOW";TAB(56);
1380 PRINT USING YY$;NC
1390 PRINT TAB(58);"---------------------"
1400 PRINT TAB(58);"---------------------"
1410 INPUT "ENTER C TO RETURN TO THE PROGRAM EXECUTION OPTIONS ";C$
1420 GOTO 700
1430 CLS
1440 CLS:PRINT TAB(30);"DEPRECIATION SCHEDULE":PRINT TAB(25);"PROJECT NAME ";A$
1450 PRINT ""
1460 PRINT "DEPRECIATION METHOD ";CH$
1470 PRINT "DEPRECIATION LIFE ";A(7);" YEARS"
1480 PRINT ""
1490 PRINT "YEAR";TAB(7);"DEPRECIATION CHARGE ";TAB(40);"BOOK VALUE AT YEAR END"
1500 PRINT "----";TAB(7);"--------------------------------";TAB(40);"-------------------------"
1510 PRINT "   0";TAB(40);
1520 PRINT USING D$;A(2)
1530 GOSUB 1640
1540 FOR GG=1 TO A(7)
1550 PRINT TAB(2);GG;
1560 PRINT TAB(7);
1570 PRINT USING D$;DA(GG);
1580 PRINT TAB(40);
1590 PRINT USING D$;BK(GG)
1600 NEXT GG
1610 PRINT ""
1620 INPUT "ENTER C TO RETURN TO THE PROGRAM EXECUTION OPTIONS ";C$
1630 GOTO 700
1640 IF (AD$="S") THEN 1660
1650 GOTO 1740
1660 RA=100/A(7)
1670 BN=A(2)
1680 FOR II= 1 TO A(7)
1690 DA(II)=(A(2)*RA) /100
1700 BK(II)=BN-DA(II)
1710 BN=BK(II)
1720 NEXT II
1730 GOTO 1850
1740 AC=A(8)
1750 RA=(AC/A(7))/100
1760 BN=A(2)
1770 FOR ZZ=1 TO A(7)
1780 DA(ZZ)=BN*RA: LE=A(7)-ZZ+1: LS=ZZ-1
1790 IF (ZZ=1) THEN 1820
1800 IF (DA(ZZ)>(BK(LS)/LE)) THEN 1820
1810 DA(ZZ)=BK(LS)/LE
1820 BK(ZZ)=BN-DA(ZZ)
1830 BN=BK(ZZ)
1840 NEXT ZZ
1850 RETURN
1860 CLS
```

Figure 8.10 *Continued*

```
1870 PRINT "                          LOAN/MORTGAGE TABLE
1880 PRINT "                          PROJECT NAME";A$
1890 PRINT "INTEREST LIFE= ";A(5);" YEARS"
1900 PRINT "INTEREST RATE= ";A(6);" %"
1910 PRINT ""
1920 PRINT "YEAR";TAB(7);"INTEREST CHARGE";TAB(30);"PRINCIPAL PAYMENT";TAB(60);"
LOAN BALANCE"
1930 O$="#####,#########.##"
1940 PRINT "  O";TAB(53);
1950 PRINT USING D$;A(4)
1960 GOSUB 2080
1970 FOR PP=1 TO A(5)
1980 PRINT TAB(2);PP;TAB(7);
1990 PRINT USING O$;IN(PP);
2000 PRINT TAB(30);
2010 PRINT USING O$;PR(PP);
2020 PRINT TAB(58);
2030 PRINT USING O$;MB(PP)
2040 NEXT PP
2050 PRINT ""
2060 INPUT "ENTER C TO RETURN TO THE PROGRAM EXECUTION OPTIONS ";C$
2070 GOTO 700
2080 RE=A(6)/100
2090 DK=((1+RE)^A(5))
2100 DL=RE*DK
2110 DM=(((1+RE)^A(5))-1)
2120 DS=DL/DM
2130 AN=A(4) *DS
2140 IN(1)=A(4) *RE
2150 PR(1)=AN-IN(1)
2160 MB(1)=A(4)-PR(1)
2170 FOR HH=2 TO A(5)
2180 IN(HH)=MB(HH-1) * RE
2190 PR(HH)=AN-IN(HH)
2200 MB(HH)=MB(HH-1)-PR(HH)
2210 NEXT HH
2220 RETURN
2230 CLS
2240 PRINT "THIS IS THE END OF THE PROGRAM
2260 END
```

Figure 8.10 *Continued*

The program starts with line 100. The BASIC instruction DEFDBL, one we have not previously discussed, results in having the variables named treated as double-precision numbers/variables rather than single-precision numbers. Unless otherwise instructed to use double-precision numbers via the DEFDBL instruction, most personal computers default to single-precision numbers. A single-precision number is only accurate to eight significant figures.

When producing estimating reports, including a feasibility estimate, it is usually desirable to have the computer print results to more than eight significant figures of accuracy. As such, the program initializes variables that will be used in reports to double-precision variables.

```
                        LOAN/MORTGAGE TABLE
                   PROJECT NAMEOFFICE BUILDING
INTEREST LIFE=   15   YEARS
INTEREST RATE=   15   %
```

YEAR	INTEREST CHARGE	PRINCIPAL PAYMENT	LOAN BALANCE
0			$880,000.00
1	132,000.00	18,495.01	861,505.00
2	129,225.75	21,269.26	840,235.80
3	126,035.36	24,459.64	815,776.10
4	122,366.42	28,128.59	787,647.60
5	118,147.13	32,347.87	755,299.70
6	113,294.95	37,200.05	718,099.60
7	107,714.94	42,780.07	675,319.60
8	101,297.93	49,197.07	626,122.50
9	93,918.38	56,576.63	569,545.90
10	85,431.88	65,063.13	504,482.80
11	75,672.41	74,822.60	429,660.20
12	64,449.02	86,045.99	343,614.20
13	51,542.13	98,952.88	244,661.30
14	36,699.20	113,795.80	130,865.50
15	19,629.83	130,865.20	0.33

```
DEPRECIATION METHOD ACCELERATED
DEPRECIATION LIFE   15   YEARS
```

YEAR	DEPRECIATION CHARGE	BOOK VALUE AT YEAR END
0		$1,000,000.00
1	$116,666.67	$883,333.33
2	$103,055.56	$780,277.78
3	$91,032.41	$689,245.37
4	$80,411.96	$608,833.41
5	$71,030.56	$537,802.85
6	$62,743.67	$475,059.18
7	$55,423.57	$419,635.61
8	$52,454.45	$367,181.16
9	$52,454.45	$314,726.71
10	$52,454.45	$262,272.26
11	$52,454.45	$209,817.80
12	$52,454.45	$157,363.35
13	$52,454.45	$104,908.90
14	$52,454.45	$52,454.45
15	$52,454.45	$0.00

Figure 8.11   Example loan amortization and depreciation schedule from feasibility estimate program.

The feasibility estimate program consists of essentially two parts: an input routine and an output routine. After the dimension instructions in lines 110 through 180, which initialize and set aside memory for eight variables, the input routine starts. The input routine receives the following input data:

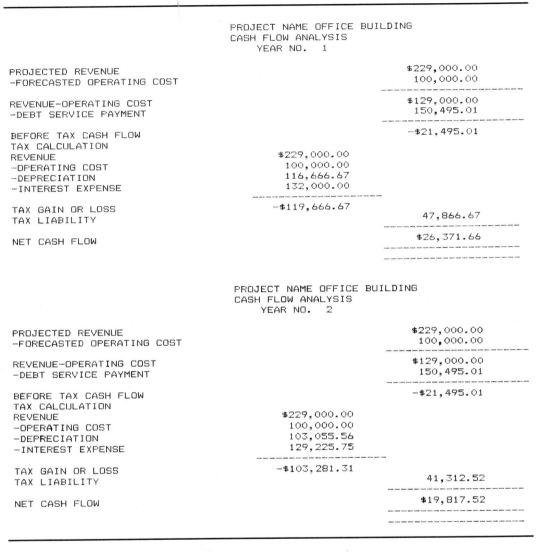

```
                        PROJECT NAME OFFICE BUILDING
                        CASH FLOW ANALYSIS
                             YEAR NO.   1

PROJECTED REVENUE                                        $229,000.00
-FORECASTED OPERATING COST                                100,000.00
                                                        ------------------
REVENUE-OPERATING COST                                   $129,000.00
-DEBT SERVICE PAYMENT                                     150,495.01
                                                        ------------------
BEFORE TAX CASH FLOW                                      -$21,495.01
TAX CALCULATION
REVENUE                         $229,000.00
-OPERATING COST                  100,000.00
-DEPRECIATION                    116,666.67
-INTEREST EXPENSE                132,000.00
                                --------------------
TAX GAIN OR LOSS                -$119,666.67
TAX LIABILITY                                              47,866.67
                                                        ------------------
NET CASH FLOW                                            $26,371.66
                                                        ------------------
                                                        ------------------


                        PROJECT NAME OFFICE BUILDING
                        CASH FLOW ANALYSIS
                             YEAR NO.   2

PROJECTED REVENUE                                        $229,000.00
-FORECASTED OPERATING COST                                100,000.00
                                                        ------------------
REVENUE-OPERATING COST                                   $129,000.00
-DEBT SERVICE PAYMENT                                     150,495.01
                                                        ------------------
BEFORE TAX CASH FLOW                                      -$21,495.01
TAX CALCULATION
REVENUE                         $229,000.00
-OPERATING COST                  100,000.00
-DEPRECIATION                    103,055.56
-INTEREST EXPENSE                129,225.75
                                --------------------
TAX GAIN OR LOSS                -$103,281.31
TAX LIABILITY                                              41,312.52
                                                        ------------------
NET CASH FLOW                                            $19,817.52
                                                        ------------------
                                                        ------------------
```

Figure 8.12   Example cash flow analysis report from feasibility estimate program.

Land cost	Loan rate	Investor's tax rate
Building cost	Depreciation method	Revenue
Equity investment	Depreciation life	Operating expense
Loan life	Depreciation rate	

The input routine consists of various input instructions that inform the program what to input and subsequently receives the input and assigns it to a defined variable. The reader should note that the program does not require the user to input the mortgage amount. Instead the program itself calculates the mortgage given the fact that the mortgage has to equal the land cost plus the building cost minus the inputted equity investment amount. The computer makes this calculation in line 370.

The program enables the user to select from either a straight-line or accelerated depreciation. The programming for this choice is contained in lines 450 through 520. The selected method is determined via the conditional BASIC instruction IF in line 490. Depending on whether the user selects the straight-line or accelerated method, the program branches to either line 500 or 520.

The input routine ends with line 690. The output routine starts in line 700. This output routine starts by giving the program a menu. By inputting A, D, L, or T, the user can print a projected cash flow for a given year, a depreciation schedule, a loan amortization schedule, or end/exit the program.

The cash flow, depreciation, and loan amortization program routines each contain the mathematics necessary to produce the reports illustrated in Figures 8.11 and 8.12. Lines 1020 and 1030 in the cash flow routine are used to format numbers contained in the reports. When entering the cash flow routine/option, the user is requested to input the year for which he wants a report. This is done in lines 900 and 910. The depreciation and loan calculations that are part of the producing the cash flow report are performed via the subroutines that start in lines 1640 and 2080, respectively. After these subroutines are completed, lines 1040 through 1400 are used to print the report illustrated in Figure 8.12. The various PRINT USING instructions, e.g., the one illustrated in line 1050, refer to one of the print format lines (line 1020 or 1030) that enable the inserting of commas and decimals in the printed numbers.

The depreciation schedules routine/option starts at line 1430. The routine uses the same subroutine (i.e., the one that starts in line 1640) as the cash flow routine to determine the individual annual depreciation amounts. The individual annual depreciation charges are printed via the program loop initiated with the FOR instruction in line 1540 and terminating with the NEXT instruction in line 1600.

The loan amortization routine/option starts in line 1860. The mathematics necessary to calculate the annual interest, principal, and outstanding mortgage is performed via the subroutine initiated in line 2080 and ends in line 2220. The calculation assumes a fixed rate amortized loan. This type of loan assumes a fixed period payment that consists of a declining interest payment and an increasing principal payment. After the subroutine completes the loan amortization mathematics, lines 1970 through 2040 are used to print the annual payments shown in Figure 8.11.

The three reports shown in Figures 8.11 and 8.12 assume the following input data:

Land cost = $100,000
Building cost = $1,000,000
Equity investment = $220,000
Loan life = 20 years
Loan rate = 15%
Depreciation method = accelerated
Depreciation rate = 175%
Depreciation life = 15 years
Investor's tax rate = 40%
Revenue = $229,000
Operating expense = $100,000

The computer program illustrated in Figure 8.10 can be used ˜ handle the same mathematics that can be performed manually. As such, one might argue that "the computer can only do what one might do manually." While this is true, it is the speed and accuracy of the computer that result in it being an effective device for preparing/processing a feasibility estimate. Perhaps even more important is the ability of the user to change one or more of the input variable amounts and have the program print the results and print the reports in a matter of minutes. Given this ability, an individual can use the program to measure the sensitivity of the results to a change of one or more variables in a matter of minutes. This enables the user to use the program to evaluate risk. In effect, the computer and the program enable the user to test "what if" conditions—a major benefit of the computer regarding construction industry applications.

PARAMETER ESTIMATING

A recently evolved preconstruction cost estimate method is the parameter estimate. This type can be used to give the owner an approximate cost of a project and also to enable the estimator to evaluate contractor bids.

Engineering News Record first published parameter cost estimating in 1966. From that time the periodical has expanded the concept of parameter estimating. Whereas at first only the gross floor area was used as a parameter, today there are several parameter measures. Contractors, owners, designers, or construction managers using *Engineering News Record*'s parameter cost breakouts allocate lump-sum costs to trades or component systems of a building's construction. Parameter measures are then chosen to divide into the trade cost, one parameter to a trade. The choice relates the parameter measure to the function of the trade. For example, structural steel cost may be related to the gross area supported, and dry-wall cost to interior area. The parameter costs can yield guidelines to estimate the cost of a similar project or to judge the validity of contractors' quotes.

Let us look at an example of collected parameter cost data. These data could easily be collected by the estimator or could be taken from published cost data such as those in *Engineering News Record*. Parameter cost data for an office building (shown in Figure 8.13) includes such information as the type of project, parameter measures, and trade data. The descriptive information regarding the type of project is used merely to classify similar types of projects. That is, should the estimator attempt to estimate an office building, he would attempt to match the future project with parameter cost data for a similar type of project. Information such as the type of frame, the exterior walls, and the design ratios would aid the estimator in selecting a similar type of project from his parameter cost library.

The parameter measures shown in Figure 8.13 indicate the actual measures for a previously constructed office building. That project has a gross enclosed floor area of 650,000 square feet, and the frame is structural steel. Other parameter measures shown in the figure may be used to relate the actual cost of the project by segments or trades.

Let us look at the data regarding the trades. In the first column a code is indicated that relates the types of work in question to one of the parameters. For example, the general conditions and fee for the office building are indicated to be a measure or function of the parameter of gross enclosed floor area. The interior masonry shown in the trade has a code of 12, indicating that the interior masonry is a function of the linear feet of partition wall. The measured linear feet of partition wall was 30,000. Dividing this quantity into the total cost amount develops a parameter cost of $6.20.

Similar parameter unit costs are developed and shown in Figure 8.13. Another column relates the percentage of trade cost amount to the total cost of the project; e.g., the interior masonry is shown as 1.18 percent. This is developed by dividing the total costs for the interior masonry—$186,000—by the total cost of the project—$15,708,000.

If the value of the parameter cost data shown in Figure 8.13 is to be used in determining a measure of preliminary cost, the estimator merely has to take off the parameter-measure quantities to obtain a historical library of parameter costs by trade. For the office building this would mean that the estimator would only have to take off 14 measures of project quantities. This compares to several hundred quantities that are characteristic of a

Type of Building	Office
Location	Troy, Mich.
Construction Start/Complete	Aug./Oct.
Type of Owner	Private
Frame	Structural Steel
Exterior Walls	Metal Curtain Wall
Special Site Work	None
Fire Rating	2-A

PARAMETER MEASURES

1. Gross Enclosed Floor Area	650,000 sf
2. Gross Area Supported (excluding slab on grade)	608,400 sf
3. Total Basement Floor Area	41,600 sf
4. Roof Area	70,000 sf
5. Net Finished Area	500,000 sf
6. Number of Floors Including Basements	26
7. Number of Floors Excluding Basements	25
8. Area of Face Brick	0
9. Area of Other Exterior Wall	150,000 sf
10. Area of Curtain Wall Including Glass	221,000 sf
11. Store-front Perimeter	300 sf
12. Interior Partitions	30,000 sf
13. HVAC	1,700 tons
14. Parking Area	890,000 sf

OTHER MEASURES

Area of Typical Floor	19,400 sf
Story Height, Typical Floor	152 in
Lobby Area	2,000 sf
Number of Plumbing Fixtures	460
Number of Elevators	12

DESIGN RATIOS

A/C Ton per Building ft^2	0.0026
Parking ft^2 per Building	1.3692

Figure 8.13   Example historical parameter estimating data.

Area or Trade	Parameter Cost			Total Cost	
	Code	Unit	Cost	$	%
General Conditions and Fee	1	sf	2.19	1,425,000	9.07
Sitework (clearing and grubbing)	1	sf	0.35	226,000	1.44
Excavation	3	sf	4.57	190,000	1.21
Foundation	2	sf	0.67	410,000	2.61
Formed Concrete	2	sf	2.71	1,650,000	10.50
Interior Masonry	12	lf	6.20	186,000	1.18
Structural Steel	2	sf	1.23	750,000	4.77
Miscellaneous Metal, Including Stairs	2	sf	0.38	230,000	1.46
Carpentry	5	sf	0.18	90,000	0.57
Waterproofing and Dampproofing	10	sf	0.10	22,000	0.14
Roofing and Flashing	4	sf	1.64	115,000	0.73
Metal Doors, Frames, Windows	5	sf	0.11	55,000	0.35
Hardware	5	sf	0.12	60,000	0.38
Glazing	11	lf	333.33	100,000	0.64
Curtain Wall	10	sf	3.96	875,000	5.57
Lath and Plaster	5	sf	0.08	40,000	0.25
Dry Wall	12	lf	28.90	867,000	5.52
Tile Work	5	sf	0.10	49,000	0.31
Accoustical Ceiling	5	sf	0.18	90,000	0.57
Resilient Flooring	5	sf	0.04	18,000	0.11
Carpet	5	sf	0.03	17,000	0.11
Painting	5	sf	0.17	87,000	0.55
Toilet Partitions	5	sf	0.03	13,000	0.08
Elevators	om	ea	70,000	70,000	0.44
Plumbing	1	sf	5.15	3,350,000	21.35
HVAC	1	sf	5.15	3,350,000	21.35
Electrical	1	sf	1.77	1,150,000	7.32
Parking, Paved	14	sf	0.25	223,000	1.42
TOTAL	1	sf	24.17	15,708,000	100.00

Figure 8.13 *Continued*

contractor's detailed estimate. The unit-cost estimate is in reality a one-parameter estimate. Typically, the parameter estimate used by an estimator would be restricted to 8 to 15 parameters.

Let us now look at how a parameter estimate can be made from previous parameter cost data. Assume we are faced with determining a preliminary cost estimate for another office project. Further assume that the office building in question is similar in quality and construction to the office building for which we have collected data in Figure 8.13. The type of project is described in Figure 8.14. The parameter measures are shown;

Trade	Parameter Cost			Total Cost	
	Code	Unit	Cost	Amount	%
General Conditions and Fee	1	sf	2.19	865,050	8.62
Sitework (clearing and grubbing)	1	sf	0.35	138,250	1.38
Excavation	3	sf	4.57	205,650	2.05
Foundation	2	sf	0.67	234,500	2.34
Formed Concrete	2	sf	2.71	948,500	9.45
Interior Masonry	12	lf	6.20	220,100	2.20
Structural Steel	2	sf	1.23	430,500	4.29
Miscellaneous Metal, Including Stairs	2	sf	0.38	133,000	1.33
Carpentry	5	sf	0.18	57,600	0.57
Waterproofing and Dampproofing	10	sf	0.10	11,000	0.11
Roofing and Flashing	4	sf	1.64	65,600	0.65
Metal Doors, Frames, Windows	5	sf	0.11	35,200	0.35
Hardware	5	sf	0.12	38,400	0.38
Glazing	11	lf	333.33	100,000	1.00
Curtain Wall	10	sf	3.96	435,600	4.34
Lath and Plaster	5	sf	0.08	25,600	0.25
Dry Wall	12	lf	28.90	1,025,950	10.22
Tile Work	5	sf	0.10	32,000	0.32
Accoustical Ceiling	5	sf	0.18	57,600	0.57
Resilient Flooring	5	sf	0.04	12,800	0.13
Carpet	5	sf	0.03	9,600	0.10
Painting	5	sf	0.17	54,400	0.54
Toilet Partitions	5	sf	0.03	9,600	0.10
Elevators	om	ea	70,000	70,000	0.70
Plumbing	1	sf	5.15	2,034,250	20.27
HVAC	1	sf	5.15	2,034,250	20.27
Electrical	1	sf	1.77	699,150	6.97
Parking, Paved	14	sf	0.25	50,000	0.50
TOTAL	1	sf	25.40	10,034,150	100.00

Figure 8.14 Using parameter data to predict/estimate cost of proposed project.

Parameter Measures

1. Gross Enclosed Floor Area	395,000 sf
2. Gross Area Supported (excluding slab on grade)	350,000 sf
3. Total Basement Floor Area	45,000 sf
4. Roof Area	40,000 sf
5. Net Finished Area	320,000 sf
6. Number of Floors Including Basements	12
7. Number of Floor Excluding Basements	11
8. Area of Face Brick	0
9. Area of Other Exterior Wall	80,000 sf
10. Area of Curtain Wall Including Glass	110,000 sf
11. Store-front Perimeter	300 sf
12. Interior Partitions	35,500 lf
13. HVAC	1,200 tons
14. Parking Area	200,000 sf

Figure 8.14 *Continued*

e.g., the office building we wish to estimate has gross enclosed floor area of 395,000 square feet. Other parameter measures are shown in the figure. The parameter cost data for the trades as determined from the previous office building project are also shown. In reality, the parameter cost data we would use for estimating would likely be an accumulation of several past projects. However, for purposes of demonstration, let us assume that these historical accumulated cost data are only the ones shown in the previous example.

Now let us consider the determination of the masonry cost. The unit parameter is identified as a function of linear feet of partition walls. We would multiply the 35,000 by $6.20 to determine the total estimated masonry cost of $220,100. We determine the column of percentages by simply taking the estimated cost of a given trade and dividing it by the calculated sum of the total estimated cost. In this manner we derive the total estimated cost of the proposed project and the components of the cost identified by trade. Thus, it is possible for the estimator to determine an approximate cost of the project and also develop component trade costs that can be used to evaluate contractor bids.

EXAMPLE PARAMETER ESTIMATING PROGRAM WRITTEN IN BASIC

An example computer program written in BASIC to store historical parameter estimating data and subsequently use the historical data base for preparing a parameter estimate is illustrated in Figure 8.15. The program illustrated essentially computerizes the procedures discussed in the preceding sections.

The program illustrated is the first program we illustrate that uses data files to store data on a data disk, greatly facilitating the collection, storage, and subsequent use of historical data. In this regard this attribute of data files and data storage can make otherwise unfeasible or questionable (in regard to benefit versus cost) management techniques or procedures such as parameter estimating feasible.

As is true of our discussion of other computer programs illustrated, we will not discuss each and every program line illustrated in Figure 8.15. Instead we will give an overview of how the program works and describe some of its unique aspects. As is also true of other programs, the program illustrated in Figure 8.15 would need some modifications and additions to be effectively used by an individual or firm. As illustrated, the program lacks some of the error routines and user instructions that are part of a more usable program.

The parameter estimating program illustrated consists of three program options/routines available to the user in lines 260 through 410.

The three options are

S: To initialize the system and define the parameters, trades, and correlations

H: To enter historical data from past projects

E: To use the program to prepare a parameter estimate for a proposed project.

Actually, the three options must be initially executed in the order shown. The user must initialize or define the parameter estimating setup (option S) before historical data can be entered. Similarly, historical data from at least one past project must be entered via option H before the user can use the program to prepare a parameter estimate using option E. Afterward the H or E options can be executed in any order.

The parameter estimating program illustrated in Figure 8.15 enables the user to uniquely define his own parameters, trades, and correlations between trades and parameters. This is a favorable attribute of the program in that it offers the user an ability to "modify" the program to fit his needs rather than require the user to adapt to a defined format or list of parameters, trades, and correlations that are part of the program.

The initialization/setup of variables routine starts in line 430. By means of a FOR/NEXT program loop, which starts in line 440 and terminates in line 550, the user defines/inputs the parameters that are to be part of the parameter estimating system. Attention is drawn to lines 490 through 520.

```
100 DEFDBL Q,D,P,M,R,T,E
110 DIM QU(15)
120 DIM CR$(40)
130 DIM PA$(40)
140 DIM PT$(15)
150 DIM TR$(40)
160 DIM PM$(40)
170 DIM MP$(40)
180 DIM PA(40)
190 DIM PQ(40)
200 DIM ES(15)
210 DIM A$(15)
220 DIM AA$(40)
230 CLS
240 LOCATE 2,30
250 CLS
260 PRINT "ENTER S: TO SET UP THE SYSTEM TO INCLUDE DEFINING THE PARAMETERS AND
TRADES
270 PRINT ""
280 PRINT "ENTER H: TO ENTER HISTORICAL DATA FOR A PAST PROJECT (NOTE: YOU CANNO
T
290 PRINT "          RUN THIS OPTION UNTIL YOU HAVE PERFORMED OPTION S: ;I.E. INI
TIALIZED
300 PRINT "          THE SYSTEM)
310 PRINT ""
320 PRINT "ENTER E: TO USE PAST DATA TO PREPARE A PARAMETER ESTIMATE (NOTE:YOU M
UST
330 PRINT "          HAVE ENTERED SOME PAST DATA, I.E. HAVE RUN OPTION H AT LEAST

340 PRINT "          ONCE BEFORE YOU RUN THIS OPTION)
350 PRINT ""
360 PRINT "ENTER P: TO RETURN TO THE PROGRAM OPTIONS
370 PRINT ""
380 INPUT "NOW ENTER S, H, E, OR P ";X$
390 IF (X$="S") THEN 430
400 IF (X$="H") THEN 1580
410 IF (X$="E") THEN 2480
420 GOTO 2440
430 CLS
440 FOR I=1 TO 15
450 CLS
460 PRINT "ENTER PARAMETER NUMBER ";I
470 PRINT ""
480 INPUT "ENTER PARAMETER NAME= ";A$(I)
490 PRINT "DO YOU WANT TO ENTER ANOTHER PARAMETER NAME?
500 INPUT "ENTER Y (YES) OR N (NO) ";B$
510 IF (B$="Y") THEN 550
520 IF (B$="N") THEN 560
530 CLS
540 CLS
550 NEXT I
560 PRINT ""
570 PRINT "YOU HAVE COMPLETED THE INPUT OF PARAMETERS
580 CLS
590 CLS
600 FOR II=1 TO 40
610 CLS
620 PRINT "ENTER TRADE NUMBER ";II
630 PRINT ""
640 INPUT "ENTER TRADE NAME= ";AA$(II)
```

Figure 8.15 Example computer program written in BASIC for parameter estimating.

```
650 CLS
660 PRINT "TRADE NAME= ";AA$(II)
670 PRINT ""
680 PRINT "YOU MUST NOW DEFINE THE PARAMETER NO. THAT THE TRADE IS A FUNCTION OF
"
690 PRINT "THE PARAMETERS ARE AS FOLLOWS:
700 PRINT "NUMBER";TAB(10);"PARAMETER NAME"
710 FOR JJ=1 TO I
720 PRINT TAB(3);JJ;TAB(10);A$(JJ)
730 NEXT JJ
740 PRINT "ENTER A NUMBER FROM 1 TO ";I;" TO IDENTIFY THE PARAMETER NUMBER=";
750 INPUT PP
760 CLS
770 PRINT "TRADE NAME= ";AA$(II)
780 PRINT ""
790 PRINT "IDENTIFIED PARAMETER IT IS A FUNCTION OF"
800 PRINT ""
810 PRINT "PARAMETER NUMBER";TAB(20);"PARAMETER NAME"
820 PRINT TAB(8);PP;TAB(20);A$(PP)
830 PRINT ""
840 CLS
850 PA(II)=PP
860 PRINT "YOU HAVE ENTERED THE FOLLOWING TRADES:
870 PRINT "NUMBER";TAB(10);"TRADE NAME";TAB(50);"TRADE A FUNCTION OF PARAMETER
880 PRINT "-----";TAB(10);"----------";TAB(50);"----------------------------"
890 FOR ZZ=1 TO II
900 PRINT TAB(3);ZZ;TAB(20);AA$(ZZ);TAB(50);A$(PA(ZZ))
910 NEXT ZZ
920 PRINT ""
930 PRINT "ENTER Y: TO ENTER ANOTHER TRADE NAME
940 PRINT "ENTER N: IF YOU DO NOT WANT TO ENTER ANOTHER TRADE NAME
950 INPUT D$
960 IF (D$="N") THEN 990
970 CLS
980 NEXT II
990 CLS
1000 PRINT "YOU HAVE NOW COMPLETED THE ENTRY OF PARAMETERS AND TRADES"
1010 PRINT ""
1020 INPUT "ENTER C TO STORE THE SET-UP ON A DATA DISK ";C$
1030 CLS
1040 PRINT "PLEASE WAIT....., THE DATA IS BEING STORED ON THE DISK
1050 GOSUB 1120
1060 PRINT ""
1070 PRINT "THE PARAMETER NAMES, TRADE NAMES, AND CORRELATIONS HAVE NOW BE STORE
D
1080 PRINT "ON THE PARAMETER ESTIMATING SYSTEM DISK."
1090 PRINT ""
1100 PRINT "ENTER C TO RETURN TO THE PROGRAM EXECUTION OPTIONS ";C$
1110 GOTO 250
1120 I$=STR$(I)
1130 II$=STR$(II)
1140 OPEN "COUNT.DAT" AS #1 LEN=5
1150 FIELD #1, 5 AS DE$
1160 RSET DE$=I$
1170 PUT #1,1
1180 RSET DE$=II$
1190 PUT #1,2
1200 CLOSE #1
1210 OPEN "METER.DAT" AS #1 LEN=45
1220 FOR JA=1 TO I
1230 FIELD #1, 45 AS PT$(JA)
```

Figure 8.15 *Continued*

```
1240 LSET PT$(JA)=A$(JA)
1250 PUT #1,JA
1260 NEXT JA
1270 CLOSE #1
1280 OPEN "TRADES.DAT" AS #1 LEN=45
1290 FOR JB=1 TO II
1300 FIELD #1, 45 AS TR$(JB)
1310 LSET TR$(JB)=AA$(JB)
1320 PUT #1,JB
1330 NEXT JB
1340 CLOSE #1
1350 OPEN "CORR.DAT" AS #1 LEN=5
1360 FOR JC=1 TO II
1370 PA$(JC)=STR$(PA(JC))
1380 FIELD #1, 5 AS CR$(JC)
1390 LSET CR$(JC)=PA$(JC)
1400 PUT #1,JC
1410 NEXT JC
1420 CLOSE #1
1430 OPEN "PART.DAT" AS #1 LEN=20
1440 FOR JD=1 TO II
1450 FIELD #1, 20 AS PM$(JD)
1460 LSET PM$(JD)="0"
1470 PUT #1,JD
1480 NEXT JD
1490 CLOSE #1
1500 OPEN "TRPAR.DAT" AS #1 LEN=20
1510 FOR JE=1 TO II
1520 FIELD #1, 20 AS MP$(JE)
1530 LSET MP$(JE)="0"
1540 PUT #1,JE
1550 NEXT JE
1560 CLOSE #1
1570 RETURN
1580 CLS
1590 CLS
1600 OPEN "COUNT.DAT" AS #1 LEN=5
1610 FIELD #1, 5 AS T$
1620 GET #1,1
1630 I$=T$
1640 GET #1,2
1650 II$=T$
1660 CLOSE #1
1670 I=VAL(I$)
1680 II=VAL(II$)
1690 OPEN "METER.DAT" AS #1 LEN=45
1700 FOR IM=1 TO I
1710 FIELD #1, 45 AS PT$(IM)
1720 GET #1,IM
1730 A$(IM)=PT$(IM)
1740 NEXT IM
1750 CLOSE #1
1760 PRINT ""
1770 CLS
1780 FOR SS=1 TO I
1790 CLS
1800 PRINT "NUMBER";TAB(10);"PARAMETER NAME"
1810 PRINT "------";TAB(10);"--------------"
1820 PRINT TAB(3);SS;TAB(10);A$(SS)
1830 PRINT ""
1840 INPUT "ENTER THE QUANTITY= ";QU(SS)
```

Figure 8.15 *Continued*

```
1850 PRINT ""
1860 NEXT SS
1870 CLS
1880 PRINT "ENTER C: TO CONTINUE AND TO ENTER THE QUANTITIES FOR THE TRADES
1890 INPUT G$
1900 CLS
1910 PRINT "THE TRADES FOR THIS PARAMETER ESTIMATING SYSTEM ARE AS FOLLOWS:
1920 PRINT ""
1930 PRINT "NUMBER";TAB(10);"TRADE NAME"
1940 PRINT "------";TAB(10);"--------------------------------"
1950 OPEN "TRADES.DAT" AS #1 LEN=45
1960 FOR ZX=1 TO II
1970 FIELD #1, 45 AS TR$(ZX)
1980 GET #1,ZX
1990 AA$(ZX)=TR$(ZX)
2000 PRINT TAB(3);ZX;TAB(10);AA$(ZX)
2010 NEXT ZX
2020 CLOSE #1
2030 PRINT ""
2040 INPUT "ENTER C TO START THE INPUT OF TRADE DOLLAR AMOUNTS ";C$
2050 CLS
2060 DD$="$$#####,###############.##"
2070 FOR UU=1 TO II
2080 CLS
2090 PRINT "NUMBER";TAB(10);"TRADE NAME"
2100 PRINT "------";TAB(10);"----------"
2110 PRINT TAB(3);UU;TAB(10);AA$(UU)
2120 PRINT ""
2130 INPUT "ENTER THE DOLLAR AMOUNT OR O (THE NUMBER) FOR THE TRADE= ";DA(UU)
2140 PRINT ""
2150 IF (DA(UU)=0) THEN 2370
2160 OPEN "CORR.DAT" AS #1 LEN=5
2170 FIELD #1, 5 AS CR$
2180 GET #1,UU
2190 CR=VAL(CR$)
2200 CLOSE #1
2210 OPEN "PART.DAT" AS #1 LEN=20
2220 FIELD #1, 20 AS PM$
2230 GET #1,UU
2240 PM=VAL(PM$)
2250 PN=PM+QU(CR)
2260 LSET PM$=STR$(PN)
2270 PUT #1,UU
2280 CLOSE #1
2290 OPEN "TRPAR.DAT" AS #1 LEN=20
2300 FIELD #1, 20 AS MP$
2310 GET #1,UU
2320 MP=VAL(MP$)
2330 MN=MP+DA(UU)
2340 LSET MP$=STR$(MN)
2350 PUT #1,UU
2360 CLOSE #1
2370 NEXT UU
2380 CLS
2390 PRINT ""
2400 PRINT "YOU HAVE COMPLETED THE ENTRY OF THE HISTORICAL DATA FOR THIS JOB
2410 PRINT ""
2420 INPUT "ENTER C TO RETURN TO THE PROGRAM OPTIONS ";C$
2430 GOTO 250
2440 CLS
2450 PRINT "THIS IS THE END OF THE PROGRAM"
```

Figure 8.15 *Continued*

```
2460 KEY ON
2470 END
2480 CLS
2490 CLS
2500 OPEN "COUNT.DAT" AS #1 LEN=5
2510 FIELD #1, 5 AS T$
2520 GET #1,1
2530 I$=T$
2540 GET #1,2
2550 II$=T$
2560 CLOSE #1
2570 I=VAL(I$)
2580 II=VAL(II$)
2590 PRINT "THE PARAMETERS THAT ARE DEFINED ON THIS DISK ARE AS FOLLOWS:
2600 PRINT "NUMBER";TAB(10);"PARAMETER NAME"
2610 PRINT "------";TAB(10);"-----------------"
2620 OPEN "METER.DAT" AS #1 LEN=45
2630 FOR IL=1 TO I
2640 FIELD #1, 45 AS PT$(IL)
2650 GET #1,IL
2660 A$(IL)=PT$(IL)
2670 PRINT TAB(3);IL;TAB(10);A$(IL)
2680 NEXT IL
2690 CLOSE #1
2700 PRINT ""
2710 PRINT "ENTER C: TO CONTINUE THE PREPARATION OF A PARAMETER ESTIMATE OPTI(
2720 INPUT V$
2730 CLS
2740 INPUT "ENTER THE NAME OF THE PROJECT= ";NA$
2750 PRINT ""
2760 CLS
2770 FOR GG=1 TO I
2780 CLS
2790 PRINT "NUMBER";TAB(10);"PARAMETER NAME"
2800 PRINT "------";TAB(10);"---------------------------"
2810 PRINT TAB(3);GG;TAB(10);A$(GG)
2820 PRINT ""
2830 INPUT "ENTER THE PARAMETER QUANTITY= ";ES(GG)
2840 PRINT ""
2850 NEXT GG
2860 INPUT "ENTER C TO HAVE THE PROGRAM CALCULATE THE ESTIMATE ";C$
2870 CLS
2880 CLS
2890 PRINT "PLEASE WAIT, THE HISTORICAL DATA FROM THE DISK IS BEING READ...."
2900 OPEN "PART.DAT" AS #1 LEN=20
2910 FOR GA=1 TO II
2920 FIELD #1, 20 AS PM$
2930 GET #1,GA
2940 PQ(GA)=VAL(PM$)
2950 NEXT GA
2960 CLOSE #1
2970 OPEN "TRPAR.DAT" AS #1 LEN=20
2980 FOR GB=1 TO II
2990 FIELD #1, 20 AS MP$
3000 GET #1,GB
3010 TQ(GB)=VAL(MP$)
3020 NEXT GB
3030 CLOSE #1
3040 CLS
3050 PRINT TAB(30);"PROJECT NAME= ";NA$
```

Figure 8.15 *Continued*

```
3060 PRINT TAB(30);"PARAMETER ESTIMATE"
3070 PRINT ""
3080 PRINT "TRADE";TAB(50);"ESTIMATED TRADE COST"
3090 PRINT "-----------------";TAB(50);"-----------------------------"
3100 TE=0
3110 OPEN "TRADES.DAT" AS #1 LEN=45
3120 FOR NN=1 TO II
3130 FIELD #1, 45 AS TR$(NN)
3140 GET #1,NN
3150 AA$(NN)=TR$(NN)
3160 NEXT NN
3170 FOR WW=1 TO II
3180 R$="$$##,###########.##"
3190 S$="##,#############.##"
3200 IF (TQ(WW)=0) THEN 3360
3210 CLOSE #1
3220 OPEN "CORR.DAT" AS #1 LEN=5
3230 FIELD #1, 5 AS CR$
3240 GET #1,WW
3250 CR=VAL(CR$)
3260 CLOSE #1
3270 ET(WW)=(TQ(WW)*ES(CR))/PQ(WW)
3280 TE=TE+ET(WW)
3290 IF (WW=1) THEN 3330
3300 PRINT AA$(WW);TAB(50);
3310 PRINT USING S$;ET(WW)
3320 GOTO 3370
3330 PRINT AA$(WW);TAB(48);
3340 PRINT USING R$;ET(WW)
3350 GOTO 3370
3360 PRINT AA$(WW);TAB(45);"NO PREVIOUS TRADE COST DATA"
3370 NEXT WW
3380 PRINT "-----------------";TAB(50);"-----------------------------"
3390 PRINT "TOTAL";TAB(48);
3400 PRINT USING R$;TE
3410 PRINT ""
3420 INPUT "ENTER C TO RETURN TO THE PROGRAM EXECUTION OPTIONS ";C$
3430 GOTO 250
```

Figure 8.15 *Continued*

These program instructions give the user the ability to define a nondefined number of parameters. In effect, the program enables the user to exit the program loop before the I counter in the loop is completed. If the user enters an N when confronted with the question in line 490, the program "jumps" out of the loop and branches to line 560.

Line 600 starts the program loop that enables the user to initialize/set up the trades and correlations for the parameter estimating system. Again the user is given the opportunity to branch out of the input routine via lines 930 through 960. This input loop starts in line 600 and ends with line 980.

After inputting each trade, the user is requested to identify (correlate) the parameter that the cost of the trade is a function of in regards to its occurrence. This is done via lines 680 through 750. When confronted with the request to identify the parameter name/number in line 740, the user enters a parameter number that is received in the input instruction in line 750.

After the user completes the entry of parameter names, trade names, and correlations, the program sends/save the setup on a data disk via lines 1120 through 1570. The instructions in these lines can be considered data file programming. In particular, the program uses random data file programming as a means of storing the setup on a data disk. Before these lines are executed by the program, the user would insert a blank initialized data disk in the disk drive to receive the data sent to the drive via the data file programming lines.

The data file programming in lines 1120 through 1570 actually create several different data files on the data disk. Because the programming performed for each of these data files is similar, we will only discuss one of these data files—the one contained in lines 1210 through 1270.

The data file created by lines 1210 through 1270 stores the names of the parameters input by the user in the setup routine; line 1210 "creates" or opens a data file that is arbitrarily named "METER." The LEN = 45 in line 1210 sets aside 45 characters to hold each parameter name. The FIELD instruction simply identifies the variable to receive the parameter name as PT$, an arbitrarily selected variable.

The program loop from lines 1220 to 1260 receives and stores the parameter names previously input by the user. The actual "putting" of the parameter name onto the data disk is done by PUT instruction in line 1250. In effect, the PUT instruction "puts" the parameter name on the data disk. After each of the parameter names is put on the data disk, the data file (in this case file named METER) is closed for input in line 1270.

Other data files are opened and closed in the same manner. After completing the storage of setup in the other disk files, the program returns to the program menu via the RETURN instruction in line 1570.

Historical parameter data from past projects is input and stored by selecting option H in line 380. When this option is selected, the program branches to line 1580. The program then "reads" the previously prepared data disk and places the parameter names and trades into the computer memory. This is done in order to enable the user to input parameter quantities and trade dollar amounts from the past project being entered.

The reading of the previously prepared data files is performed in lines 1600 through 1750. The only difference between the reading of the data files and the previously described storing of the data on the data disk is that a GET instruction is used to "get" the data instead of the previously described PUT instruction.

After reading the data disk, the loop started in line 1780 enables the user to enter the parameter quantities and trade costs. After receiving the data input, the program proceeds to store the entered historical data via the data filing programming in lines 2160 through 2360.

The preparation of a parameter estimate program option is selected by entering an E in line 380. The program then branches to line 2480. In this option/routine, the user merely inputs the estimated quantities for the previously defined estimate, and the program proceeds to print an estimate, by trade, for the proposed project.

The preparation of an estimate starts by having the program first read the data disk. This is done in lines 2500 through 2690.

This reading of the data disk places the names of the parameters into the computer memory such that the user can input the parameter quantities for the project being estimated. After the quantities are input, using the program loop from lines 2770 through 2850, the program proceeds to read previously stored historical data from data files.

The reading of the historical data, including parameter quantities and trade costs, is read using the data filing programming in lines 2900 through 3030. The data file read contains the cumulation parameter quantities and trade costs from all past projects entered.

The printing of the parameter estimate for the proposed project starts in line 3040. The calculation of the printed trade costs is performed by multiplying the inputted quantity of a parameter times the historical trade cost per parameter measure that is stored in the data file. Actually, the trade cost per parameter measure is not stored in the data file. Instead, the cumulative trade cost is divided by the cumulative parameter quantity, of which the trade is a function, as defined in the CORR data file.

A sample of a printed parameter estimate for a proposed project is illustrated in Figure 8.16. In addition to printing the estimated cost for each trade and the estimated cost for the entire project, the program also prints the historical trade costs per parameter measure used as the data base for preparing the estimate.

```
                              PROJECT NAME= OFFICE BUILDING
                              PARAMETER ESTIMATE

TRADE                                    ESTIMATED TRADE COST
--------------                           ---------------------------

EXCAVATION                                      $42,395.04
CONCRETE                                         89,757.35
CONCRETE FORMING                                 58,382.42
MASONRY                                         114,180.63
CARPENTRY                                        32,673.29
STRUCTURAL STEEL                                 24,123.00
ELECTRICAL                                       38,190.54
PLUMBING                                         65,655.00
MECHANICAL                                       26,455.00
----------------                                 ---------------------------
TOTAL                                           $491,812.28


ASSUMED DATA BASE FOR THE PARAMETER ESTIMATE
TRADE                      PARAMETER              TRADE $/UNIT PAR
-----                      ---------              -----------------

EXCAVATION                 SECT. AREA                    7.93
CONCRETE                   FLOOR AREA                    3.27
CONCRETE FORMING           FLOOR AREA                    2.13
MASONRY                    LIN FT. OF WALLS             26.23
CARPENTRY                  HEIGHT                       347.59
STRUCTURAL STEEL           NO. OF FLOORS              4,824.60
ELECTRICAL                 HEIGHT                       406.28
PLUMBING                   NO. OF FLOORS             13,131.00
MECHANICAL                 NO. OF FLOORS              5,291.00
```

Figure 8.16 Example parameter estimate prepared from parameter estimating program.

9: Detailed Estimating Applications

INTRODUCTION

No task is more fundamental to the existence of a construction firm than the estimating task. The task entails the projection of numerous types of costs incurred when constructing a proposed project. Included in these costs are direct labor, material, equipment, subcontractor, job overhead, and company overhead costs. The accurate estimating of each of these costs influences the potential profit or loss on a project.

A contractor expends many hours preparing estimates for projects, some projects on which he is low bidder and subsequently builds, other projects on which he is an unsuccessful bidder. A firm may expend in excess of 100 hours preparing a single estimate.

Even though a contractor may expend many hours preparing an estimate, the estimate may turn out to be inaccurate. The author's experience leads him to the conclusion that a contractor seldom, if ever, prepares a construction estimate with a 100 percent degree of accuracy. In fact he may frequently prepare estimates that are 6 percent or more accurate relevant to the actual cost of building a project.

The end result is that the typical construction firm has a need to lessen the hours required to prepare an estimate while at the same time improve the accuracy of the estimate. The computer gives the firm the potential to address both of these concerns.

While a computer can aid in the construction estimating task, there is in fact considerable misconception as to what a computer can and cannot do in regard to estimating. First of all, the computer cannot prepare an estimate for a firm by itself; it is not a substitute for the construction firm's "hunches" and know-how obtained from years of on-site experience. Instead, the computer should be viewed as a tool that the construction firm can use to help it prepare an estimate.

While computers will undoubtedly be used in the future to actually read construction drawings via a pen and a plotter, this should not be viewed as a practical or even feasible approach today. Instead, the computer should be viewed as having the following applications to detailed contractor estimating:

- The ability to efficiently and accurately perform the many mathematical calculations that are part of the estimating function.
- The ability to perform spreadsheet calculations (add columns and rows of data) and subject the results to "what if conditions."
- The ability to store (via data base programming and data files) vast amounts of historical project data that subsequently aids in the estimating and predicting of future costs and events.
- The ability to use a common data base to integrate several firm and project functions, including estimating and job cost control.

In this chapter we will illustrate the use of a computer to perform estimating mathematical conversions. We will do this by the illustration of an example program written in BASIC.

In this chapter we will also discuss business spreadsheet programs. Programs such as VISICALC, MULTIPLAN, etc., have been widely sold to computer users in many businesses. We will discuss their application to construction estimating in regard to performing spreadsheet calculations and building a financial model that can be subject to "what if" conditions.

Finally, we will illustrate an example spreadsheet program the author has written using BASIC. While the program is somewhat repetitive of the spreadsheet program illustrated in Chapter 4, the program in this chapter is more extensive and complete. Most importantly we will demonstrate how the program creates a data base that can serve as a basis for integrating yet another project management function, that of job cost control discussed in the following chapter.

We will not illustrate the concept of storing vast amounts of historical data that can be subsequently used for predicting/estimating a future cost or event. We will illustrate this capability of computers to estimating in our discussion of equipment management/estimating that is presented in Chapter 12.

ESTIMATING CONVERSIONS: AN EXAMPLE BASIC COMPUTER PROGRAM

The preparation of a construction estimate entails the making of many mathematical calculations and conversions. Many of these conversions are necessitated by the fact that there is a need to convert from the dimensions on the construction drawings to another unit. For example, even though the size of a concrete footing may be shown in feet and inches on the drawings, the construction estimator is likely to want to measure the concrete placement quantity in cubic yards.

The fact that a mixed unit of measure, feet and inches, is used by the designer in preparing construction drawings increases the number of required calculations and mathematical conversions even more.

Prior to the use of a computer, the contractor expended considerable nonproductive time performing the above type of conversions. Even more importantly, owing to human error, the contractor occasionally made mathematical errors in performing these calculations and conversions that led to inaccurate project estimates.

The efficiency and accuracy of mathematical calculations and conversions is greatly enhanced by a computer and a software computer program. While relatively simple in design and sophistication relative to data base programming, many of these calculation conversion programs are in wide use by contractors.

A relatively simple and short estimating conversion program is illustrated in Figure 9.1. The program has been written to make commonly required mathematical conversions that are part of estimating excavation, concrete, concrete forming, rebar, carpentry, and structural steel plates.

We will now give a brief overview of the estimating conversion program illustrated in Figure 9.1. The reader will note that we have not included error routines, data editing routines, etc., that are a necessary part of a complete program.

After clearing the computer monitor in line 100, the program enables the user to select the type of material/item being estimated. This selection menu is given in lines 130 through 270. Depending on the user's selection, the program then branches to different program lines/routines.

Let us follow the program through the E, or excavation, option. The program branches to line 400. After executing lines 400, 405, and 410, the program branches to subroutines 2000 and 2050. The first subroutine asks the user if the dimensions to be input are in feet, in feet and inches, or in inches only. Subroutine 2050 is used to test the user selection and send the program to yet another subroutine, either subroutine 2200, 2300, or 2400. These subroutines are used to enable the user to input the excavation dimensions. Also, the converting of the three linear dimensions into a cubic yard quantity is performed by these subroutines.

The above-noted types of tasks and mathematics are needed for other materials. The programming for the conversions for these materials is done by using the same subroutines.

```
100 CLS
110 PRINT "ESTIMATING QUANTITY TAKE-OFF CONVERSION PROGRAMS
120 PRINT ""
130 PRINT "ENTER E:  TO DETERMINE EXCAVATION QUANTITY
140 PRINT "ENTER C:  TO DETERMINE CONCRETE QUANTITY
150 PRINT "ENTER F:  TO DETERMINE CONCRETE FORMING QUANTITY
160 PRINT "ENTER R:  TO DETERMINE REBAR QUANTITY
170 PRINT "ENTER W:  TO DETERMINE CARPENTRY QUANTITY
180 PRINT "ENTER S:  TO DETERMINE STEEL QUANTITY
200 PRINT "ENTER T:  TO STOP/TERMINATE THE PROGRAM
210 INPUT CH$
220 IF (CH$="E") THEN 400
230 IF (CH$="C") THEN 600
240 IF (CH$="F") THEN 800
250 IF (CH$="R") THEN 1000
260 IF (CH$="W") THEN 1200
270 IF (CH$="S") THEN 1400
280 PRINT "THIS IS THE END OF THE PROGRAM"
290 END
400 CLS
405 PRINT "EXCAVATION CONVERSIONS
410 PRINT ""
415 GOSUB 2000
420 GOSUB 2050
425 CLS
430 PRINT "EXCAVATION QUANTITY
435 PRINT "WIDTH=";WC;" FEET
440 PRINT "LENGTH=";LC;" FEET"
445 PRINT "DEPTH=";DC;" FEET
450 PRINT ""
455 PRINT VB;" CU.YDS."
460 PRINT VA;" CU.FT."
465 PRINT VC;" CU.INCHES"
470 INPUT "ENTER C TO CONTINUE";C$
475 GOTO 100
600 CLS
605 PRINT "CONCRETE QUANTITY
610 PRINT ""
615 GOSUB 2000
620 GOSUB 2050
625 CLS
630 PRINT "CONCRETE QUANTITY
635 PRINT "WIDTH= ";WC;" FEET
640 PRINT "LENGTH= ";LC;" FEET
645 PRINT "DEPTH= ";DC;" FEET
650 PRINT ""
655 PRINT VB;" CU.YDS"
660 PRINT VA;" CU.FT.
665 PRINT VC;" CU.INCHES"
670 INPUT "ENTER C TO CONTINUE ";C$
675 GOTO 100
800 CLS
```

Figure 9.1 Example estimating mathematical conversion program written in BASIC.

```
805 PRINT "CONCRETE FORMING CONVERSIONS
810 PRINT ""
815 GOSUB 2000
820 GOSUB 2070
825 CLS
830 PRINT "CONCRETE FORMING QUANTITY
835 PRINT "WIDTH= ";WC;" FEET
840 PRINT "LENGTH= ";LC;" FEET
845 PRINT ""
850 PRINT VA;" SFCA
855 INPUT "ENTER C TO CONTINUE";C$
860 GOTO 100
1000 CLS
1005 PRINT "REBAR CONVERSIONS"
1010 PRINT ""
1015 INPUT "ENTER REBAR SIZE IN # OF 8THS, E.G. 7 = ";E
1020 INPUT "ENTER LENGTH OF BAR IN FEET = ";L
1025 INPUT "ENTER NO. OF BARS = ";N
1030 T=L*N
1035 D=E/8
1040 W=(490/1728)*(D*D/4)*3.14*12
1045 WA=T*W
1050 WC=WA/2000
1055 PRINT ""
1060 PRINT "REBAR QUANTITY"
1065 PRINT ""
1070 PRINT "SIZE= ";E
1075 PRINT "DEAMETER= ";D
1080 PRINT "NO. OF BARS= ";N
1085 PRINT "LENGTH OF BARS (IN FEET) = ";L
1090 PRINT "TOTAL LENGTH OF BARS (IN FEET) = ";T
1095 PRINT "WEIGHT PER FOOT= ";W
1100 PRINT "TOTAL WEIGHT OF BARS= ";WA; "LBS."
1105 PRINT "TOTAL WEIGHT OF BARS= ";WC;" TONS"
1110 INPUT "ENTER C TO CONTINUE";C$
1115 GOTO 100
1200 CLS
1205 PRINT "CARPENTRY CONVERSIONS
1210 PRINT ""
1215 INPUT "ENTER LENGTH IN FEET= ";LC
1220 INPUT "ENTER WIDTH IN INCHES= ";W
1225 INPUT "ENTER DEPTH IN INCHES= ";D
1230 INPUT "ENTER NO. OF BOARDS= ";N
1235 FB=(W*D*LC*N)/12
1240 CLS
1245 PRINT "CARPENTRY QUANTITY
1250 PRINT ""
1255 PRINT "SIZE= ";W;" INCHES X ";D;" INCHES
1260 PRINT "LENGTH= ";LC
1265 PRINT "NO. OF BOARDS= ";N
1270 PRINT ""
1275 PRINT FB;" BOARD FEET
1280 FC=FB/1000
1285 PRINT FC;"MFDM
1290 INPUT "ENTER C TO CONTINUE";C$
1295 GOTO 100
1400 CLS
1405 PRINT "STEEL CONVERSIONS
1410 PRINT ""
1415 GOSUB 2000
1420 GOSUB 2050
```

Figure 9.1 *Continued*

```
1425 CLS
1430 PRINT "STEEL QUANTITIES
1435 PRINT "WIDTH= ";WC;" FEET
1440 PRINT "LENGTH= ";LC;" FEET"
1445 PRINT "DEPTH= ";DC;" FEET"
1450 PRINT ""
1455 PRINT VB;" CU.YDS."
1460 PRINT VA;" CU.FT."
1465 WD=VA*490
1470 WE=WD/2000
1475 PRINT WD;" LBS"
1480 PRINT WE;" TONS"
1485 INPUT "ENTER C TO CONTINUE ";C$
1490 GOTO 100
2000 PRINT "ENTER F: IF DIMENSIONS ARE TO BE ENTERED IN FEET"
2005 PRINT "ENTER FI: IF DIMENSIONS ARE TO BE ENTERED IN FEET AND INCHES"
2010 PRINT "ENTER I: IF DIMENSIONS ARE TO BE ENTERED IN INCHES"
2015 INPUT U$
2020 RETURN
2050 IF (U$="F") THEN GOSUB 2200
2055 IF (U$="FI") THEN GOSUB 2300
2060 IF (U$="I") THEN GOSUB 2400
2065 RETURN
2070 IF (U$="F") THEN GOSUB 2500
2075 IF (U$="FI") THEN GOSUB 2600
2080 IF (U$="I") THEN GOSUB 2700
2085 RETURN
2200 CLS
2205 INPUT "ENTER WIDTH IN FEET= ";WC
2210 INPUT "ENTER LENGTH IN FEET= ";LC
2215 INPUT "ENTER DEPTH IN FEET= ";DC
2220 VA=WC*LC*DC
2225 VB=VA/27
2230 VC=VB*1728
2235 RETURN
2300 CLS
2305 PRINT "ENTER FEET AND INCHES OF WIDTH"
2310 INPUT "ENTER FEET= ";WA
2315 INPUT "ENTER INCHES= ";WB
2320 WC=WA+(WB/12)
2325 PRINT "ENTER FEET AND INCHES OF LENGTH"
2330 INPUT "ENTER FEET= ";LA
2335 INPUT "ENTER INCHES= ";LB
2340 LC=LA + (LB/12)
2345 PRINT "ENTER FEET AND INCHES OF DEPTH"
2350 INPUT "ENTER FEET= ";DA
2355 INPUT "ENTER INCHES= ";DB
2360 DC=DA +(DB/12)
2365 VA=WC*LC*DC
2370 VB=VA/27
2375 VC=VA*1728
2380 RETURN
2400 CLS
2405 INPUT "ENTER WIDTH IN INCHES= ";W
2410 INPUT "ENTER LENGTH IN INCHES= ";L
2415 INPUT "ENTER DEPTH IN INCHES= ";D
2420 WC=W/12
2425 LC=L/12
2430 DC=D/12
2435 VA=WC*LC*DC
2440 VB=VA/27
```

Figure 9.1 *Continued*

```
2445 VC=VA*1728
2450 RETURN
2500 CLS
2505 INPUT "ENTER WIDTH IN FEET= ";WC
2510 INPUT "ENTER LENGTH IN FEET= ";LC
2515 VA=WC*LC
2520 RETURN
2600 CLS
2605 PRINT "ENTER FEET AND INCHES OF WIDTH"
2610 INPUT "ENTER FEET= ";WA
2615 INPUT "ENTER INCHES= ";WB
2620 WC=WA + (WB/12)
2625 PRINT "ENTER FEET AND INCHES OF DEPTH"
2630 INPUT "ENTER FEET= ";LA
2635 INPUT "ENTER INCHES= ";LB
2640 LC=LA +(LB/12)
2645 VA=WC*LC
2650 RETURN
2700 CLS
2705 PRINT "ENTER WIDTH IN INCHES= ";W
2710 PRINT "ENTER LENGTH IN INCHES= ";L
2715 WC=W/12
2720 LC=L/12
2725 VA=WC*LC
2730 RETURN
```

Figure 9.1 *Continued*

After the subroutines for the excavation work are executed, the program resumes in line 425. The program proceeds to print the converted quantities as well as the input dimensions. An example of a printout for the excavation and other materials is illustrated in Figure 9.2.

After printing the excavation report, line 475 returns the user to the material selection menu.

More sophisticated estimating mathematical calculations and conversion programs than the one illustrated in Figure 9.1 are available and in use by contractors. However, all these programs operate on the same principle and programming concepts illustrated in Figure 9.1.

BUSINESS SPREADSHEET PROGRAMS AND CONSTRUCTION ESTIMATING

The rapid growth of the use of microcomputers by various types of businesses has resulted in the evolution of a considerable amount of business-type programs. Business programs such as VISICALC, VISIPLOT, MULTIPLAN, LOTUS 123, etc., are in wide use.

The above-noted types of programs are not written for exclusive use by the construction industry. They are written with enough flexibility to be used by a wide range of businesses, including a manufacturing industry,

```
EXCAVATION QUANTITY
WIDTH= 7  FEET
LENGTH= 6  FEET
DEPTH= 2  FEET

 3.111111  CU.YDS.
 84  CU.FT.
 5376  CU.INCHES




CONCRETE QUANTITY
WIDTH=  6.5  FEET
LENGTH=  9.25  FEET
DEPTH=  9.75  FEET

 21.71181  CU.YDS
 586.2188  CU.FT.
 37518  CU.INCHES




CONCRETE FORMING QUANTITY
WIDTH=  7.5  FEET
LENGTH=  8.33  FEET

 62.475  SFCA




REBAR CONVERSIONS

ENTER REBAR SIZE IN # OF 8THS, E.G. 7 = ? 7
ENTER LENGTH OF BAR IN FEET = ? 15
ENTER NO. OF BARS = ? 26

REBAR QUANTITY

SIZE=  7
DEAMETER=  .875
NO. OF BARS=  26
LENGTH OF BARS (IN FEET) =  15
TOTAL LENGTH OF BARS (IN FEET) =  390
WEIGHT PER FOOT=  2.045123
TOTAL WEIGHT OF BARS=  797.5978 LBS.
TOTAL WEIGHT OF BARS=  .3987989  TONS




CARPENTRY QUANTITY

SIZE=  6  INCHES X  4  INCHES
LENGTH=  6
NO. OF BOARDS=  25

 300  BOARD FEET
 .3 MFBM
```

Figure 9.2 Example output from conversion program.

```
STEEL QUANTITIES
WIDTH=  8  FEET
LENGTH=  22  FEET
DEPTH=  4  FEET




26.07408  CU.YDS.
704  CU.FT.
344960  LBS
172.48  TONS
```

Figure 9.2 *Continued*

a dentist, a car dealer, or a contractor. While broad based, the programs may lack some of the programming routines that are "ideal" for a given industry. Nonetheless, owing to their wide use and flexibility, a short discussion of a spreadsheet application is included in this section.

One of the most popular business application programs is the electronic spreadsheet program. The program enables the user to create a spreadsheet that can be updated and widely adaptable. The ease of performing "what if" analysis has led to its prime use in budgeting/forecasting, but almost any application could be utilized.

One example of such a program is MULTIPLAN. Like other spreadsheet programs, MULTIPLAN consists of a matrix of rows (255) × columns (63). Each cell can potentially contain a word or group of words (alpha entry) or a numerical value or equation to calculate and return a numerical value (value entry). The computer screen, which only has room for 22 rows and from 3 to 63 columns, depending on their width, provides a window that can be moved around to view/use different portions of the spreadsheet.

By using the commands and subcommands that appear on the menu at the bottom of the screen, the user establishes the format, the template, that guides the entry of data onto the spreadsheet. The template is simply an electronic sheet on which columns, labels, formulas, and possibly some, but not all, of the data values for calculation have been established for future application. Once created and saved on disk, the template can be reused repeatedly or further expanded/modified.

Perhaps the most critical phase of the estimating process is the final summarization of costs that takes place immediately prior to the submission of the contractor's bid. During these last hours, subcontractors/material suppliers phone in their prices, scopes of work, and any revisions to same.

The estimator must compare and analyze these quickly and be aware of their position relative to their competitors, so as to deal with them accordingly. At some point prices must be plugged into the estimate summary covering all phases of the work so that the estimate overhead may be adjusted and the summations checked. From this point on all changes are handled as external adjustments. The process, while essential and unavoidable, provides margin for error. A dangerous situation can occur if mathematical or judgmental errors exist. The sometimes frantic nature of the final minutes preceding the bid deadline often invites errors.

The microcomputer and an electronic spreadsheet program can be used to alleviate some of the problems encountered on bid day. By creating an electronic estimate summary sheet to replace the typical paper form, with the necessary mathematical functions embedded in the template, the problems associated with closing the estimate and having it checked can be virtually eliminated. An example estimate template created with MULTIPLAN is illustrated in Figure 9.3.

```
PROJECT:                         BID DATE:
ARCHITECT:                       PROJECT DURATION (MOS.):      1.0
LOCATION:

        ESTIMATE SECTIONS        SUB.    MATERIAL          LABOR
------------------------------  -----  ----------------  ----------------
1.   GENERAL REQUIREMENTS
2A.  SITE WORK-EXCAV., ETC.
2B.  BIT. PAVING, LANDSCAPING
2C.  DEMOLITION
3A.  CONCRETE FOUNDATIONS
3B.  CONCRETE FLOORS, ETC.
3C.  STRUCT. CONCRETE, PRECAST
3D.  RE-STEEL, MISC. ADJ.
4.   MASONRY
5A.  STRUCT. & MISC. STEEL
5B.  METAL DECKING
6A.  ROUGH CARPENTRY, HDW.
6B.  FINISH CARPENTRY, ETC.
7A.  WATERPROOFING, INSUL.
7B.  PREFORMED METAL PANELS
7C.  ROOFING
7D.  SEALANTS
8A.  HOLLOW METAL, FIN. HDW.
8B.  SPECIALTY DOORS
8C.  GLASS & GLAZING, WINDOWS
9A.  DRYWALL, PLASTER, ACOUST.
9C.  PAINTING, WALLCOVERING
10.  MISC. SPECIALTIES
11.  EQUIPMENT
12.  FURNISHINGS
13.  SPECIAL CONSTRUCTION
14.  CONVEYING SYSTEMS
15.  MECHANICAL SYSTEMS
16.  ELECTRICAL SYSTEMS
```

Figure 9.3 Example spreadsheet template from a business spreadsheet program.

```
TOTALS                                    $0.00              $0.00

OVERHEAD ADJUSTMENTS
  BASED ON:
            $0.00

BUILDER'S RISK INS.                       $0.00
OWNER'S PROT. INS.                        $0.00
UMBRELLA INS.                             $0.00
INS. & SOC. SECURITY                      $0.00
PERFORMANCE BOND                          $0.00
STATE SALES TAX                           $0.00
CONTINGENCY

ADJUSTMENTS TOTAL                         $0.00

ADJUSTED COST                             $0.00

MARGIN (ENTER BELOW)
        0%                                $0.00
                                     ====================
*BASE BID*                                $0.00
                                     ====================


                         SUBCONTRACTOR
                              BID
                           SUMMARYS

SECT.:
        SUBCONTRACTOR           BID AMOUNT             SCOPE



SECT.:
        SUBCONTRACTOR           BID AMOUNT             SCOPE



SECT.:
        SUBCONTRACTOR           BID AMOUNT             SCOPE
```

Figure 9.3 *Continued*

In addition to preparing the necessary summations, the spreadsheet program can also calculate overhead items that are typically figures on early projections of cost. This is done automatically and updated continually, as figures change, by formulas embedded in the overhead adjustments section of the spreadsheet. A filled in template is illustrated in Figure 9.4.

Analysis of subcontractor/material supplier bids can be handled with the subcontractor bid summary section of the spreadsheet. An example is illustrated in Figure 9.5. Located adjacent to the estimate spreadsheet are a series of smaller spreadsheets set up for entry of subcontractor/material supplier bid information. If an item is to be subcontracted indicated by a

```
PROJECT: MONMOUTH WTP
ARCHITECT: WELLS ENGINEERS
LOCATION: MONMOUTH, IL.
BID DATE: 4 FEB. 1983
PROJECT DURATION (MOS.):      7.0
```

ESTIMATE SECTIONS	SUB.	MATERIAL	LABOR
1. GENERAL REQUIREMENTS		$17406.00	$36055.00
2A. SITE WORK–EXCAV., ETC.	Y	$28386.00	$135.00
2B. BIT. PAVING, LANDSCAPING		$0.00	$0.00
2C. DEMOLITION		$0.00	$0.00
3A. CONCRETE FOUNDATIONS	N	$180.00	$32429.00
3B. CONCRETE FLOORS, ETC.	N	$15378.00	$14681.00
3C. STRUCT. CONCRETE, PRECAST	N	$1016.00	$2096.00
3D. RE–STEEL, MISC. ADJ.	Y	$9398.00	$5355.00
4. MASONRY	Y	$7000.00	$0.00
5A. STRUCT. & MISC. STEEL	Y	$6985.00	$1866.00
5B. METAL DECKING		$0.00	$0.00
6A. ROUGHH CARPENTRY, HDW.	N	$1577.00	$2571.00
6B. FINISH CARPENTRY, ETC.		$0.00	$0.00
7A. WATERPROOFING, INSUL.		$0.00	$0.00
7B. PREFORMED METAL PANELS		$0.00	$0.00
7C. ROOFING	Y	$7480.00	$0.00
7D. SEALANTS	N	$60.00	$160.00
8A. HOLLOW METAL, FIN. HDW.	Y	$1348.00	$160.00
8B. SPECIALTY DOORS	Y	$625.00	$0.00
8C. GLASS & GLAZING, WINDOWS		$0.00	$0.00
9A. DRYWALL, PLASTER, ACOUST.		$0.00	$0.00
9C. PAINTING, WALLCOVERING		$0.00	$0.00
10. MISC. SPECIALTIES		$0.00	$0.00
11. EQUIPMENT	Y	$1250.00	$1120.00
12. FURNISHINGS		$0.00	$0.00
13. SPECIAL CONSTRUCTION		$0.00	$0.00
14. CONVEYING SYSTEMS		$0.00	$0.00
15. MECHANICAL SYSTEMS	Y	$18209.00	$0.00
16. ELECTRICAL SYSTEMS		$0.00	$0.00
TOTALS		$116298.00	$96628.00

Figure 9.4   Example filled in spreadsheet template.

```
         OVERHEAD ADJUSTMENTS
            BASED ON:
                        $276423.14
         ---------------------------------------------------------
         BUILDER'S RISK INS.                           $4.34
         OWNER'S PROT. INS.                          $317.89
         UMBRELLA INS.                               $359.35
         INS. & SOC. SECURITY                      $16049.17
         PERFORMANCE BOND                           $3317.08
         STATE SALES TAX                            $1377.45
         CONTINGENCY
         --------------------------------      ------------------
         ADJUSTMENTS TOTAL                         $21425.28
                                               ------------------
         ADJUSTED COST                            $234351.28

         MARGIN (ENTER BELOW)
                 7%                                $16404.59
                                               ==================
         *BASE BID*                              $250755.87
                                               ==================
```

Figure 9.4 *Continued*

Y or N in the Sub. column of the estimate summary sheet, the estimator uses the MULTIPLAN function "GOTO" to move to the appropriate subcontractor summary. Prices and scopes of work can then be entered. Upon choosing the appropriate subcontract/material supply price, the amount can be automatically transferred to the estimate summary, which is then appropriately updated to reflect the new price. A sufficient number of summary locations could be created to handle even the largest projects.

Finally, the spreadsheet program can calculate the base bid from the most current adjusted cost when the estimator simply inputs the appropriate profit margin. The flexibility of the electronic spreadsheet allows for continual change in prices and markup rates until virtually seconds before the bid must be submitted, with the assurance that calculations on inputted numbers are accurate.

AN EXAMPLE ESTIMATE SPREADSHEET COMPUTER PROGRAM WRITTEN IN BASIC

In this section we will illustrate a program written in BASIC that enables the user to input data for a proposed estimate, save the input via data files, and print a detailed estimate report. The reader will remember that we wrote a relatively small estimate spreadsheet program as a means of teaching/illustrating the BASIC language in Chapter 4.

The program we will now illustrate is more extensive and complex than the one illustrated in Chapter 4. In addition to being more extensive

```
                              SUBCONTRACTOR
                                   BID
                              SUMMARYS
--------------------------------------------------------------------------

SECT.:2A-EXCAV.
          SUBCONTRACTOR           BID AMOUNT                    SCOPE
------------------------------    ------------------    --------------------
OUR ESTIMATE                        $28386.00  ALL EXC. & BACKFILL
SPURGEON CONST.                     $32500.00  ALL




--------------------------------------------------------------------------


SECT.:3D-REINF. STEEL
          SUBCONTRACTOR           BID AMOUNT                    SCOPE
------------------------------    ------------------    --------------------
MATHIS-KELLEY                       $5845.00   17 TONS RESTEEL   (MESH @ 16.3
GATE CITY                           $4950.00   15.9 TON RESTEEL
HOWARD                              $5688.00   14 TON RESTEEL  (MESH-19.00/C)




--------------------------------------------------------------------------


SECT.:4-MASONRY
          SUBCONTRACTOR           BID AMOUNT                    SCOPE
------------------------------    ------------------    --------------------
C&W                                 $6586.00   (ZONOLITE)
DENNIS                              $8232.00   ZONOLITE
KAUFMAN                             $7460.00   ZONOLITE
O. BAUM                             $7215.00   ZONOLITE
```

Figure 9.5 Subcontractor bid summaries obtained from use of business spreadsheet program.

and more complex, the program illustrated in this section has the following three features that were not characteristic of the earlier one:

- The program enables the estimating of labor, material, and subcontractors for a proposed project.
- The inputted estimate data can be stored on a data disk.
- The stored data collected by the program can subsequently be used as a basis for a job cost control program.

The last feature of our program is especially noteworthy. The program will in effect store a complete estimate (the labor, material, and subcontract amounts for defined work items) on a data disk. Using a job cost control program (one will be illustrated in the following chapter), the stored estimate data can be used as a basis of calculating percent complete, identifying cost overruns, and the profit or loss realized on individual work items as the project progresses.

In effect, the estimate spreadsheet program illustrated in this section and the job cost control program illustrated in the following chapter can be viewed as a single estimating/job cost control system. We will limit our discussion to the estimating spreadsheet in this chapter. While the program illustrated is in effect a spreadsheet program and also makes use of data file programming, the reader should especially focus on the integrated feature of the program that will "attach" with the job cost control program in the next chapter.

Let us now turn our attention to the program. It is illustrated in Figure 9.6. After dimensioning various variables in lines 120 through 250, the user can select to either prepare an estimate or print a previously inputted estimate. These two options are given to the user in lines 330 and 350. Naturally, the user cannot print an estimate that has not been inputted. Therefore, it is necessary to input "B" (to enter an estimate) before it can be printed.

When the user inputs a B in line 430, the program branches to line 470. The user inputs the project name, date of estimate, project owner name, and project location in lines 480 through 520. The program then starts a program loop in line 560.

The program is designed such that the user prepares the overall project estimate by means of defining and estimating the cost of various work items. These user-defined work items are grouped by work classifications the user defines. The program is designed such that the user can define up to 15 classifications, each of which can be used to further define 15 work item names. The end result is that the user can define 225 work items (15 work items for 15 classifications).

The J variable in the program loop starting in line 560 is used to set up/identify the work classifications used for grouping the work items. Example work classifications are illustrated in the example report in Figure 9.7 obtained from the program shown in Figure 9.6.

After defining and inputting a work classification on line 630, another program loop is started (within the J loop) in line 670. This L loop is used to define the work item names and the estimate data. After defining/inputting the work item name in line 840, the program proceeds to ask the user if the work item is to be subcontracted. This question is asked via the INPUT instruction in line 920.

The purpose of the question as to whether or not the item is subcontracted relates to the fact that if the item is subcontracted the user merely has to input the amount. On the other hand, if the defined work item is not subcontracted, the program branches to line 940. In this and following program lines the user inputs the units of measure for the defined work item, the quantity of work, the labor productivity, the average labor rate, and the material unit cost for the work item.

On the other hand, if the work item is subcontracted, the program branches to line 3860. The user inputs the subcontract amount and using line 4030, the program branches back within the L loop (specifically to line 990).

After defining/inputting a work item name, and the requested estimating data, the user is given an option to enter another work item (by "countering" 1 in the L loop), define another work classification (by "countering" 1 in the J loop), or ending the data input for the estimate. These options are offered the user via lines 1030 through 1130. If the user inputs a W (to input another work item) or a C (to input another work classification), the process for inputting a work item and/or work classification discussed above starts over again.

When the user has completed the data input for the estimate for the proposed project, he enters a D in line 1090. The program then branches to line 1330.

Starting in line 1330, the program proceeds to inform the user that the estimate data will be stored on a data disk. The actual storing of the estimate data on a data disk is accomplished via the data file programming in lines 1440 through 1960.

The data file storing is accomplished via several data files. The data file name GCT in line 1450 is used to store the number of work classifications defined for the estimate. The data file named GEN opened in line 1500 is used to store the project name, estimate date, project owner, and project location. The data file named GLS opened in line 1610 is used to store the defined work classification names.

The work item names and inputted estimate data are stored in data files via lines 1700 through 1920. Two somewhat different types of data files are created in this program loop. In line 1735 a data file is opened to receive the work item name and estimate data. The variables used to store this data on the data disk are defined via the FIELD instruction in line 1740.

```
100 KEY OFF
110 DEFDBL S
120 DIM NC$(15)
130 DIM LC$(15)
140 DIM LT(15)
150 DIM WC$(15,15)
160 DIM UC$(15,15)
170 DIM QC(15,15)
180 DIM MC(15,15)
190 DIM SU$(15,15)
200 DIM SU(15,15)
210 DIM PN$(4)
220 DIM KC$(15)
230 DIM KC(15)
240 DIM LR(15,15)
250 DIM LP(15,15)
260 CLS
270 CLS
280 GOTO 100
290 PRINT TAB(20);"PREPARATION OF AN ESTIMATE SYSTEM DISK
300 PRINT ""
310 PRINT TAB(28);"PROGRAM EXECUTION OPTION
320 PRINT ""
330 PRINT "ENTER B: TO BEGIN THE PREPARATION OF A NEW ESTIMATE
340 PRINT ""
350 PRINT "ENTER P: TO PRINT ONE OF THE VARIOUS TYPES OF ESTIMATING REPORTS
360 PRINT ""
370 PRINT "ENTER M: TO RETURN TO THE PROGRAM MAIN MENU
380 PRINT ""
390 INPUT T$
400 IF (T$="B") THEN 470
410 IF (T$="P") THEN 2050
420 IF (T$="M") THEN 260
430 CLS
440 PRINT "YOU HAVE MADE AN INPUT ERROR, YOU MUST ENTER B, A, M, OR P
450 PRINT ""
460 GOTO 290
470 CLS
480 CLS
490 INPUT "ENTER THE PROJECT NAME= ";PN$(1)
500 INPUT "ENTER THE DATE= ";PN$(2)
510 INPUT "ENTER PROJECT OWNER NAME= ";PN$(3)
520 INPUT "ENTER PROJECT LOCATION= ";PN$(4)
530 CLS
540 INPUT "ENTER C TO CONTINUE ";C$
550 CLS
560 FOR J=1 TO 15
570 PRINT "ENTER D: TO INPUT THE WORK CLASSIFICATION NAME NO. ";J
580 INPUT R$
590 IF (R$="D") THEN 600
600 CLS
610 PRINT "ENTER WORK CLASSIFICATION NO. ";J
620 PRINT ""
630 INPUT NC$(J)
640 PRINT ""
650 CLS
660 KC(J)=0
670 FOR L=1 TO 15
680 PRINT "WORK CLASSIFICATION= ";NC$(J)
690 PRINT ""
```

Figure 9.6   Example preparation of estimate program written in BASIC.

```
700 PRINT "YOU WILL NOW INPUT THE WORK ITEM NO. ";J;" - ";L
710 PRINT ""
720 PRINT "ENTER D: TO DIRECTLY DEFINE A WORK ITEM NAME WITHOUT VIEWING WORK ITE
M
730 PRINT "        NAMES ON THE HISTORICAL WORK ITEM DISK"
740 INPUT T$
750 IF (T$="D") THEN 770
760 CLS
770 CLS
780 PRINT "WORK CLASSIFICATION NO. ";J;
790 PRINT " : ";NC$(J)
800 PRINT ""
810 PRINT "ENTER WORK ITEM NO. ";J;" - ";L
820 PRINT "(LIMIT THE NAME TO 30 CHARACTERS)
830 PRINT ""
840 INPUT "ENTER WORK ITEM NAME= ";WC$(J,L)
850 CLS
860 PRINT "WORK ITEM NO.";TAB(30);J;" - ";L
870 PRINT "WORK ITEM NAME";TAB(30);WC$(J,L)
880 PRINT ""
890 PRINT "IS THIS ITEM TO BE SUBCONTRACTED"
900 PRINT "ENTER Y: IF THE ITEM IS TO BE SUBCONTRACTED"
910 PRINT "ENTER N: IF THE ITEM IS NOT TO BE SUBCONTRACTED"
920 INPUT J$
925 IF (J$="Y") THEN 927
926 GOTO 930
927 INPUT "ENTER SUBCONTR AMT ";SU(J,L)
930 CLS
940 INPUT "ENTER UNITS= ";UC$(J,L)
950 INPUT "ENTER QUANTITY OF WORK= ";QC(J,L)
960 INPUT "ENTER LABOR PRODUCTITITY= ";LP(J,L)
970 INPUT "ENTER AVERAGE LABOR COST/HOUR= ";LR(J,L)
980 INPUT "ENTER MATERIAL UNIT COST= ";MC(J,L)
990 CLS
1000 SU$(J,L)=STR$(SU(J,L))
1010 KC(J)=KC(J)+1
1020 CLS:PRINT "ENTER ONE OF THE FOLLOWING:"
1030 PRINT ""
1040 PRINT "ENTER W: TO ENTER ANOTHER WORK ITEM FOR THIS ESTIMATE"
1050 PRINT "ENTER C: TO ENTER ANOTHER WORK CLASSIFICATION FOR THIS ESTIMATE"
1060 PRINT "ENTER D: IF YOU HAVE COMPLETED THE WORK CLASSIFICATIONS AND WORK ITE
MS AND
1070 PRINT "        WANT TO PLACE THE DATA ON AN ESTIMATE DISK"
1080 PRINT "ENTER T: TO ABORT THE DATA ENTRY AND NOT HAVE THE ENTERED DATA STORE
D"
1090 INPUT H$
1100 IF (H$="W") THEN 1150
1110 IF (H$="C") THEN 1190
1120 IF (H$="T") THEN 1220
1130 IF (H$="D") THEN 1330
1140 CLS
1150 CLS
1160 NEXT L
1170 CLS
1180 GOTO 100
1190 CLS
1200 NEXT J
1210 CLS
1220 CLS
1230 PRINT "YOU HAVE INDICATED THAT YOU WANT TO TERMINATE DATA ENTRY FOR THE PRO
```

Figure 9.6 *Continued*

```
JECT AND
1240 PRINT "NOT STORE THE ENTERED DATA ON AN ESTIMATING DISK.
1250 PRINT ""
1260 PRINT "ARE YOU SURE? IF YOU ENTER Y (YES) THE ENTERED DATA WILL BE LOST
1270 PRINT ""
1280 PRINT "ENTER Y: IF YOU WNAT TO TERMINATE AND NOT STORE THE ENTERED DATA"
1290 PRINT "ENTER N: IF YOU MADE A MISTAKE IN SELECTING YOUR OPTIONS AND YOU WAN
T TO
1300 PRINT "          SELECT AN OPTION AGAIN
1310 INPUT XV$
1320 IF (XV$="Y") THEN 270
1330 CLS
1340 PRINT "THE ENTERED ESTIMATING DATA WILL NOW BE STORED ON AN ESTIMATING DATA
DISK
1350 PRINT ""
1360 PRINT "YOU MUST NOW REMOVE THE HISTORICAL WORK ITEM DATA DISK AND REPLACE I
T WITH
1370 PRINT "AN INITIALIZED DISK ON WHICH YOU WILL STORE THE ENTERED DATA FOR THE
PROJECT
1380 PRINT "NAMED: ";PN$(1)
1390 PRINT "ENTER D: TO STORE THE ENTERED DATA ON THE INSERTED ESTIMATING DISK
1400 INPUT VV$
1410 IF (VV$="D") THEN 1420
1420 CLS
1430 PRINT "PLEASE WAIT WHILE THE DATA IS BEING PLACED ON THE DISK...."
1440 JC$=STR$(J)
1450 OPEN "GCT.DAT" AS #1 LEN=6
1460 FIELD #1, 6 AS GC$
1470 LSET GC$=JC$
1480 PUT #1, 1
1490 CLOSE #1
1500 OPEN "GEN.DAT" AS #1 LEN=45
1510 FIELD #1, 45 AS PD$
1520 LSET PD$=PN$(1)
1530 PUT #1, 1
1540 LSET PD$=PN$(2)
1550 PUT #1,2
1560 LSET PD$=PN$(3)
1570 PUT #1,3
1580 LSET PD$=PN$(4)
1590 PUT #1, 4
1600 CLOSE #1
1610 OPEN "GLS.DAT" AS #1 LEN=45
1620 FOR HG=1 TO J
1630 KC$(HG)=STR$(KC(HG))
1640 FIELD #1, 40 AS HC$, 5 AS HN$
1650 LSET HC$=NC$(HG)
1660 LSET HN$=KC$(HG)
1670 PUT #1,HG
1680 NEXT HG
1690 CLOSE #1

1700 FOR BI=1 TO J
1710 PR=KC(BI)
1720 EX=BI
1730 FOR BO=1 TO PR
1740 FIELD #1, 30 AS WD$, 15 AS UD$, 15 AS QD$, 15 AS PD$, 15 AS RD$, 15 AS MD$,
15 AS SD$
1750 LSET WD$=WC$(BI,BO)
1760 LSET UD$=UC$(BI,BO)
1770 LSET QD$=STR$(QC(BI,BO))
```

Figure 9.6 *Continued*

```
1780 LSET PD$=STR$(LP(BI,BO))
1790 LSET RD$=STR$(LR(BI,BO))
1800 LSET MD$=STR$(MC(BI,BO))
1810 LSET SD$=SU$(BI,BO)
1820 PUT #1,BO
1830 FIELD #2, 15 AS LLQ$, 15 AS LLH$, 15 AS LLD$, 15 AS LLM$, 15 AS LLS$
1840 LSET LLQ$="0"
1850 LSET LLH$="0"
1860 LSET LLD$="0"
1870 LSET LLM$="0"
1880 LSET LLS$="0"
1890 PUT #2,BO
1900 NEXT BO
1910 CLOSE #1
1920 CLOSE #2
1930 NEXT BI
1940 OPEN "UPDA.DAT" AS #1 LEN=12
1950 PUT #1,1
1960 CLOSE #1
1970 PRINT ""
1980 PRINT "THE DATA FOR PROJECT ";PN$(1);
1990 PRINT " HAS NOW BEEN STORED ON THE DISK"
2000 PRINT ""
2010 INPUT "ENTER C TO RETURN TO THE PROGRAM OPTIONS ";C$
2020 GOTO 270
2030 GOTO 4040
2040 CLS
2050 CLS
2060 INPUT "OF THE PROJECT YOU HAVE STORED ON THE DISK ";C$
2070 PRINT ""
2080 CLS
2090 OPEN "GEN.DAT" AS #1 LEN=45
2100 FIELD #1, 45 AS PD$
2110 GET #1,1
2120 PN$(1)=PD$
2130 GET #1,2
2140 PN$(2)=PD$
2150 GET #1,3
2160 PN$(3)=PD$
2170 GET #1,4
2180 PN$(4)=PD$
2190 CLOSE #1
2200 PRINT "PROJECT NAME:";TAB(30);PN$(1)
2210 PRINT ""
2220 PRINT "ESTIMATE DATE:";TAB(30);PN$(2)
2230 PRINT ""
2240 PRINT "PROJECT OWNER:";TAB(30);PN$(3)
2250 PRINT ""
2260 PRINT "PROJECT LOCATION:";TAB(30);PN$(4)
2270 PRINT ""
2280 PRINT "ENTER C: IF THIS IS THE CORRECT DISK AND YOU WANT TO CONTINUE THIS O
PTION
2290 PRINT "ENTER P: TO RETURN TO THE PROGRAM OPTIONS
2300 INPUT H$
2310 IF (H$="C") THEN 2340
2320 IF (H$="P") THEN 270
2330 CLS
2340 CLS
2350 PRINT "PLEASE WAIT WHILE THE REST OF THE ESTIMATING DATA DISK IS READ....
2360 OPEN "GCT.DAT" AS #1 LEN=6
```

Figure 9.6 *Continued*

```
2370 FIELD #1, 6 AS GC$
2380 GET #1,1
2390 JC$=GC$
2400 CLOSE #1
2410 JC=VAL(JC$)
2420 FOR HN=1 TO JC
2430 OPEN "GLS.DAT" AS #1 LEN=45
2440 FIELD #1, 40 AS HC$, 5 AS HN$
2450 GET #1,HN
2460 NC$(HN)=HC$
2470 KC$(HN)=HN$
2480 CLOSE #1
2490 KC=VAL(KC$(HN))
2500 EX=HN
2510 CLOSE #2
2520 FOR HM=1 TO KC
2530 FIELD #1, 30 AS WD$, 15 AS UD$, 15 AS QD$, 15 AS PD$, 15 AS RD$, 15 AS MD$,
 15 AS SD$
2540 GET #1,HM
2550 WC$(HN,HM)=WD$
2560 UC$(HN,HM)=UD$
2570 QC(HN,HM)=VAL(QD$)
2580 LP(HN,HM)=VAL(PD$)
2590 LR(HN,HM)=VAL(RD$)
2600 MC(HN,HM)=VAL(MD$)
2610 SU(HN,HM)=VAL(SD$)
2620 NEXT HM
2630 CLOSE #1
2640 NEXT HN
2650 PRINT ""
2660 PRINT " THE ESTIMATING DATA ON THE DISK HAS NOW BEEN READ"
2670 PRINT ""
2680 INPUT "ENTER C TO CONTINUE AND SELECT YOUR PRINT OPTION ";C$
2690 CLS
2700 PRINT "ENTER D: TO OBTAIN A HARD COPY OF A DETAILED ESTIMATE REPORT
2710 PRINT ""
2720 INPUT PY$
2730 IF (PY$="D") THEN 2740
2740 CLS
2750 PRINT "YOU CANNOT RUN THIS OPTION UNLESS YOU HAVE ATTACHED A PRINTER
2760 PRINT ""
2770 PRINT "TURN THE PRINTER ON NOW IF YOU HAVE NOT ALREADY DONE THIS
2780 PRINT ""
2790 INPUT "ENTER C TO PRINT A HARD COPY OF THE DETAILED REPORT FOR THE JOB ";C$
2800 CLS
2810 PRINT "PLEASE WAIT WHILE THE HARD COPY REPORT IS PRINTED"
2820 PRINT ""
2830 OPEN "LPT1:" FOR OUTPUT AS #1
2840 WIDTH #1,132
2850 PRINT #1,CHR$(15);TAB(45);"DETAILED PROJECT ESTIMATE"
2860 PRINT #1,""
2870 PRINT #1,CHR$(15);TAB(42);"PROJECT NAME:";TAB(67);PN$(1)
2880 PRINT #1,TAB(42);"DATE PROJECT ESTIMATED";TAB(67);PN$(2)
2890 FT=0
2900 PRINT #1,TAB(42);"PROJECT OWNER:";TAB(67);PN$(3)
2910 FS#=0
2920 PRINT #1,TAB(42);"PROJECT LOCATION:";TAB(67);PN$(4)
2930 FL#=0
2940 PRINT #1,""
```

Figure 9.6 *Continued*

```
2950 FM#=0
2960 JC=VAL(JC$)
2970 FOR KF=1 TO JC
2980 KC=VAL(KC$(KF))
2990 PRINT #1,"WORK CLASSIFICATION:   ";NC$(KF)
3000 I$="$$##,#######.##"
3010 Z$="##,#######.##"
3020 GL#=0
3030 GM#=0
3040 GS#=0
3050 GT#=0
3060 PRINT #1,CHR$(15);"WORK ITEM";TAB(32);"QUANTITY";TAB(49);"UNITS";TAB(65);"L
ABOR COST";TAB(82);"MATERIAL COST";TAB(99);"SUB CONTRACT";TAB(116);"TOTAL COST"
3070 PRINT #1,CHR$(15);"-------------------------";TAB(32);"-------------";TAB(4
9);"----------";TAB(65);"----------------";TAB(82);"---------------";TAB(99);"---
--------------";TAB(116);"-----------------"
3080 FOR KO=1 TO KC
3090 LC#=QC(KF,KO)*LP(KF,KO)*LR(KF,KO)
3100 DM#=QC(KF,KO)*MC(KF,KO)
3110 PRINT #1,WC$(KF,KO);TAB(31);
3120 PRINT #1,USING Z$;QC(KF,KO);
3130 PRINT #1,TAB(49);UC$(KF,KO);TAB(65);
3140 PRINT #1,USING Z$;LC#;
3150 PRINT #1,TAB(82);
3160 PRINT #1,USING Z$;DM#;
3170 PRINT #1,TAB(99);
3180 PRINT #1,USING Z$;SU(KF,KO);
3190 TT#=LC# + DM# +SU(KF,KO)
3200 PRINT #1,TAB(116);
3210 PRINT #1,USING Z$;TT#
3220 GL#=GL# + LC#
3230 GM#=GM# + DM#
3240 GS#=GS# + SU(KF,KO)
3250 NEXT KO
3260 PRINT #1,          "--------------------------";TAB(32);"-------------";TAB(4
9);"----------";TAB(65);"----------------";TAB(82);"---------------";TAB(99);"---
--------------";TAB(116);"-----------------"
3270 PRINT #1,"TOTAL ";NC$(KF);TAB(63);
3280 PRINT #1,USING I$;GL#;
3290 FL#=FL# + GL#
3300 PRINT #1,TAB(80);
3310 PRINT #1,USING I$;GM#;
3320 FM#=FM# + GM#
3330 PRINT #1,TAB(97);
3340 FS#=FS# + GS#
3350 PRINT #1,USING I$;GS#;
3360 GT#=GL# + GM# + GS#
3370 PRINT #1,TAB(114);
3380 PRINT #1,USING I$;GT#;
3390 PRINT #1,""
3400 PRINT #1,""
3410 NEXT KF
3420 LPRINT ""
3430 PRINT #1,              "--------------------------";TAB(32);"-------------";TAB(4
9);"----------";TAB(65);"----------------";TAB(82);"---------------";TAB(99);"---
--------------";TAB(116);"-----------------"
3440 PRINT #1,""
3450 PRINT #1,"PROJECT TOTALS";
3460 PRINT #1,TAB(63);
3470 PRINT #1,USING I$;FL#;
```

Figure 9.6 *Continued*

```
3480 PRINT #1,TAB(80);
3490 PRINT #1,USING I$;FM#;
3500 PRINT #1,TAB(97);
3510 PRINT #1,USING I$;FS#;
3520 FT#=FL#+FM#+FS#
3530 PRINT #1,TAB(114);
3540 PRINT #1,USING I$;FT#;
3550 PRINT #1,CHR$(18)
3560 PRINT "ENTER C TO RETURN TO PROGRAM OPTIONS"
3570 INPUT C$
3580 CLOSE #1
3590 CLOSE #2
3600 GOTO 270
3610 CLS
3620 PRINT "WORK ITEM NO.";TAB(30);J;" - ";L
3630 PRINT "WORK ITEM NAME";TAB(30);WC$(J,L)
3640 PRINT ""
3650 PRINT "YOU HAVE INDICATED IT WILL BE SUBCONTRACTED
3660 GOTO 3730
3670 CLS
3680 PRINT "WORK ITEM NO.";TAB(30);J;" - ";L
3690 PRINT "WORK ITEM NAME";TAB(30);WC$(J,L)
3700 PRINT ""
3710 PRINT "YOU HAVE INDICATED IT WILL NOT BE SUBCONTRACTED"
3720 GOTO 3730
3730 PRINT ""
3740 PRINT "IS THIS CORRECT?"
3750 PRINT ""
3760 PRINT "ENTER Y: IF IT IS CORRECT AND YOU WANT TO CONTINUE
3770 PRINT "ENTER N: IF IT IS NOT CORRECT AND YOU WANT TO REENTER YOUR OPTION
3780 INPUT K$
3790 IF (K$="Y") THEN 3820
3800 IF (K$="N") THEN 860
3810 CLS
3820 IF (J$="Y") THEN 3860
3830 SU(J,L)=0
3840 SU$(J,L)=STR$(SU(J,L))
3850 GOTO 930
3860 CLS
3870 PRINT "ENTER SUBCONTRACT AMOUNT (ENTER NUMBER WITHOUT $ SIGN OR COMMAS)
3880 PRINT ""
3890 INPUT "ENTER SUBCONTRACT AMOUNT = ";SU(J,L)
3900 PRINT ""
3910 PRINT "ENTERED SUBCONTRACT AMOUNT";TAB(30);
3920 SW$="$$##,############.##"
3930 PRINT USING SW$;SU(J,L)
3940 IF (B$="C") THEN 990
3950 IF (B$="W") THEN 3860
3960 CLS
3970 PRINT ""
3980 GOTO 3910
3990 QC(J,L)=0
4000 LP(J,L)=0
4010 LR(J,C)=0
4020 MC(J,L)=0
4030 GOTO 990
4040 CLS
4050 PRINT "THIS IS THE END OF THE PROGRAM
4060 KEY ON
4070 END
```

Figure 9.6 *Continued*

DETAILED PROJECT ESTIMATE

PROJECT NAME: OFFICE BUILDING
DATE PROJECT ESTIMATED   4-5-85
PROJECT OWNER: XYZ PARTNERSHIP
PROJECT LOCATION: PEORIA ILLINOIS

WORK CLASSIFICATION: CONCRETE PLACEMENT

WORK ITEM	QUANTITY	UNITS	LABOR COST	MATERIAL COST	SUB CONTRACT	TOTAL COST
WALL FOOTINGS	86.00	CU YD	1,419.00	4,472.00	0.00	5,891.00
PAD FOOTINGS	124.00	CU YD	2,618.88	6,324.00	0.00	8,942.88
WALLS	235.00	CU YD	4,408.60	11,280.00	0.00	15,688.60
SLAB ON GRADE	97.00	CU YD	2,010.08	5,044.00	0.00	7,054.08
CIRC. COLUMNS	111.00	CU YD	2,504.16	5,439.00	0.00	7,943.16
RECT. COLUMNS	89.00	CU YD	1,543.75	4,272.00	0.00	5,815.75
BEAMS	0.00		0.00	0.00	34,565.00	34,565.00
EXT. CONCRETE	0.00		0.00	0.00	34,355.00	34,355.00
TOTAL CONCRETE PLACEMENT			$14,504.47	$36,831.00	$68,920.00	$120,255.47

WORK CLASSIFICATION: CONCRETE FORMING

WORK ITEM	QUANTITY	UNITS	LABOR COST	MATERIAL COST	SUB CONTRACT	TOTAL COST
WALL FOOTINGS	3,465.00	SFCA	7,207.20	1,247.40	0.00	8,454.60
PAD FOOTINGS	4,555.00	SFCA	11,660.80	2,869.65	0.00	14,530.45
WALLS	4,565.00	SFCA	24,833.60	1,962.95	0.00	26,796.55
SUSPENDED SLABS	6,545.00	SFCA	33,379.50	2,225.30	0.00	35,604.80
CIRC. COLUMNS	345.00	SFCA	1,269.60	117.30	0.00	1,386.90
RECT. COLUMNS	765.00	SFCA	2,065.50	344.25	0.00	2,409.75
EXT. COLUMNS	0.00		0.00	0.00	2,365.00	2,365.00
GUTTERS	0.00		0.00	0.00	6,545.00	6,545.00
TOTAL CONCRETE FORMING			$80,416.20	$8,766.85	$8,910.00	$98,093.05

WORK CLASSIFICATION: MASONRY

WORK ITEM	QUANTITY	UNITS	LABOR COST	MATERIAL COST	SUB CONTRACT	TOTAL COST
FACE BRICK	5,765.00	EA.	9,800.50	2,594.25	0.00	12,394.75
CONCRETE BLOCK	7,655.00	EA.	15,922.40	3,597.85	0.00	19,520.25
CINDER BLOCK	875.00	EA.	1,636.25	411.25	0.00	2,047.50
STONE	0.00		0.00	0.00	54,555.00	54,555.00
LINTELS	0.00		0.00	0.00	3,545.00	3,545.00
TOTAL MASONRY			$27,359.15	$6,603.35	$58,100.00	$92,062.50
PROJECT TOTALS			$122,279.82	$52,201.20	$135,930.00	$310,411.02

Figure 9.7 Example detailed estimate report obtained from estimate program.

```
                           DETAILED LABOR ESTIMATE


                    PROJECT NAME:            OFFICE BUILDING
                    DATE PROJECT ESTIMATED:  4-5-85
                    PROJECT OWNER:           XYZ PARTNERSHIP
                    PROJECT LOCATION:        PEORIA ILLINOIS
```

WORK CLASSIFICATION: CONCRETE PLACEMENT

WORK ITEM	UNITS	QUANTITY	LABOR PROD.	LABOR RATE	LABOR COST	UNIT COST
WALL FOOTINGS	CU YD	86	1.1	15	1,419.00	16.50
PAD FOOTINGS	CU YD	124	1.32	16	2,618.88	21.12
WALLS	CU YD	235	1.34	14	4,408.60	18.76
SLAB ON GRADE	CU YD	97	1.35	15.35	2,010.08	20.72
CIRC. COLUMNS	CU YD	111	1.41	16	2,504.16	22.56
RECT. COLUMNS	CU YD	89	1.13	15.35	1,543.75	17.35
TOTAL LABOR COST FOR CLASSIFICATION					$14,504.47	

WORK CLASSIFICATION: CONCRETE FORMING

WORK ITEM	UNITS	QUANTITY	LABOR PROD.	LABOR RATE	LABOR COST	UNIT COST
WALL FOOTINGS	SFCA	3465	.13	16	7,207.20	2.08
PAD FOOTINGS	SFCA	4555	.16	16	11,660.80	2.56
WALLS	SFCA	4565	.34	16	24,833.60	5.44
SUSPENDED SLABS	SFCA	6545	.34	15	33,379.50	5.10
CIRC. COLUMNS	SFCA	345	.23	16	1,269.60	3.68
RECT. COLUMNS	SFCA	765	.15	18	2,065.50	2.70
TOTAL LABOR COST FOR CLASSIFICATION					$80,416.20	

WORK CLASSIFICATION: MASONRY

WORK ITEM	UNITS	QUANTITY	LABOR PROD.	LABOR RATE	LABOR COST	UNIT COST
FACE BRICK	EA.	5765	.1	17	9,800.50	1.70
CONCRETE BLOCK	EA.	7655	.13	16	15,922.40	2.08
CINDER BLOCK	EA.	875	.11	17	1,636.25	1.87
TOTAL LABOR COST FOR CLASSIFICATION					$27,359.15	
TOTAL LABOR COST FOR PROJECT					$122,279.82	

Figure 9.7 *Continued*

A second type of data file (used for a separate purpose) is opened in line 1825. The variables in this data file are all initialized to 0 via lines 1840 through 1880. The purpose of these is to assign the value 0 to the initial actual cost data that will be subsequently updated with actual cost data via the use of the job cost control program described in the next chapter. The

UNIT COST ESTIMATE

PROJECT NAME: OFFICE BUILDING
DATE PROJECT ESTIMATED: XYZ PARTNERSHIP
PROJECT OWNER: XYZ PARTNERSHIP
PROJECT LOCATION: PEORIA ILLINOIS

| WORK CLASSIFICATION: | | CONCRETE PLACEMENT | | | | |
WORK ITEM	UNITS	QUANTITY	LABOR COST	UNIT LABOR $	MATL. COST	UNIT MATL. $
WALL FOOTINGS	CU YD	86	1,419.00	16.50	4,472.00	52.00
PAD FOOTINGS	CU YD	124	2,618.88	21.12	6,324.00	51.00
WALLS	CU YD	235	4,408.60	18.76	11,280.00	48.00
SLAB ON GRADE	CU YD	97	2,010.08	20.72	5,044.00	52.00
CIRC. COLUMNS	CU YD	111	2,504.16	22.56	5,439.00	49.00
RECT. COLUMNS	CU YD	89	1,543.75	17.35	4,272.00	48.00

SUMMARY OF WORK CLASSIFICATION: CONCRETE PLACEMENT
LABOR COST= $14,504.47
MATERIAL COST= $36,831.00
TOTAL COST= $51,335.47

| WORK CLASSIFICATION: | | CONCRETE FORMING | | | | |
WORK ITEM	UNITS	QUANTITY	LABOR COST	UNIT LABOR $	MATL. COST	UNIT MATL. $
WALL FOOTINGS	SFCA	3465	7,207.20	2.08	1,247.40	0.36
PAD FOOTINGS	SFCA	4555	11,660.80	2.56	2,869.65	0.63
WALLS	SFCA	4565	24,833.60	5.44	1,962.95	0.43
SUSPENDED SLABS	SFCA	6545	33,379.50	5.10	2,225.30	0.34
CIRC. COLUMNS	SFCA	345	1,269.60	3.68	117.30	0.34
RECT. COLUMNS	SFCA	765	2,065.50	2.70	344.25	0.45

SUMMARY OF WORK CLASSIFICATION: CONCRETE FORMING
LABOR COST= $80,416.20
MATERIAL COST= $8,766.85
TOTAL COST= $89,183.05

| WORK CLASSIFICATION: | | MASONRY | | | | |
WORK ITEM	UNITS	QUANTITY	LABOR COST	UNIT LABOR $	MATL. COST	UNIT MATL. $
FACE BRICK	EA.	5765	9,800.50	1.70	2,594.25	0.45
CONCRETE BLOCK	EA.	7655	15,922.40	2.08	3,597.85	0.47
CINDER BLOCK	EA.	875	1,636.25	1.87	411.25	0.47

SUMMARY OF WORK CLASSIFICATION: MASONRY
LABOR COST= $27,359.15
MATERIAL COST= $6,603.35
TOTAL COST= $33,962.50

PROJECT NAME: OFFICE BUILDING
TOTAL LABOR COST $122,279.82
TOTAL MATERIAL COST $52,201.20
TOTAL LABOR & MATL. COST $174,481.02

Figure 9.7 *Continued*

user should note the use of the FIELD #1 and FIELD #2 instructions in lines 1740 and 1830. The #1 and #2 refer to the data channels opened and used to send data to the disk drive. Depending on the type of computer and operating system, a programmer may be limited to using a single data channel or multiple channels.

After the estimate data is stored on a data disk, the program informs the user that the data storage is compiled via lines 1980 and 1990. The program then returns the user to the program options.

Once a project estimate has been inputted and stored on a data disk, the program illustrated in Figure 9.6 can be used to print a detailed estimate report for the project. An example of such a report is illustrated in Figure 9.7.

The user can produce a report such as the one illustrated in Figure 9.7 by entering a P when given the option in the program menu in lines 330 through 420. When a P is entered, the program branches to line 2050.

When the program branches to line 2050, the program reads the data file named GEN and prints the project name, estimate date, project owner, and location on the monitor. Assuming the user indicates that the proper data disk is in the drive, the user enters C. The program proceeds to read the rest of the previous inputted estimate data from the data disk. This is done via the data file programming in lines 2360 through 2640.

Once the program reads the estimate data from the data disk, the program proceeds to print a detailed estimate for the project. This is accomplished using lines 2830 through 3550. An example of the report for inputted estimate data is illustrated in Figure 9.7.

Given program modifications and additional programming routines, it would be possible to format and print additional types of reports, including a unit price estimate report, a labor cost estimate report, a subcontractor estimate report, etc. The program could also be extended to enable the estimating of equipment costs and job overhead items.

As noted previously, perhaps the most important characteristic of the program illustrated is that the inputted estimate data is stored on a data disk. Given the ability to read back this inputted estimate data, it becomes possible to integrate the illustrated estimate spreadsheet program with other project management functions, including planning and scheduling and job cost control. The "tieing" of the job cost function to the illustrated estimate spreadsheet program is demonstrated in the following chapter.

10: Job Cost Control Applications

INTRODUCTION

Perhaps the two most important tasks a construction firm performs are the preparation of an estimate for a project and the job cost control of the project in progress. One could justifiably view the estimating task as setting the potential for profit and the job cost control function as the task that enables the realization of the project.

Project estimating was discussed in the preceding chapter. In this chapter we will address the job cost control function and illustrate the application of the computer to performing the task. However, the fact that we are discussing estimating and job cost control in two separate chapters should not lead the reader to the conclusion that they are independent functions. The fact is that the prepared estimate serves as the basis for the subsequent cost control function. This will be illustrated in our discussion of an example job cost control program written in BASIC that is included in this chapter.

Before illustrating an example job cost control program, we will first discuss the important or critical components of a good job cost control program, independent of whether it is a manual or computer system. In the following section we will discuss the integrating of several project management functions to form a system. This discussion precedes our illustration of the example job cost control BASIC program that does in fact integrate job estimating and cost control.

Various job cost control computer programs are in wide use in the construction industry today. In fact, next to various accounting packages, including payroll and general ledger programs, job cost programs are probably most widely used (the reader is referred to our application survey study discussed in Chapter 1).

While abundant and frequent in use, the many so-called job cost control programs in use today are not equally as good in regard to their usefulness to the construction industry. Many have been modified from use in other businesses to work for construction. Given this approach, some lack the unique features characteristic of the needs of the constructor. It is with this in mind that we have included the following two sections in this chapter prior to illustrating an example job cost control computer program.

BASIC INGREDIENTS OF A GOOD JOB COST CONTROL PROGRAM/REPORT FOR CONSTRUCTION

The very term *job cost control report* means different things to different people. The ingredients of the report vary considerably in practice.

The mere posting of total job cost, as a job progresses, against the total budgeted cost for the project has been referred by some as a job cost system and/or report. The author does not view this as a control system at all. Instead it is a "reporting" system, one that merely keeps track of the cost of the project relative to a budget. Such an approach would only inform the contractor of a potential cost overrun when in fact the cost expended summed to an amount greater than the total estimate, at a time much too late to correct the cause for the overrun.

Some firms have expanded the above approach to a job cost control system to the actual recording of ongoing costs for pieces of a job, the pieces being referred to as work items, relative to an overall cost budget/estimate for the individual work items. While this is an improvement on the mere recording of total job cost aggregated into a single amount, such an approach still should be viewed as more of a reporting system than a job cost control system. In such an approach the contractor would only be able to detect a cost overrun on a specific work item, when again the ongoing cost exceeded the budgeted/estimated amount.

Disregarding the above two approaches to a job cost control program leads us to the question, what are the ingredients of a good job cost control system/report? The author proposes the following necessary ingredients for each individual work item defined for the system:

1. Quantity of work to be done (determined as part of the estimating function).

2. Quantity of effort (in man-hours) budgeted for the above-estimated quantity of work (determined as part of the estimating function).
3. Quantity of work put in place to date (as determined for an in-progress job from field reporting).
4. Quantity of effort (in man-hours) expended to date (as determined from field reporting and payroll accounting for an in-progress job).

The above four types of information enable the job cost control system/report user to detect a potential problem or cost overrun *before* the actual overrun occurs. This early detection may enable the report user to correct the field inefficiency early, before it causes financial harm to the firm.

Given these four types of information on a work item basis, it is possible to calculate percent complete by quantity of work put in place relative to the overall quantity of work to be performed and compare this percentage to the percentage of effort (hours) expended to date, relative to the total estimated effort or hours. For example, the comparison may indicate that wall forms are 20 percent complete as to quantity put in place. However, the job cost control system/report may indicate that 30 percent of the budgeted labor hours have been expended to date.

The fact that 30 percent of the effort (hours) is expended and only 20 percent of the work is accomplished to date may "flag" a troublesome potential cost overrun, one that should get the attention of the contractor. A similar analysis would be made as a function of time (perhaps weekly or monthly) for each and every work item.

The end result is that the four above types of information on a work item basis are an absolute and necessary part of a job cost control system/report, an example of which will be illustrated later in this chapter. Anything less than this is a reporting system, not a control system.

Not to be overlooked as a necessary ingredient of a job cost control system is the need for accurate field reporting that supports the system/report. This need, along with approaches to getting good field reporting, was discussed in Chapter 6 in detail. As such we will not repeat the discussion here.

PERFORMING PROJECT MANAGEMENT FUNCTIONS AS A SYSTEM

In performing project management functions systematically, the contractor performs several more or less separate steps. Essentially, he plans work and subsequently controls the work. Both the planning and the control functions consist of more definitive steps. For example, planning entails estimating, activity planning, material scheduling, cash budgeting, etc.

While it is possible for a contractor to perform these functions independently, this may prove too time consuming and costly for the small- or medium-sized contractor. It is, however, possible to perform them as interrelated functions. Many of the individual project management functions can be interrelated and performed as a system via a common data base. This concept of an integrated project management estimating/planning/control system is illustrated in Figure 10.1.

The key to an effective system—one that facilitates planning and controlling—is the definition of work items or segments that are to be the cost objects of the system. This definition can provide the base for collecting labor, material, and overhead costs whereby historical work item data can be collected from ongoing and past projects. The data serves as the basis for planning, estimating, and budgeting future projects. These projects are in turn controlled through the monitoring and comparing of work item costs and progress to the plan and the estimate.

Let us now illustrate the concept of an integrated project management estimating/planning/control system by walking through the cycle shown in Figure 10.1.

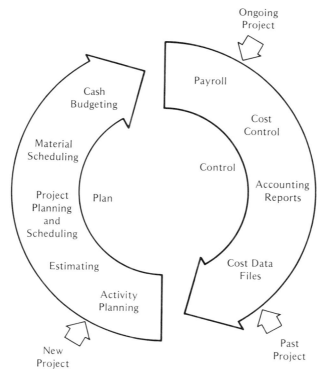

Figure 10.1 Integrated estimating system.

Assume that the company has already defined its work items and has collected labor productivity and material usage data for the work items from the performance of past projects. We will enter the cycle shown in Figure 10.1 at the starting point of a new project.

QUANTITY TAKEOFF

Faced with a new project, a contractor starts the project management process by taking off quantities from the project drawings. Let us assume that one of the work items or cost objects in a specific contractor's system is defined as the placement of formwork for concrete walls. The contractor would systematically review construction drawings such as those illustrated in Figure 10.2 and calculate the amount of work to be performed. The calculations and calculated quantity of work are usually placed on an estimating sheet such as that shown in Figure 10.3. Assume that for the project being estimated, School 106, the contractor estimates that he will have to perform 50,000 square feet of contact area of formwork for concrete walls. This quantity is shown in Figure 10.3.

Activity Planning

The objective of activity planning is to determine the optimal combination of resources to be used in performing the required quantity and quality of work. Activity planning means determining the best crew size, combination of labor crafts, and types of equipment to be used to perform the projected work.

Too often in the construction industry the traditional methods of performing a job have been accepted, and the lack of innovation has weighed heavily on the industry, causing low productivity. By comparing different combinations of labor and equipment, a company can spot inefficiencies and in effect optimize performance. The goal of the activity planning function should be to establish the number of employees by type of labor craft to be employed along with the type of equipment to be utilized for the method. Given the combination of resources available, the work item data from past projects could be used to effectively predict or plan each new project. Productivity can be established as units of work item per manhour.

Productivity records are structured from the data collected from the performance of the work in question on past projects. For example, let us assume a contractor has performed forming for concrete walls on five previous projects. Through the collection of data at the project sites, let us

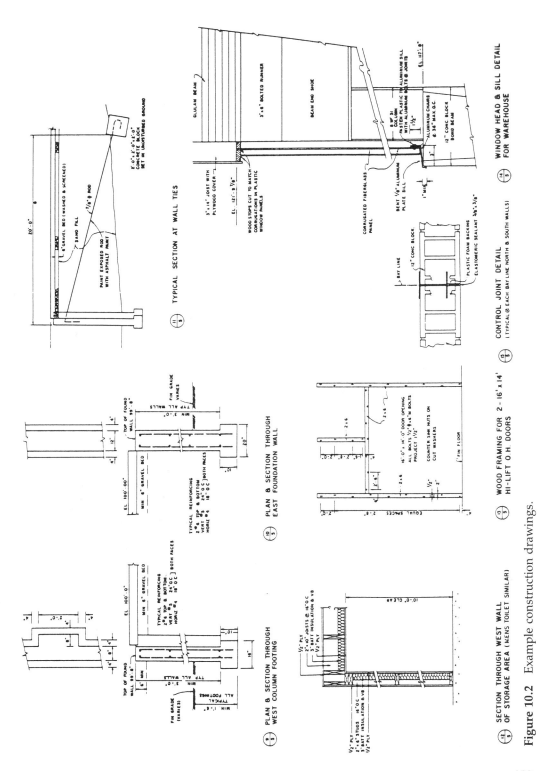

Figure 10.2 Example construction drawings.

183

PRACTICAL FORM 316	QUANTITY SHEET										

PROJECT	SCHOOL 106		ESTIMATOR	JJA	ESTIMATE NO	EXAMPLE
LOCATION	ANYWHERE		EXTENSIONS		SHEET NO	
ARCHITECT ENGINEER	JKA		CHECKED	SLL	DATE	9-12-X0

CLASSIFICATION

DESCRIPTION	NO.	DIMENSIONS						ft^2		ESTIMATED QUANTITY	UNIT
		Length	Height								
03101											
FORM - CONC WALL											
Northeast WALL	1	120.0'	10.0'					1200			
" "	1	140.0'	10.0'					1400			
" "	1	180.0'	8.0'					1440			
Southeast WALL	1	420.0'	12.0'					5040			
Northwest WALL	1	220.0'	12.0'					2640			
" "	1	260.0'	12.0'					3120			
" "	1	260.0'	10.0'					2600			
Southwest WALL	1	540.0'	12.0'					6480			
Annex - North W	2	180.0'	10.0'					3600			
Annex - East W	2	140.0'	12.0'					3360			
Annex - South W	2	380.0'	12.0'					9120			
Annex - West W	2	500.0'	10.0'					10000			
										50000	sfca

Figure 10.3　Placing quantity takeoff quantities on an estimating sheet.

HISTORY DATA
FORMING CONCRETE WALLS

Unit of Measure: Productivity:

SFCA = Square Feet of Contract Area   Man-hours/100 SFCA

Project	Date Completed	Quantity of Work Performed	Crew Size	Duration (Hours)	Man-hours	Productivity Man-hours/ 100 SFCA	Cum. Productivity Cum. Man-hours/ 100 SFCA
School 101	7/5/XO	20,000	10	200	2000	10.0	10.0
Hospital 102	8/8/XO	24,000	15	140	2100	8.75	9.32
School 103	9/6/XO	40,000	8	400	3200	8.00	8.69
Office Building 104	11/5/XO	18,000	8	200	1600	8.88	8.72
School 105	2/3/XO	41,000	20	270	5400	13.2	10.00

Figure 10.4 Collected historical work item data.

assume that the contractor has collected the data shown in Figure 10.4. Based on the performance of five projects, the contractor's cumulative average productivity for placing formwork (expressed in man-hours per 100 square feet of contact area of forms placed) is 10.0 man-hours per 100 square feet of contact area of forming.

Let us further assume that the project being considered by the contractor, School 106, is judged to have similar characteristics represented by the average of the five projects summarized in Figure 10.4. In other words the cumulative productivity shown in Figure 10.4 for forming is judged to be representative of the productivity expected on School 106.

Based on the calculated quantity of work to be performed for formwork (50,000 SFCA, as shown in Figure 10.3) and the calculated productivity for formwork (10.0 man-hours/100 SFCA, as shown in Figure 10.4), the estimated duration of man-hours for the formwork to be performed on School 106 can be calculated. This calculation is illustrated in Figure 10.5.

Given the calculated 5000 man-hours, the contractor can now decide upon crew size and then estimate the resulting required work days. For example, he may consider the three different crew sizes indicated in Figure

---

CALCULATION OF MAN-HOURS FOR SCHOOL 106
FORMWORK—CONCRETE WALLS

---

1. Quantity of Work to be Performed:
   Quantity Takeoff   =   50,000 square feet of
                                            contract area (SFCA)

2. Assumed Productivity:
   Cumulative Productivity   =   10.0 man-hours/100 SFCA

3. Calculated Duration (Man-hours)
   (Quantity of Work to Perform)
   X Productivity   =   (50,000 SFCA) X

$$10 \frac{\text{Man-hours}}{100 \text{ SFCA}} = 5{,}000 \text{ man-hours}$$

Figure 10.5   Calculated durations.

10.6 to be feasible for School 106. Assume that the contractor judges that based on considerations of manpower availability and productivity, he will use 10 men to perform the work. Based on this crew size selection, a 500-hour duration or 12.5 work weeks (assuming a 40-hour work week) is selected, as illustrated in Figure 10.6. This calculated duration will now be used to calculate a cost estimate for the forming work and an overall project schedule.

The point is that the common work item—the formwork for concrete walls—is being utilized to integrate the quantity takeoff function and activity planning. Other work items would be taken off and planned in the same manner.

We will now proceed to see how the common work item concept will facilitate other contractor project management functions, including estimating, project planning, and control.

DETERMINATION OF CREW SIZE AND DURATION
FORMWORK—CONCRETE WALLS

Work to be Performed: 50,000 square feet of contract area (SFCA)
Required Man-hours: 5,000

Possible Crews:	Size of Crew	Resulting Duration (Hours)	Resulting Duration (Weeks)
	8	625	15.6
	10	500	12.5
	12	416	10.4
Selected Crew:	Size of Crew	Resulting Duration (Hours)	Resulting Duration (Weeks)
	10	500	12.5

Figure 10.6   Three possible crews.

Estimating Direct Cost

No single management function plays a more important role in the financial success of the company than estimating. The secret competitive bidding process that characterizes the industry emphasizes the need for accurate estimates. Too often in the construction industry a company establishes part of its estimate from "the seat of its pants." With little other than a vague recollection of past performances of the work in question, the estimator is faced with predicting future costs based on hunches and unreliable word-of-mouth information. Admittedly, each time a company undertakes a new project, the project will likely be somewhat unique as to factors that dictate cost. However, knowledge of structured past project data, along with recognition of varying and unique project conditions, can result in reduced uncertainty in the estimator's project bid.

The estimating function can make great use of past project data regarding the performance of individual work items. For example, let us consider the forming of concrete walls work item illustrated in Figures 10.4 to 10.6. In Figure 10.6 we calculated an expected work item duration of 500 hours or 12.5 work weeks for the forming of concrete walls for School 106. The direct labor cost component of the cost estimate for the forming of concrete walls can be determined by multiplying the work item duration in hours by the crew cost per hour.

We assumed in Figure 10.6 that the contractor decided to use 10 craftsmen to do the forming operation. Let us assume that the average wage rate plus labor fringes for each craftsman is $18. Based on this craftsman cost per hour and the duration calculated and illustrated in Figure 10.6, the estimated direct labor cost for the concrete work is calculated as illustrated in Figure 10.7. The direct material cost can be established through identification of quantities of material for individual work items (referred to as the quantity takeoff), material wastage factors as indicated from historical data, and the relevant material prices.

DETERMINATION OF DIRECT LABOR COST
FORMWORK–CONCRETE WALLS

Estimated Man-hours Duration: 500 hours

Cost per Craftsman: $18.00/hour

Estimated Direct Labor Cost = Duration (Hours × Craftsman rate/hour
               × Number of Craftsmen

Estimated Direct Labor Cost = 500 hours × 18.00 $/hours × 10

Estimated Direct Labor Cost = $90,000.00

Figure 10.7 Calculating the direct labor cost.

In addition to labor and material cost components of a contractor's estimate, equipment and overhead costs must be determined. A construction company often spends many hours attempting to be very accurate in its estimates of project labor and material costs. However, too often this effort is followed by a less than detailed approach to equipment costs and overhead cost allocation. For example, after determining direct labor and material costs for a project, a construction company may add 40 percent of the summed direct costs to cover equipment costs and overhead cost and profit. Such a procedure often leads to substantial inaccuracy in the total project bid price. Less than accurate overhead allocation usually can be traced to a company's lack of a cost accounting system. Inability to develop an accurate application rate and base along with an analysis of the over- and underapplied overhead leads to unprofitable estimates.

Project Planning and Scheduling

Closely related to the management functions of activity planning and estimating is that of overall project planning and scheduling. The purpose of a contractor's overall project planning and scheduling function is to integrate all of the planned project activities into an overall project schedule that is compatible with project time and cost objectives. A project plan and schedule are often prepared with a bar chart or a CPM diagram.

A project plan and schedule are prepared by constructing the technological and resource logic between the various required construction activities that are part of the overall project. It is possible for the contractor to define project activities for the project planning and scheduling function to be compatible with the same work items/activities that are defined for the quantity takeoff, activity planning, and estimating functions.

For example, the previously discussed work item/activity identified as forming concrete walls can be defined as one of the activities on a bar chart or CPM diagram for an overall project plan and schedule. This is illustrated in Figure 10.8. The activity duration used for calculations performed via the project plan and schedule is the duration previously calculated in Figure 10.6.

The point here is that the overall project plan and schedule can be prepared in conjunction with other project management functions if a common data base (i.e., work items) is utilized. This use of a common data base for several functions enhances the benefit/cost ratio for any one of the functions relative to performing the functions independently.

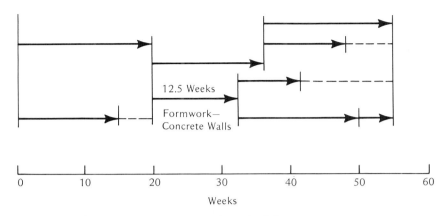

Figure 10.8 Work item as an activity on the schedule.

Resource Scheduling

Closely related to the management functions of planning and scheduling is project resource scheduling, including the scheduling of labor, material, purchases, and equipment. The quantity takeoff segment of estimating establishes what resources are required. Overall project planning and scheduling dictates when the resources are needed.

By establishing the resource requirements for the individual project activities and subsequently summing them via the prepared overall project plan and schedule, it becomes possible to determine the cumulative demand for any project resource as a function of time.

Let us consider the labor resource for the project plan and schedule illustrated in Figure 10.8. This simplified illustration is shown again in Figure 10.9 with the labor requirement for each activity shown in the block alongside the activity arrow. Note that the labor resource requirement for forming concrete walls is the 10 laborers selected as the crew in Figure 10.6.

By summing the cumulative laborers required for activities occurring simultaneously, the overall labor resource requirements at any one point in time can be established as shown in Figure 10.9.

While laborers may not be a critical resource to a specific project, the process illustrated in Figure 10.9 could be performed for any resource we might consider. Once again, the common work item/activity is utilized to perform another project management function—resource scheduling.

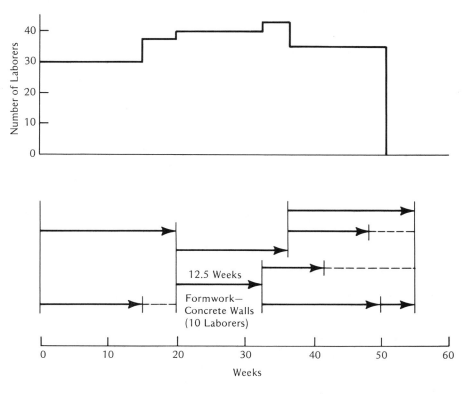

Figure 10.9 Schedule with labor requirements.

Cash Budgeting

The benefits of preparing cash budgets have been well documented. However, the fact remains that construction companies are often negligent in their preparation of cash budgets. As a result, many of the problems these companies have can be traced to the lack of adequate preparation and updating of project cash budgets. The cash budget must include the identification of expected dollar amounts of cash receipts and disbursements and the time at which the various receipts and disbursements occur. The amounts of the receipts are determined by the contractor's total project bid. The disbursements are, for the most part, identified by the estimating function.

The activities plan establishes the time at which disbursements will have to be made. The timing of receipts of cash from the project owner are determined in part by the activities plan and in part by the owner–contractor project payment agreement.

The cash budget for a project is essential for determining financing needs as a function of time. Because deferred payment for work performed is very common, and because of low working-capital ratios, the construction company is often faced with the need to secure financing at various times during a construction project. The amount of this financing and its cost should be determined before the project is bid. This is necessary so that the interest cost can be reflected in the estimate of the project costs, and subsequently in the project bid. Financing costs are as much a part of project cost as are the labor or material costs. Their identification in the project estimate is essential to a profitable estimate and also to the project bid.

The very ability to obtain financing at a critical time in the project schedule is often dependent on how soon the company initiates the search for funds. The availability and cost of loan money from financial institutions varies as a function of many economic factors. Unless a plan exists for obtaining funds in advance, the construction company may find itself without a source of funds when they are needed. The preparation of these supporting schedules and the cash budget is facilitated by the use of a common set of work items. Just as the work items can serve as the base for establishing work segment durations, costs, and resource schedules, the cash budget and its supporting schedules can be produced as a function of the defined work items.

Let us assume that the direct labor cost for each of the project activities illustrated in Figure 10.9 is determined as was done for the forming of concrete walls in Figure 10.5. By plotting the direct labor cost for each activity, as is done in Figure 10.10, it is possible to determine the cumulative cash requirement for the direct labor requirement as a function of time. Similarly, the total project cash requirement for the project as a function of time can be determined by performing a similar process for all of the component costs of the project.

When a proposed project becomes reality, the contractor's project management function does not terminate. Planning, which includes estimating and the preparation of budgets, provides the potential for a profitable project. But it is the control function that brings these potential profits to reality.

Payroll

The labor component of the control function is initiated with the performance of the payroll obligation. The payroll function is fundamental to the daily operation of any firm that is dependent on the use of labor. The

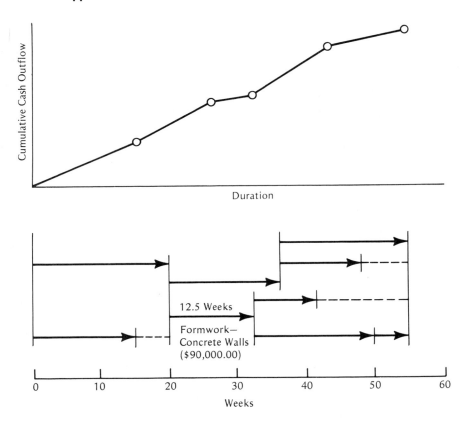

Figure 10.10   Plotting the planned cash flow.

preparation of employee paychecks, the establishing of withholding liabilities, and the filing of required forms to taxing bodies requires the company to document individual employee hours worked. Time cards are often
limited to documenting total time worked by a given employee. With only
a slight modification of the time card, it is impossible to document labor
time to specific segments of work performed by the employee.

The work item cost objects that are used for documenting labor hours
can be the same work items that are used for project planning, scheduling,
and estimating. In this manner historical work item files are established
from past projects and in turn used to aid the planning and estimating of
future projects.

As is true of the definition of work items that serve planning and
estimating, practical considerations must guide the defining of work items
for data collection. Considerations such as the ability to differentiate time

to specific work items, the cost of collecting and processing the data, and the benefits to be gained from the processed data all play a part in work item definition.

As with labor, procedures can trace material to specific work items. From this collected data material standards and wastage factors can be established for planning and estimating future projects. Equally important is the role material placement work item standards can have in the control of both material and labor costs.

Cost Control

In order to have an effective cost control program, the trend of the cost must be determined as soon as possible and compared against the progress of the plan so that required corrective action can be taken. The monitoring of production costs cannot be overemphasized in regard to the operation of the construction company and its projects.

The need to have a means of quickly documenting and monitoring project production and costs is emphasized by the fact that the construction company's planned production and costs are often less than accurate estimates. Regardless of the soundness of the company's planning and estimating practices, numerous factors prevent the plan and estimate from being totally deterministic. The ever-changing environment surrounding construction work, its variability, and the industry's high dependence on labor productivity all inject uncertainty into the project plan and estimate. The result is that plan and performance differences are partly due to lack of control and partly due to a less than accurate plan. Independent of the cause, early recognition of inefficiencies and deviations from planned progress are essential to corrective management decisions.

Effective project control of labor and material costs can be gained through documenting material quantities and labor hours for previously defined work items. Let us assume that for a work item such as the previously defined forming of concrete walls, the company estimates 50,000 square feet of contact area (SFCA) of work to be performed. On the basis of historical work item data collected from previous projects, the company estimates that it will need 10 carpenter man-hours per 100 SFCA of work. The total estimated man-hours for the work item is therefore 5000. Let us now assume that the company receives the contract to do the work. Further, assume that inspection of the work after a month of placing forms indicates that 5000 SFCA of work has been put in place. This determination of work performed is necessary for progress billings. In fact, the documentation of work performed in work items can result in more accurate billings.

On the basis of payroll records structured to report labor hours to work items, 1250 carpenter-hours have been charged to the wall-forming-related work. Analysis of the material put in place indicates that 10 percent of the work is completed. However, based on an estimate of 5000 man-hours, the cost accounting system indicates that 25 percent of the estimated labor hours and cost have already been expended. This calculation is shown in Figure 10.11. Assuming that labor hours should be proportional to the wall forming performed, it appears that the company is faced with a substantial labor cost overrun.

The variation in the percentages of labor hours versus material placed should receive attention immediately. It may be that it can be explained and is not reason for alarm. However, it may also be indicative of inefficiencies. The early detection of these inefficiencies can bring corrective action before cost overruns become excessive.

Merely comparing actual costs with estimated costs does not always give a good measure of performance. It can be that excessive overtime labor costs are hidden by high labor productivity. Looked at another way, the benefit of high employee productivity may be hidden because of the inefficiencies of management in scheduling work. The point to be made is that

---

Estimate

Quantity of work to be performed = 50,000 square feet of contact area (SFCA)

History productivity data: $\dfrac{10 \text{ carpenter-hours}}{100 \text{ SFCA}}$

Estimated carpenter-hours = $\dfrac{50,000 \text{ SFCA } (10 \text{ hr})}{100 \text{ SFCA}}$ = 5000 carpenter-hours

Accumulated Project Data

1250 carpenter-hours to date = 25% of estimated hours
10% of work performed, i.e., 5000 SFCA

Projected Cost Overrun

10% of work equated to 1250 hours expended,
therefore, 100% of work equates to 12,500 hours

Projected hours	=	12,500
Estimated hours	=	5,000
Estimated overrun in hours	=	7,500

Figure 10.11 Calculation of cost/control report.

effective cost control is achieved by analyzing the factors that make up the total cost. In the case of material costs, it is necessary to analyze the purchase price as well as the budget price, and the amount of material used as well as the estimated amount from the quantity takeoff. Similarly, the analysis of the components of overhead costs must be analyzed in order to effectively control the total overhead cost.

AN EXAMPLE JOB COST CONTROL COMPUTER PROGRAM WRITTEN IN BASIC

Given the need to monitor the cost of a construction project as a function of time, there have been many job cost control computer programs written. Some of these programs interface with an accounts payable and perhaps a payroll software program. Yet other job cost control software programs "stand alone."

Because of the large data memory storage capacity of the computer, it becomes possible to integrate several sometimes independently performed business or project functions. In this section we will illustrate a software program for job cost control that interfaces with the estimate spreadsheet program described in Chapter 9.

The objective of the integrated job cost control program illustrated in this chapter is to produce a report that enables a user to determine the following as a function of time for any single work item:

1. Quantity of work budgeted/estimated
2. Labor hours of effort budgeted/estimated
3. Quantity of work put in place to date
4. Labor hours of effort expended to date

Items 1 and 2 are in fact determined by the estimate spreadsheet program illustrated in Chapter 9. The reader will remember that the estimate spreadsheet program had the capability to store the inputted estimate data for each and every defined work item on a data disk. This stored data will now be read by our job cost control program and actual quantities of work and hours (effort) will be compared against the estimated quantities. Such a program/system will enable the user to monitor the progress of each work item and spot troublesome work items, i.e., those going over budget.

The example job cost control computer program is illustrated in Figure 10.12. Example reports obtained from the program are illustrated in Figure 10.13.

```
100 KEY OFF
120 DEFDBL S,B,A,L,M,R,T,P
130 DIM LLQ(15,15)
140 DIM LLH(15,15)
150 DIM LLD(15,15)
160 DIM LLM(15,15)
170 DIM LLS(15,15)
180 DIM NC$(15)
190 DIM LC$(15)
200 DIM LT(15)
210 DIM WC$(15,15)
220 DIM UD$(15,15)
230 DIM QC(15,15)
240 DIM MC(15,15)
250 DIM SU$(15,15)
260 DIM SU(15,15)
270 DIM PN$(4)
280 DIM KC$(15)
290 DIM KC(15)
300 DIM LR(15,15)
310 DIM LP(15,15)
320 DIM ACS(15,15)
330 DIM UC$(15,15)
340 CLS
350 CLS
360 PRINT "ENTER E: TO ENTER ACTUAL COSTS FOR AN ON-GOING PROJECT PREVIOUSLY EST
IMATED"
370 PRINT "ENTER P: TO PRINT ONE OF SEVERAL DIFFERENT JOB COST REPORTS"
380 PRINT "ENTER M: TO EXIT AND RETURN TO THE PROGRAM MAIN MENU"
390 PRINT ""
400 INPUT K$
410 IF (K$="E") THEN 440
420 IF (K$="P") THEN 2470
430 IF (K$="M") THEN 340
440 CLS
450 PRINT "TO RUN THIS OPTION YOU MUST INSERT THE JOB ESTIMATE DATA DISK FOR WHI
CH
460 PRINT "YOU WANT TO INPUT DATA-THE ACTUAL COST DATA WILL BE STORED ON THE SAM
E DISK."
470 PRINT ""
480 PRINT "INSERT THE ESTIMATE DATA DISK IN THE DRIVE NOW IF YOU HAVE NOT ALREAD
Y DONE THIS
490 PRINT ""
500 INPUT "AFTER INSERTING THE DISK, ENTER C TO READ THE NAME OF THE PROJECT ";C
$
510 OPEN "GEN.DAT" AS #1 LEN=45
520 FIELD #1, 45 AS PD$
530 GET #1,1
540 PN$(1)=PD$
550 GET #1,2
560 PN$(2)=PD$
570 GET #1,3
580 PN$(3)=PD$
590 GET #1,4
600 PN$(4)=PD$
610 CLOSE #1
620 CLS
630 PRINT "PROJECT NAME: ";TAB(30);PN$(1)
640 PRINT "DATE PROJECT ESTIMATED";TAB(30);PN$(2)
650 PRINT "PROJECT OWNER:";TAB(30);PN$(3)
660 PRINT "PROJECT LOCATION:";TAB(30);PN$(4)
```

Figure 10.12 Example BASIC program for job cost control.

```
670 PRINT ""
680 PRINT "ENTER C: IF THIS IS THE CORRECT ESTIMATING DISK AND YOU WANT TO CONTI
NUE
690 PRINT "ENTER P: TO RETURN TO THE PROGRAM OPTIONS
700 INPUT H$
710 IF (H$="C") THEN 740
720 IF (H$="P") THEN 350
730 CLS
740 CLS
750 PRINT "PLEASE WAIT WHILE THE ESTIMATING DATA FOR THE PROJECT IS READ FROM TH
E DISK"
760 OPEN "GCT.DAT" AS #1 LEN=6
770 FIELD #1, 6 AS GC$
780 GET #1,1
790 JC$=GC$
800 CLOSE #1
810 JC=VAL(JC$)
820 FOR HN=1 TO JC
830 OPEN "GLS.DAT" AS #1 LEN=45
840 FIELD #1, 40 AS HC$, 5 AS HN$
850 GET #1,HN
860 NC$(HN)=HC$
870 KC$(HN)=HN$
880 CLOSE #1
890 KC=VAL(KC$(HN))
900 EX=HN
910 GOSUB 5510
920 FOR HM=1 TO KC
930 FIELD #1, 30 AS WD$, 15 AS UD$, 15 AS QD$, 15 AS PD$, 15 AS RD$, 15 AS MD$,1
5 AS SC$
940 GET #1,HM
950 WC$(HN,HM)=WD$
960 UD$(HN,HM)=UD$
970 QC(HN,HM)=VAL(QD$)
980 LP(HN,HM)=VAL(PD$)
990 LR(HN,HM)=VAL(RD$)
1000 MC(HN,HM)=VAL(MD$)
1010 SU(HN,HM)=VAL(SC$)
1020 FIELD #2, 15 AS LLQ$, 15 AS LLH$, 15 AS LLD$, 15 AS LLM$, 15 AS LLS$
1030 GET #2,HM
1040 LLQ(HN,HM)=VAL(LLQ$)
1050 LLH(HN,HM)=VAL(LLH$)
1060 LLD(HN,HM)=VAL(LLD$)
1070 LLM(HN,HM)=VAL(LLM$)
1080 LLS(HN,HM)=VAL(LLS$)
1090 NEXT HM
1100 CLOSE #1
1110 CLOSE #2
1120 NEXT HN
1130 OPEN "UPDA.DAT" AS #1 LEN=12
1140 FIELD #1, 12 AS UP$
1150 GET #1,1
1160 LD$=UP$
1170 CLOSE #1
1180 PRINT ""
1190 PRINT "THE ESTIMATING DATA ON THE DISK HAS NOW BEEN READ"
1200 PRINT ""
1210 PRINT "ENTER C: TO CONTINUE WITH THE ENTER ACTUAL COST DATA OPTION"
1220 PRINT "ENTER P: TO EXIT THIS OPTION AND RETURN TO PROGRAM OPTIONS
1230 INPUT L$
1240 IF (L$="P") THEN 350
```

Figure 10.12 *Continued*

```
1250 IF (L$="C") THEN 1270
1260 CLS
1270 CLS
1280 INPUT "NOW ENTER DATE OF THIS COST CONTROL UPDATE, E.G. 9-12-82 ";DA$
1290 CLS
1300 PRINT "ENTER C TO START THE INPUT OF ACTUAL COST DATA AS OF ";DA$
1310 INPUT C$
1320 FOR KN=1 TO JC
1330 GOTO 4840
1340 KL=VAL(KC$(KN))
1350 FOR KM=1 TO KL
1360 CLS
1370 PRINT "WORK CLASSIFICATION: ";NC$(KN)
1380 IF (SU(KN,KM)>0) THEN 1800
1390 PRINT ""
1400 PRINT "WORK ITEM: ";WC$(KN,KM)
1410 PRINT "UNITS OF WORK: ";UD$(KN,KM)
1420 PRINT ""
1430 PRINT "ENTER 0'S (THE NUMBER) IF NO ACTIVITY":PRINT ""
1440 PRINT "DESCRIPTION";TAB(20);"ORIGINAL EST";TAB(37);"ACT. TO THIS DATE";TAB(
60);"THIS PERIOD"
1450 PRINT "------------------";TAB(20);"------------------";TAB(38);"-----------
--";TAB(60);"------------------"
1460 OO$="##,########.##"
1470 PRINT "QUANTITY OF WORK";TAB(20);
1480 PRINT USING OO$;QC(KN,KM);
1490 PRINT TAB(40);
1500 PRINT USING OO$;LLQ(KN,KM);
1510 PRINT TAB(60);
1520 INPUT ACQ
1530 BLH=QC(KN,KM)*LP(KN,KM)
1540 PRINT "LABOR HOURS";TAB(20);
1550 PRINT USING OO$;BLH;
1560 PRINT TAB(40);
1570 PRINT USING OO$;LLH(KN,KM);
1580 PRINT TAB(60);
1590 INPUT ACH
1600 PRINT "LABOR DOLLARS";TAB(20);
1610 BUD=BLH*LR(KN,KM)
1620 PRINT USING OO$;BUD;
1630 PRINT TAB(40);
1640 PRINT USING OO$;LLD(KN,KM);
1650 PRINT TAB(60);
1660 INPUT ACD
1670 MT=MC(KN,KM)*QC(KN,KM)
1680 PRINT "MATERIAL DOLLARS";TAB(20);
1690 PRINT USING OO$;MT;
1700 PRINT TAB(40);
1710 PRINT USING OO$;LLM(KN,KM);
1720 PRINT TAB(60);
1730 INPUT ACM
1740 PRINT "ENTER C: IF THE DATA IS CORRECT AND YOU WANT TO PROCEED TO THE NEXT
WORK ITEM
1750 PRINT "ENTER F: TO EXIT OPTION AND RETURN TO PROGRAM OPTIONS (YOU WILL LOSE
 INPUTED
1760 PRINT "          ACTUAL COST DATA FOR THIS PERIOD).
1770 INPUT V$
1780 IF (V$="F") THEN 350
1790 IF (V$="C") THEN 1990
1800 CLS
1810 PRINT "WORK ITEM: ";WC$(KN,KM)
```

Figure 10.12 *Continued*

```
1820 PRINT ""
1830 PRINT "SUBCONTRACTED ITEM"
1840 UU$="##,########.##"
1850 PRINT "ORIGINAL SUBCONTRACT AMOUNT= ";TAB(55);
1860 PRINT USING UU$;SU(KN,KM)
1870 PRINT "SUBCONTRACT $ EXPENDED TO DATE";TAB(55);
1880 PRINT USING UU$;LLS(KN,KM)
1890 PRINT ""
1900 INPUT "ENTER SUBCONTRACT $ EXPENDED THIS PERIOD= ";ACS(KN,KM)
1910 PRINT USING UU$;ACS(KN,KM)
1920 PRINT ""
1930 PRINT "ENTER C: IF THE ENTERED AMOUNT IS CORRECT AND CONTINUE TO NEXT WORK
ITEM
1940 PRINT "ENTER F: TO EXIT OPTION AND RETURN TO PROGRAM OPTIONS (YOU WILL LOSE
YOUR
1950 PRINT "        ACTUAL INPUTED DATA FOR THIS UPDATE"
1960 INPUT MM$
1970 IF (MM$="C") THEN 1990
1980 IF (MM$="F") THEN 350
1990 LLO(KN,KM)=LLO(KN,KM)+ACO
2000 LLH(KN,KM)=LLH(KN,KM)+ACH
2010 LLD(KN,KM)=LLD(KN,KM)+ACD
2020 LLM(KN,KM)=LLM(KN,KM)+ACM
2030 LLS(KN,KM)=LLS(KN,KM)+ACS(KN,KM)
2040 NEXT KM
2050 NEXT KN
2060 CLS
2070 PRINT "YOU HAVE COMPLETED THE ENTRY OF UPDATED DATA FOR PROJECT: ";PN$(1)
2080 PRINT ""
2090 PRINT "ENTER D: TO STORE THE UPDATED DATA ON THE PROJECT DATA DISK"
2100 INPUT IJ$
2110 IF (IJ$="D") THEN 2120
2120 CLS
2130 PRINT "THE UPDATED DATA FOR PROJECT: ";PN$(1)
2140 PRINT "WILL NOW BE STORED ON THE DATA DISK FOR THE PROJECT
2150 PRINT ""
2160 PRINT "YOU MUST NOW PLACE THE DATA DISK (THE ONE ON WHICH THE ORIGINAL ESTI
MATE WAS STORED)
2170 PRINT "FOR PROJECT ";PN$(1)
2180 PRINT "IN THE DISK DRIVE"
2190 PRINT "IF THE ESTIMATING DATA DISK IS IN THE DRIVE, ENTER C TO START THE ST
ORAGE OF
2200 INPUT "OF THE UPDATED DATA ON THE DRIVE ";C$
2210 CLS
2220 PRINT "PLEASE WAIT WHILE THE DATA IS BEING STORED ON THE DISK
2230 FOR YA=1 TO JC
2240 KC=VAL(KC$(YA))
2250 EX=YA
2260 GOSUB 5510
2270 CLOSE #1
2280 FOR YB=1 TO KC
2290 FIELD #2, 15 AS LLO$, 15 AS LLH$, 15 AS LLD$, 15 AS LLM$, 15 AS LLS$
2300 LSET LLO$=STR$(LLO(YA,YB))
2310 LSET LLH$=STR$(LLH(YA,YB))
2320 LSET LLD$=STR$(LLD(YA,YB))
2330 LSET LLM$=STR$(LLM(YA,YB))
2340 LSET LLS$=STR$(LLS(YA,YB))
2350 PUT #2,YB
2360 NEXT YB
2370 CLOSE #2
2380 NEXT YA
```

Figure 10.12 *Continued*

```
2390 OPEN "UPDA.DAT" AS #1 LEN=12
2400 FIELD #1, 12 AS UP$
2410 LSET UP$=DA$
2420 CLOSE #1
2430 PRINT ""
2440 PRINT "THE UPDATED DATA HAS NOW BEEN STORED"
2450 INPUT "ENTER C TO CONTINUE ";C$
2460 GOTO 350
2470 CLS
2480 PRINT "IN THIS OPTION YOU CAN PRINT ONE OF THE FOLLOWING REPORTS"
2490 PRINT "(NOTE: YOU MUST INSERT THE APPROPRIATE JOB ESTIMATE DISK TO ENABLE A
 REPORT)
2500 PRINT "DO THAT NOW IF YOU WANT A REPORT!"
2510 PRINT ""
2520 PRINT "SH: TO PRINT A HARD COPY OF A SUMMARY REPORT
2530 PRINT "ENTER SUB: TO PRINT A HARD COPY OF A SUBCONTRACTOR REPORT FOR THE PR
OJECT"
2540 PRINT "ENTER  M: TO EXIT AND RETURN TO THE MAIN MENU
2550 INPUT "NOW ENTER YOUR OPTION ";R$
2560 IF (R$="M") THEN 350
2570 IF (R$="SH") THEN 2590
2580 IF (R$="SUB") THEN 2590
2590 OPEN "GEN.DAT" AS #1 LEN=45
2600 FIELD #1, 45 AS PD$
2610 GET #1,1
2620 PN$(1)=PD$
2630 GET #1,2
2640 PN$(2)=PD$
2650 GET #1,3
2660 PN$(3)=PD$
2670 GET #1,4
2680 PN$(4)=PD$
2690 CLOSE #1
2700 CLS
2710 PRINT "PROJECT NAME: ";TAB(30);PN$(1)
2720 PRINT "DATE PROJECT ESTIMATED";TAB(30);PN$(2)
2730 PRINT "PROJECT OWNER: ";TAB(30);PN$(3)
2740 PRINT "PROJECT LOCATION:";TAB(30);PN$(4)
2750 PRINT ""
2760 PRINT "ENTER C: IF THIS IS THE CORRECT DISK AND YOU WANT TO PROCEED"
2770 INPUT FF$
2780 IF (FF$="C") THEN 2790
2790 IF (R$="SH") THEN 2810
2800 IF (R$="SUB") THEN 4070
2810 CLS
2820 INPUT "ENTER TODAY'S DATE=";TD$
2830 CLS
2840 PRINT "PLEASE WAIT WHILE THE SUMMARY REPORT IS PRINTED ON THE PRINTER"
2850 OPEN "LPT1:" FOR OUTPUT AS #1
2860 WIDTH #1,132
2870 PRINT #1,CHR$(15);TAB(45);"SUMMARY COST REPORT"
2880 PRINT #1,""
2890 PRINT #1,CHR$(15);TAB(42);"PROJECT NAME:";TAB(67);PN$(1)
2900 PRINT #1,TAB(42);"PROJECT OWNER:";TAB(67);PN$(3)
2910 PRINT #1,TAB(42);"PROJECT LOCATION:";TAB(67);PN$(4)
2920 PRINT #1,""
2930 PRINT #1,"DATE PROJECT ORIGINALLY ESTIMATED: ";PN$(2)
2940 PRINT #1, "DATE OF THIS REPORT: ";TD$
2950 PRINT #1,  ""
2960 JC=VAL(JC$)
2970 PRINT #1,""
```

Figure 10.12 *Continued*

```
2980 RBD=0!
2990 RBT=0!

3000 RLD=0!
3010 RLH=0!
3020 RDV=0!
3030 RHV=0!
3040 FOR XX=1 TO JC
3050 KC=VAL(KC$(XX))
3060 PRINT #1,"CLASSIFICATION: ";NC$(XX)
3070 PRINT ""
3080 PRINT #1,"WORK ITEM";TAB(29);"*******************INITIAL ESTIMATE*************
";TAB(75);"***************ACTUAL TO DATE****************"
3090 PRINT #1,"DESCRIPTION";TAB(21);"UNIT";TAB(29);"QUANTITY";TAB(43);"MATERIAL
$";TAB(64);"LABOR $";TAB(75);"QUANTITY";TAB(85);"MATERIAL $";TAB(102);"LABOR $";
TAB(119);"COMPL.";TAB(126);"BUDGET"
3100 PRINT #1,"------------------";TAB(21);"------";TAB(29);"----------";TAB(41
);"----------------";TAB(58);"------------------";TAB(75);"--------";TAB(85);"------
----------";TAB(102);"------------------";TAB(119);"-----";TAB(126);"------"
3110 TBD=0!
3120 TBT=0!
3130 TLD=0!
3140 TLH=0!
3150 TDV=0!
3160 THV=0!
3170 FOR YY=1 TO KC
3180 WI$=LEFT$(WC$(XX,YY),20)
3190 PRINT #1,WI$;TAB(21);
3200 IF (SU(XX,YY)>0) THEN 3220
3210 GOTO 3250
3220 PRINT #1,"WORK ITEM IS SUBCONTRACTED-NO MATERIAL OR LABOR COST"
3230 GOTO 3740
3240 PRINT #1,WI$;TAB(21);
3250 UNT$=LEFT$(UC$(XX,YY),7)
3260 PRINT #1,UNT$;
3270 PRINT #1,TAB(29);
3280 UD$="#,######.#"
3290 PRINT #1,USING UD$;QC(XX,YY);
3300 PRINT #1,TAB(41);
3310 UT$="#,#######.##"
3320 MT=QC(XX,YY)*MC(XX,YY)
3330 TBD=TBD+MT
3340 PRINT #1,USING UT$;MT;
3350 PRINT #1,TAB(58);
3360 BL=QC(XX,YY)*LP(XX,YY)*LR(XX,YY)
3370 TBT=TBT+BL
3380 PRINT #1,USING UT$;BL;
3390 PRINT #1,TAB(73);
3400 IF (LLQ(XX,YY)=0) THEN 3430
3410 LIQ=LLQ(XX,YY)
3420 GOTO 3440
3430 LIQ=0!
3440 PRINT #1,USING UD$;LIQ;
3450 PRINT #1,TAB(85);
3460 IF (LLM(XX,YY)=0) THEN 3490
3470 LIM=LLM(XX,YY)
3480 GOTO 3500
3490 LIM=0!
3500 PRINT #1,USING UT$;LIM;
3510 TLD=TLD+LIM
3520 PRINT #1,TAB(100);
```

Figure 10.12 *Continued*

```
3530 IF (LLD(XX,YY)=0) THEN 3560
3540 LID=LLD(XX,YY)
3550 GOTO 3570
3560 LID=0!
3570 PRINT #1,USING UT$;LID;
3580 TLH=TLH+LID
3590 PRINT #1,TAB(118);
3600 UY$="###.#"
3610 IF (LLQ(XX,YY)=0) THEN 3650
3620 PC=LLQ(XX,YY)/QC(XX,YY)*100
3630 PCA=PC/100
3640 GOTO 3660
3650 PC=0!
3660 PRINT #1,USING UY$;PC;
3670 PRINT #1,TAB(126);
3680 CK=LLD(XX,YY)/BL*100
3690 IF (CK>PC) THEN 3720
3700 TK$="-----"
3710 GOTO 3730
3720 TK$="OVER"
3730 PRINT #1,TK$
3740 NEXT YY
3750 PRINT #1,"--------------------";TAB(21);"-------";TAB(29);"----------";TAB(41
);"----------------";TAB(58);"----------------";TAB(75);"--------";TAB(85);"------
-----------";TAB(102);"----------------";TAB(119);"-----";TAB(126);"------"
3760 NT$=LEFT$(NC$(XX),20)
3770 PRINT #1,"TOTALS FOR ";NT$;
3780 PRINT #1,TAB(41);
3790 PRINT #1,USING UT$;TBD;
3800 PRINT #1,TAB(58);
3810 PRINT #1,USING UT$;TBT;
3820 PRINT #1,TAB(85);
3830 PRINT #1,USING UT$;TLD;
3840 PRINT #1,TAB(100);
3850 PRINT #1,USING UT$;TLH
3860 PRINT #1,""
3870 RBD=RBD+TBD
3880 RBT=RBT+TBT
3890 RLD=RLD+TLD
3900 RLH=RLH+TLH
3910 NEXT XX
3920 PRINT #1,""
3930 PRINT #1,"--------------------";TAB(21);"-------";TAB(29);"----------";TAB(41
);"----------------";TAB(58);"----------------";TAB(75);"--------";TAB(85);"------
-----------";TAB(102);"----------------";TAB(119);"-----";TAB(126);"------"
3940 PRINT #1,"--------------------";TAB(21);"-------";TAB(29);"----------";TAB(41
);"----------------";TAB(58);"----------------";TAB(75);"--------";TAB(85);"------
-----------";TAB(102);"----------------";TAB(119);"-----";TAB(126);"------"
3950 PRINT #1,"TOTALS FOR PROJECT";TAB(41);
3960 PRINT #1,USING UT$;RBD;
3970 PRINT #1,TAB(58);
3980 PRINT #1,USING UT$;RBT;
3990 PRINT #1,TAB(85);
4000 PRINT #1,USING UT$;RLD;
4010 PRINT #1,TAB(100);
4020 PRINT #1,USING UT$;RLH
4030 PRINT #1,""
4040 PRINT #1,""
4050 CLOSE #1
4060 GOTO 350
```

Figure 10.12 *Continued*

```
4070 CLS
4080 INPUT "ENTER TODAY'S DATE=";TD$
4090 CLS
4100 PRINT "PLEASE WAIT WHILE THE SUBCONTRACTOR REPORT IS PRINTED"
4110 OPEN "LPT1:" FOR OUTPUT AS #1
4120 WIDTH #1,132
4130 PRINT #1,CHR$(15);TAB(45);"SUBCONTRACTOR COST REPORT"
4140 PRINT #1,""
4150 PRINT #1,CHR$(15);TAB(42);"PROJECT OWNER:";TAB(67);PN$(1)
4160 PRINT #1,TAB(42);"PROJECT OWNER:";TAB(67);PN$(3)
4170 PRINT #1,TAB(42);"PROJECT LOCATION";TAB(67);PN$(4)
4180 PRINT #1,""
4190 PRINT #1,"DATE PROJECT ORIGINALLY ESTIMATED: ";PN$(2)
4200 PRINT #1,"DATE OF THIS REPORT: ";TD$
4210 PRINT #1,""
4220 JC=VAL(JC$)
4230 RBD=0!
4240 RBT=0!
4250 FOR XX=1 TO JC
4260 KC=VAL(KC$(XX))
4270 TBD=0!
4280 TBT=0!
4290 PRINT #1,"CLASSIFICATION: ";NC$(XX)
4300 FOR YY=1 TO KC
4310 IF (SU(XX,YY)=0) THEN 4330
4320 GOTO 4370
4330 NEXT YY
4340 PRINT #1,"NO SUBCONTRACTED ITEMS FOR THIS WORK CLASSIFICATION"
4350 PRINT #1,""
4360 GOTO 4690
4370 PRINT #1,"WORK ITEM DESCRIPTION";TAB(30);"INTIAL SUBC. CONTRACT";TAB(60);"P
AID TO DATE";TAB(90);"TO BE PAID"
4380 PRINT #1,"-------------------------";TAB(30);"---------------------------";TA
B(60);"---------------------";TAB(90);"-----------------------"
4390 FOR CC=1 TO KC
4400 IF (SU(XX,CC)=0) THEN 4530
4410 WI$=LEFT$(WC$(XX,CC),25)
4420 UT$="##,#######.##"
4430 PRINT #1,WI$;
4440 PRINT #1,TAB(34);
4450 PRINT #1,USING UT$;SU(XX,CC);
4460 PRINT #1,TAB(64);
4470 PRINT #1,USING UT$;LLS(XX,CC);
4480 TPP=SU(XX,CC)-LLS(XX,CC)
4490 PRINT #1,TAB(94);
4500 PRINT #1,USING UT$;TPP
4510 TBD=TBD+SU(XX,CC)
4520 TBT=TBT+LLS(XX,CC)
4530 NEXT CC
4540 PRINT #1,"-----------------------------";TAB(30);"----------------------------";TA
B(60);"-------------------";TAB(90);"-----------------------"
4550 PRINT #1,"TOTALS FOR ";
4560 NT$=LEFT$(NC$(XX),20)
4570 PRINT #1,NT$;
4580 PRINT #1,TAB(34);
4590 UT$="##,#######.##"
4600 PRINT #1,USING UT$;TBD;
4610 PRINT #1,TAB(64);
4620 PRINT #1,USING UT$;TBT;
4630 PRINT #1,TAB(94);
4640 STT=TBD-TBT
```

Figure 10.12 *Continued*

```
4650 PRINT #1,USING UT$;STT
4660 RBD=RBD+TBD
4670 RBT=RBT+TBT
4680 PRINT #1,""
4690 NEXT XX
4700 PRINT #1,""
4710 PRINT #1,"------------------------";TAB(30);"------------------------";TA
B(60);"------------------------";TAB(90);"------------------------"
4720 PRINT #1,"------------------------";TAB(30);"------------------------";TA
B(60);"------------------------";TAB(90);"------------------------"
4730 PRINT #1,"TOTALS FOR PROJECT";TAB(34);
4740 UT$="##,########.##"
4750 PRINT #1,USING UT$;RBD;
4760 PRINT #1,TAB(64);
4770 PRINT #1,USING UT$;RBT;
4780 PRINT #1,TAB(94);
4790 AMT=RBD-RBT
4800 PRINT #1,USING UT$;AMT
4810 CLOSE #1
4820 GOTO 350
4830 CLS
4840 CLS
4850 PRINT "WORK CLASSIFICATION NO.:";KN;"   ";NC$(KN)
4860 PRINT ""
4870 PRINT "WORK ITEMS FOR THIS CLASSIFICATION ARE AS FOLLOWS:
4880 PRINT "";TAB(5);
4890 KL=VAL(KC$(KN))
4900 FOR ZA=1 TO KL
4910 PRINT WC$(KN,ZA),
4920 NEXT ZA
4930 PRINT ""
4940 PRINT ""
4950 PRINT "ENTER Y: IF YOU WANT TO ENTER CURRENT PERIOD DATA FOR ONE OR MORE WO
RK ITEMS
4960 PRINT "ENTER N: IF YOU DO NOT WANT TO ENTER DATA FOR ANY OF THESE WORK ITEM
S
4970 INPUT B$
4980 IF (B$="Y") THEN 1340
4990 IF (B$="N") THEN 5000
5000 CLS
5010 PRINT "YOU HAVE INDICATED THAT NO DATA IS TO BE ENTERED FOR THE FOLLOWING:
5020 PRINT "WORK CLASSIFICATION: ";NC$(KN)
5030 PRINT "WORK ITEMS:"
5040 PRINT "";TAB(5);
5050 FOR ZB=1 TO KL
5060 PRINT WC$(KN,ZB),
5070 NEXT ZB
5080 CLS
5090 PRINT "PLEASE WAIT WHILE THE REST OF THE ESTIMATING DATA DISK IS READ....
5100 OPEN "GCT.DAT" AS #1 LEN=6
5110 FIELD #1, 6 AS GC$
5120 GET #1,1
5130 JC$=GC$
5140 CLOSE #1
5150 JC=VAL(JC$)
5160 FOR HN=1 TO JC
5170 OPEN "GLS.DAT" AS #1 LEN=45
5180 FIELD #1, 40 AS HC$, 5 AS HN$
5190 GET #1,HN
5200 NC$(HN)=HC$
5210 KC$(HN)=HN$
```

Figure 10.12 *Continued*

```
5220 CLOSE #1
5230 KC=VAL(KC$(HN))
5240 EX=HN
5250 GOSUB 5510
5260 FOR HM=1 TO KC
5270 FIELD #1, 30 AS WD$, 15 AS UD$, 15 AS QD$, 15 AS PD$, 15 AS RD$, 15 AS MD$,
  15 AS SD$
5280 GET #1,HM
5290 WC$(HN,HM)=WD$
5300 UC$(HN,HM)=UD$
5310 QC(HN,HM)=VAL(QD$)
5320 LP(HN,HM)=VAL(PD$)
5330 LR(HN,HM)=VAL(RD$)
5340 MC(HN,HM)=VAL(MD$)
5350 SU(HN,HM)=VAL(SD$)
5360 FIELD #2, 15 AS LLQ$, 15 AS LLH$, 15 AS LLD$, 15 AS LLM$, 15 AS LLS$
5370 GET #2, HM
5380 LLQ(HN,HM)=VAL(LLQ$)
5390 LLH(HN,HM)=VAL(LLH$)
5400 LLD(HN,HM)=VAL(LLD$)
5410 LLM(HN,HM)=VAL(LLM$)
5420 LLS(HN,HM)=VAL(LLS$)
5430 NEXT HM
5440 CLOSE #1
5450 CLOSE #2
5460 NEXT HN
5470 PRINT ""
5480 PRINT " THE ESTIMATING DATA ON THE DISK HAS NOW BEEN READ"
5490 PRINT ""
5500 RETURN
5510 IF (EX=1) THEN 5530
5520 GOTO 5560
5530 OPEN "EA.DAT" AS #1 LEN=120
5540 OPEN "SA.DAT" AS #2 LEN=75
5550 GOTO 6310
5560 IF (EX=2) THEN 5580
5570 GOTO 5610
5580 OPEN "EB.DAT" AS #1 LEN=120
5590 OPEN "SB.DAT" AS #2 LEN=75
5600 GOTO 6310
5610 IF (EX=3) THEN 5630
5620 GOTO 5660
5630 OPEN "EC.DAT" AS #1 LEN=120
5640 OPEN "SC.DAT" AS #2 LEN=75
5650 GOTO 6310
5660 IF (EX=4) THEN 5680
5670 GOTO 5710
5680 OPEN "ED.DAT" AS #1 LEN=120
5690 OPEN "SD.DAT" AS #2 LEN=75
5700 GOTO 6310
5710 IF (EX=5) THEN 5730
5720 GOTO 5760
5730 OPEN "EF.DAT" AS #1 LEN=120
5740 OPEN "SE.DAT" AS #2 LEN=75
5750 GOTO 6310
5760 IF (EX=6) THEN 5780
5770 GOTO 5810
5780 OPEN "EG.DAT" AS #1 LEN=120
5790 OPEN "SF.DAT" AS #2 LEN=75
5800 GOTO 6310
5810 IF (EX=7) THEN 5830
```

Figure 10.12 *Continued*

```
5820 GOTO 5860
5830 OPEN "EH.DAT" AS #1 LEN=120
5840 OPEN "SG.DAT" AS #2 LEN=75
5850 GOTO 6310
5860 IF (EX=8) THEN 5880
5870 GOTO 5910
5880 OPEN "EJ.DAT" AS #1 LEN=120
5890 OPEN "SH.DAT" AS #2 LEN=75
5900 GOTO 6310
5910 IF (EX=9) THEN 5930
5920 GOTO 5960
5930 OPEN "EK.DAT" AS #1 LEN=120
5940 OPEN "SK.DAT" AS #2 LEN=75
5950 GOTO 6310
5960 IF (EX=10) THEN 5980
5970 GOTO 6010
5980 OPEN "EL.DAT" AS #1 LEN=120
5990 OPEN "SL.DAT" AS #2 LEN=75
6000 GOTO 6310
6010 IF (EX=11) THEN 6030
6020 GOTO 6060
6030 OPEN "EM.DAT" AS #1 LEN=120
6040 OPEN "SM.DAT" AS #2 LEN=75
6050 GOTO 6310
6060 IF (EX=12) THEN 6080
6070 GOTO 6110
6080 OPEN "EN.DAT" AS #1 LEN=120
6090 OPEN "SN.DAT" AS #2 LEN=75
6100 GOTO 6310
6110 IF (EX=13) THEN 6130
6120 GOTO 6160
6130 OPEN "ER.DAT" AS #1 LEN=120
6140 OPEN "SO.DAT" AS #2 LEN=75
6150 GOTO 6310
6160 IF (EX=14) THEN 6180
6170 GOTO 6210
6180 OPEN "ES.DAT" AS #1 LEN=120
6190 OPEN "SQ.DAT" AS #2 LEN=75
6200 GOTO 6310
6210 IF (EX=15) THEN 6230
6220 GOTO 6260
6230 OPEN "ET.DAT" AS #1 LEN=120
6240 OPEN "SR.DAT" AS #2 LEN=75
6250 GOTO 6310
6260 IF (EX=16) THEN 6280
6270 GOTO 6310
6280 OPEN "EU.DAT" AS #1 LEN=120
6290 OPEN "SS.DAT" AS #2 LEN=75
6300 GOTO 6310
6310 RETURN
6320 CLS
6330 PRINT "WORK ITEM NO.";TAB(30);J;" - ";L
6340 PRINT "WORK ITEM NAME";TAB(30);WC$(J,L)
6350 PRINT ""
6360 PRINT "YOU HAVE INDICATED IT WILL BE SUBCONTRACTED
6370 GOTO 6430
6380 CLS
6390 PRINT "WORK ITEM NO.";TAB(30);J;" - ";L
6400 PRINT "WORK ITEM NAME";TAB(30);WC$(J,L)
6410 PRINT ""
6420 PRINT "YOU HAVE INDICATED IT WILL NOT BE SUBCONTRACTED"
```

Figure 10.12 *Continued*

```
6430 IF (J$="Y") THEN 6460
6440 SU(J,L)=0
6450 SU$(J,L)=STR$(SU(J,L))
6460 CLS
6470 PRINT "ENTER SUBCONTRACT AMOUNT (ENTER NUMBER WITHOUT $ SIGN OR COMMAS)
6480 PRINT ""
6490 INPUT "ENTER SUBCONTRACT AMOUNT = ";SU(J,L)
6500 PRINT ""
6510 PRINT "ENTERED SUBCONTRACT AMOUNT";TAB(30);
6520 SW$="$$###,############.##"
6530 PRINT USING SW$;SU(J,L)
6540 IF (B$="C") THEN 2420
6550 IF (B$="W") THEN 6460
6560 CLS
6570 PRINT ""
6580 GOTO 6510
6590 QC(J,L)=0
6600 LP(J,L)=0
6610 LR(J,C)=0
6620 MC(J,L)=0
6630 GOTO 2420
6640 CLS
6650 PRINT "THIS IS THE END OF THE PROGRAM
6660 KEY ON
6670 END
```

Figure 10.12 *Continued*

Let us now turn our attention to the example job cost control computer program illustrated in Figure 10.12. The program starts by dimensioning program variables in lines 110 through 330.

The user is then given an opportunity to enter ongoing project data for a previously estimated project or print a job cost control report. Obviously, one must enter ongoing data before one can print a report. Therefore, it is necessary to enter an E in the program menu routine in lines 360 through 430.

When an E is input, meaning the user wants to input ongoing project data, the program branches to line 440.

The program informs the user that he must insert the previously prepared estimate data disk in the disk drive. These instructions are contained in lines 450 through 500.

The program proceeds to read the data file GEN starting in line 510. The project name, date estimated, project owner, and location are printed on the monitor. This program routine enables the user to determine if the proper estimate data disk is in the disk drive.

Assuming the proper estimate data disk is in the drive and the user enters C to specify this, the program branches to line 740. The program then proceeds to read the entire previously prepared estimate into memory.

This is done by the data file programming in lines 760 through 1170. The data file names that are opened and read in this program routine are the data files previously created by the estimate spreadsheet program described in the previous chapter.

Once the program has read the estimate data into computer memory, the disk has been read. This program proceeds to a routine that enables the user to input actual ongoing project cost data. After instructing the user to input the data of the cost update and receiving the data in lines 1280 and 1290, the program starts a loop using the variable KN in line 1320. The KN loop starting in line 1320 iterates JC times, JC being equal to the number of work classifications on the data disk. The KM loop starting in line 1350 iterates KL times, the number of work items defined within the classification that was defined in the estimate spreadsheet program.

The program then tests to determine if work item (i.e., work item number KN classification) KM (work item number within a given classification) is subcontracted. It does this by testing if the work item subcontract amount is greater than zero. This is done in line 1380 by the IF instruction. If the subcontract amount is not greater than 0, the item is not subcontracted. In this case the program proceeds to request actual ongoing data. On the other hand, if the item is subcontracted, the program branches to line 1800.

When the program branches to line 1800, the program requests the user to input the subcontract amount paid during the time period between the last cost report and the date of the current data entry. After receiving the subcontract data, the program branches to the data input loop.

If the work item within the KN and KM loops is not subcontracted, the program requests the user to enter the quantity of work performed, the labor hours expended, the labor cost expended, and the material cost expended. This data input routine is programmed in lines 1400 through 1730.

As the input work item input data is requested from the user in lines 1400 through 1730, the program prints on the monitor the initial estimate amounts and the cumulative ongoing job costs and quantities that have been previously inputted by the job cost program. The program reads two data files to do this. First, it reads the data file used to store the initial project estimate, the data file previously being created via the estimate program. The program also reads the historical data file that stores the ongoing project job costs and quantities.

After the data for each work item is inputted (either cost and quantities or subcontract amounts), the program proceeds to update the inputted job cost data. The variables used to keep the ongoing project data are updated to reflect the previous cumulative totals plus the costs and quantities just inputted. This is done in lines 1990 through 2030.

After all the data for all the work items are input, the program proceeds to store it on a data disk. The data file programming to store the cumulative cost and quantity data is contained in lines 2290 through 2370. After the data are stored, the program returns the user to the program options. This is done in line 2460, which returns the program to line 350.

Assuming the user has previously input job cost data, it becomes possible to print one of two job cost reports using the program illustrated in Figure 10.12. The user accesses the printing of job cost reports option by inputting a P when given the option in lines 360 through 430. The program then branches to line 2470.

In lines 2510 through 2580, the user is given the opportunity to select one of two reports: a summary report or a subcontractor report. Examples of these reports are illustrated in Figure 10.13.

Independent of which report the program user selects, the program first reads the data file named GEN in lines 2590 through 2690 and prints the project name, date of initial estimate, project owner, and location on the monitor. This enables the user to determine if the correct data disk is in the disk drive. Assuming that the correct data disk is in the disk drive, the program branches to line 2810 if the summary report was previously selected or line 4070 if the subcontractor report was previously selected by the user. Starting at each of these lines, the printer is activated and the programming proceeds to print the reports illustrated in Figure 10.13.

The job costs reports illustrated can be used to aid the contractor in monitoring the progress of his ongoing projects and detect possible cost overruns. The program illustrated can be modified/extended to yield additional job cost reports, including a labor cost report, a variance report, etc. The program illustrated is relatively incomplete in that it only illustrates two types of reports. However, the program does illustrate well the concept of tying/integrating two or more functions together (in this case estimating and job cost control) via a common data file. Computers and their data storage capability enable this desirable feature. As time progresses, the reader will witness even more fully integrated construction industry computer software systems.

```
                              SUMMARY COST REPORT

                        PROJECT NAME:        OFFICE BUILDING
                        PROJECT OWNER:       XYZ PARTNERSHIP
                        PROJECT LOCATION:    PEORIA ILLINOIS

DATE PROJECT ORIGINALLY ESTIMATED: 4-5-85
DATE OF THIS REPORT: 6-4-85


CLASSIFICATION: CONCRETE PLACEMENT
WORK ITEM          ****************INITIAL ESTIMATE************* **************ACTUAL TO DATE***************
DESCRIPTION     UNIT    QUANTITY   MATERIAL $        LABOR $     QUANTITY  MATERIAL $      LABOR $      COMPL. BUDGET
--------------- ------- ---------- --------------- --------------- -------- --------------- --------------- ----- ------
WALL FOOTINGS   CU YD       86.0    4,472.00        1,419.00        34.0    1,243.00         464.00      39.5 -----
PAD FOOTINGS    CU YD      124.0    6,324.00        2,618.88        54.0    2,345.00         893.00      43.5 -----
WALLS           CU YD      235.0   11,280.00        4,408.60       212.0    9,234.00       4,000.00      90.2 OVER
SLAB ON GRADE   CU YD       97.0    5,044.00        2,010.08        68.0    4,343.00       1,834.00      70.1 OVER
CIRC. COLUMNS   CU YD      111.0    5,439.00        2,504.16        67.0    4,323.00       1,894.00      60.4 OVER
RECT. COLUMNS   CU YD       89.0    4,272.00        1,543.75        67.0    3,244.00       1,234.00      75.3 OVER
BEAMS           WORK ITEM IS SUBCONTRACTED-NO MATERIAL OR LABOR COST
EXT. CONCRETE   WORK ITEM IS SUBCONTRACTED-NO MATERIAL OR LABOR COST
--------------- ------- ---------- --------------- --------------- -------- --------------- --------------- ----- ------
TOTALS FOR CONCRETE PLACEMENT       36,831.00       14,504.47                24,732.00      10,319.00

CLASSIFICATION: CONCRETE FORMING
WORK ITEM          ****************INITIAL ESTIMATE************* **************ACTUAL TO DATE***************
DESCRIPTION     UNIT    QUANTITY   MATERIAL $        LABOR $     QUANTITY  MATERIAL $      LABOR $      COMPL. BUDGET
--------------- ------- ---------- --------------- --------------- -------- --------------- --------------- ----- ------
WALL FOOTINGS   SFCA     3,465.0    1,247.40        7,207.20     3,233.0      989.00        6,845.00      93.3 OVER
PAD FOOTINGS    SFCA     4,555.0    2,869.65       11,660.80     4,200.0    1,998.00        9,856.00      92.2 -----
WALLS           SFCA     4,565.0    1,962.95       24,833.60     4,123.0    1,845.00       21,345.00      90.3 -----
SUSPENDED SLABS SFCA     6,545.0    2,225.30       33,379.50     5,987.0    1,543.00       35,346.00      91.5 OVER
CIRC. COLUMNS   SFCA       345.0      117.30        1,269.60       320.0      116.00        1,200.00      92.8 OVER
RECT. COLUMNS   SFCA       765.0      344.25        2,065.50       685.0      320.00        1,956.00      89.5 OVER
EXT. COLUMNS    WORK ITEM IS SUBCONTRACTED-NO MATERIAL OR LABOR COST
GUTTERS         WORK ITEM IS SUBCONTRACTED-NO MATERIAL OR LABOR COST
--------------- ------- ---------- --------------- --------------- -------- --------------- --------------- ----- ------
TOTALS FOR CONCRETE FORMING          8,766.85       80,416.20                 6,811.00      76,548.00

CLASSIFICATION: MASONRY
WORK ITEM          ****************INITIAL ESTIMATE************* **************ACTUAL TO DATE***************
DESCRIPTION     UNIT    QUANTITY   MATERIAL $        LABOR $     QUANTITY  MATERIAL $      LABOR $      COMPL. BUDGET
--------------- ------- ---------- --------------- --------------- -------- --------------- --------------- ----- ------
FACE BRICK      EA.      5,765.0    2,594.25        9,800.50     2,455.0    1,265.00        4,765.00      42.6 OVER
CONCRETE BLOCK  EA.      7,655.0    3,597.85       15,922.40     3,765.0    1,865.00        7,600.00      49.2 -----
CINDER BLOCK    EA.        875.0      411.25        1,636.25       454.0      200.00          856.00      51.9 OVER
STONE           WORK ITEM IS SUBCONTRACTED-NO MATERIAL OR LABOR COST
LINTELS         WORK ITEM IS SUBCONTRACTED-NO MATERIAL OR LABOR COST
--------------- ------- ---------- --------------- --------------- -------- --------------- --------------- ----- ------
TOTALS FOR MASONRY                   6,603.35       27,359.15                 3,330.00      13,221.00


--------------- ------- ---------- --------------- --------------- -------- --------------- --------------- ----- ------

--------------- ------- ---------- --------------- --------------- -------- --------------- --------------- ----- ------
TOTALS FOR PROJECT                  52,201.20      122,279.82                34,873.00     100,088.00
```

Figure 10.13 Example reports from job cost control program.

```
                              SUBCONTRACTOR COST REPORT


                         PROJECT OWNER:        OFFICE BUILDING
                         PROJECT OWNER:        XYZ PARTNERSHIP
                         PROJECT LOCATION      PEORIA ILLINOIS


DATE PROJECT ORIGINALLY ESTIMATED: 4-5-85
DATE OF THIS REPORT: 6-4-85


CLASSIFICATION: CONCRETE PLACEMENT
WORK ITEM DESCRIPTION     INTIAL SUBC. CONTRACT     PAID TO DATE            TO BE PAID
----------------------    -------------------------  -------------------------  -------------------------

BEAMS                          34,565.00                 21,233.00                 13,332.00
EXT. CONCRETE                  34,355.00                 23,235.00                 11,120.00
----------------------    -------------------------  -------------------------  -------------------------
TOTALS FOR CONCRETE PLACEMENT  68,920.00                 44,468.00                 24,452.00



CLASSIFICATION: CONCRETE FORMING
WORK ITEM DESCRIPTION     INTIAL SUBC. CONTRACT     PAID TO DATE            TO BE PAID
----------------------    -------------------------  -------------------------  -------------------------

EXT. COLUMNS                    2,365.00                  1,456.00                    909.00
GUTTERS                         6,545.00                  4,565.00                  1,980.00
----------------------    -------------------------  -------------------------  -------------------------
TOTALS FOR CONCRETE FORMING     8,910.00                  6,021.00                  2,889.00



CLASSIFICATION: MASONRY
WORK ITEM DESCRIPTION     INTIAL SUBC. CONTRACT     PAID TO DATE            TO BE PAID
----------------------    -------------------------  -------------------------  -------------------------

STONE                          54,555.00                 25,434.00                 29,121.00
LINTELS                         3,545.00                  1,655.00                  1,890.00
----------------------    -------------------------  -------------------------  -------------------------
TOTALS FOR MASONRY             58,100.00                 27,089.00                 31,011.00


----------------------    -------------------------  -------------------------  -------------------------
----------------------    -------------------------  -------------------------  -------------------------

TOTALS FOR PROJECT            135,930.00                 77,578.00                 58,352.00
```

Figure 10.13 *Continued*

LABOR COST REPORT

PROJECT NAME   OFFICE BUILDING
PROJECT OWNER: XYZ PARTNERSHIP
PROJECT LOCATION: PEORIA ILLINOIS

DATE PROJECT ORIGINALLY ESTIMATED: 4-5-85
DATE OF THIS REPORT: 6-4-85

CLASSIFICATION: CONCRETE PLACEMENT

WORK ITEM DESCRIPTION	UNITS OF WORK	% COMPL.	ESTIMATED LABOR $	ESTIMATED LABOR HRS	ACTUAL LABOR $	ACTUAL LABOR HRS	PROJECTED $ LABOR VAR.	PROJ. HRS LABOR VAR.	OVER BUDGET
WALL FOOTINGS	CU YD	39.5	1,419.00	95	464.00	36	-245.35	-4	----
PAD FOOTINGS	CU YD	43.5	2,618.88	164	893.00	85	-568.29	32	OVER
WALLS	CU YD	90.2	4,408.60	315	4,000.00	300	25.36	18	OVER
SLAB ON GRADE	CU YD	70.1	2,010.08	131	1,834.00	95	606.06	5	OVER
CIRC. COLUMNS	CU YD	60.4	2,504.16	157	1,894.00	93	633.66	-2	OVER
RECT. COLUMNS	CU YD	75.3	1,543.75	101	1,234.00	85	95.44	12	OVER
BEAMS	WORK ITEM IS SUBCONTRACTED-NO MATERIAL OR LABOR COST								
EXT. CONCRETE	WORK ITEM IS SUBCONTRACTED-NO MATERIAL OR LABOR COST								
TOTALS FOR			14,504.47	961	10,319.00	694	546.89	60	

CLASSIFICATION: CONCRETE FORMING

WORK ITEM DESCRIPTION	UNITS OF WORK	% COMPL.	ESTIMATED LABOR $	ESTIMATED LABOR HRS	ACTUAL LABOR $	ACTUAL LABOR HRS	PROJECTED $ LABOR VAR.	PROJ. HRS LABOR VAR.	OVER BUDGET
WALL FOOTINGS	SFCA	93.3	7,207.20	450	6,845.00	432	129.00	13	OVER
PAD FOOTINGS	SFCA	92.2	11,660.80	729	9,856.00	695	-971.73	25	OVER
WALLS	SFCA	90.3	24,833.60	1,552	21,345.00	1,423	-1,200.34	23	OVER
SUSPENDED SLABS	SFCA	91.5	33,379.50	2,225	35,346.00	2,346	5,260.82	339	OVER
CIRC. COLUMNS	SFCA	92.8	1,269.60	79	1,200.00	76	24.15	3	OVER
RECT. COLUMNS	SFCA	89.5	2,065.50	115	1,956.00	95	118.94	-9	OVER
EXT. COLUMNS	WORK ITEM IS SUBCONTRACTED-NO MATERIAL OR LABOR COST								
GUTTERS	WORK ITEM IS SUBCONTRACTED-NO MATERIAL OR LABOR COST								
TOTALS FOR			80,416.20	5,151	76,548.00	5,067	3,360.83	394	

CLASSIFICATION: MASONRY

WORK ITEM DESCRIPTION	UNITS OF WORK	% COMPL.	ESTIMATED LABOR $	ESTIMATED LABOR HRS	ACTUAL LABOR $	ACTUAL LABOR HRS	PROJECTED $ LABOR VAR.	PROJ. HRS LABOR VAR.	OVER BUDGET
FACE BRICK	EA.	42.6	9,800.50	577	4,765.00	324	1,389.00	184	OVER
CONCRETE BLOCK	EA.	49.2	15,922.40	995	7,600.00	455	-470.08	-70	----
CINDER BLOCK	EA.	51.9	1,636.25	96	856.00	49	13.53	-2	OVER
STONE	WORK ITEM IS SUBCONTRACTED-NO MATERIAL OR LABOR COST								
LINTELS	WORK ITEM IS SUBCONTRACTED-NO MATERIAL OR LABOR COST								
TOTALS FOR			27,359.15	1,668	13,221.00	828	932.45	112	
TOTALS FOR PROJECT			122,279.82	7,780	100,088.00	6,589	4,840.17	567	

Figure 10.13 *Continued*

11: Planning and Scheduling Applications

INTRODUCTION

Planning and scheduling techniques, e.g., the critical-path method (CPM), are controversial management tools in the construction industry. Some contractors prepare detailed schedules and "live" by them; others prepare no schedules whatsoever and if they are required to do so by the owner, merely go through the motions without using the plan and schedule.

One of the major arguments a contractor gives against the use of formalized plans and schedules relates to the fact that he believes the time and cost it takes to prepare a formalized schedule does not outweigh the benefit of its use. The contractor might also argue that given all the uncertain events that characterize a construction project, the prepared plan soon becomes outdated.

The use of the computerized scheduling system can alleviate both of the above-noted contractor concerns. For one, the computer can handle the data processing that is part of the CPM process with ease. Second, the computer can easily handle uncertain events. Updating a formalized plan such as a CPM diagram is virtually effortless with a computer. Even better, the use of a computer lets the contractor play "what if" games even before the uncertainties occur. By using the computer to play the "what if" games prior to the actual event, the contractor can use a planning and scheduling technique and the computer to "manage around" the uncertain events when they do occur.

Given the benefits of performing scheduling techniques via the computer, the increased use of computers in the construction industry should result in scheduling tools such as CPM playing a more important part of the contractor's everyday management practices.

Before illustrating the performance of CPM scheduling via the computer, we will first discuss the mathematical calculations that are part of the CPM process. The premise is that the user of a computer software system, including a CPM system, should first understand the calculation process.

It should be noted that some contractors prefer the use of the bar chart versus that of a network model such as the critical-path method (see Figure 11.1 for a bar chart).

Bar charts, although widely used, have many limitations. In particular, the bar chart does not clearly show what course of action the contractor should take when a particular activity's actual duration is not equal to its planned duration.

Pipeline Project: Progress Date Sept. 27

Estimated Progress
Actual Progress

Activity	Quan.	Start	Finish	Sept. 4-8	Sept. 11-15	Sept. 18-22	Sept. 25-29	Oct. 2-6	Oct. 9-13	Oct. 16-20	Oct. 23-29	Oct. 30 Nov. 3
Dig Hole	8 cu. yd	Sept. 11	Sept. 20		100							
Obtain Subbase	2 cu. yd	Sept. 11	Oct. 2		75							
Obtain Pipe	8 pipes	Sept. 11	Oct. 12		50							
Have Pipe	—	Oct. 13	Oct. 16							■		
Fine Grade	—	Sept. 21	Sept. 27				100					
Place Subbase	—	Oct. 3	Oct. 6					■				
Compact Subbase	—	Oct. 9	Oct. 18						■			
Place Pipe	—	Oct. 19	Oct. 26								■	
Excess Subbase	—	Oct. 9	Oct. 10						■			
Backfill	7 cu. yd	Oct. 27	Nov. 2									■

Figure 11.1 An example bar chart.

In defense of the use of the bar chart, it should be noted that it is capable of modeling any of the possible logic relationships that may exist between two activities. In particular, the bar chart can model an activity that starts after another activity has started but before it is finished. On the other hand, network models must separate two such activities into several incremental activities in order to properly model them.

NETWORK MODELS AND PROJECT PLANNING

The use of networks has greatly facilitated the task of project planning. In regard to project planning, a network is a diagrammatic representation of the project's activities. Whereas the bar chart is restricted in its ability to identify the complex interrelationships that exist between project activities and in its ability to indicate optimal activity timing, calculations on a network can be made by means of the model that indicate optimal activity timing decisions. As a result, the network model has become a widely used project planning tool.

When constructing a network to represent a project, either arrow notation or circle notation may be used. An arrow notation network is constructed by using arrows to represent activities. The relation, or logic, between activities is represented by connecting the arrows by means of circles (often referred to as network nodes). The nodes represent events that are points in time. For example, a node placed on the end of an activity represents the event "the activity is finished and following activities may start." Figure 11.2 illustrates several small arrow notation activity networks. The letter on each of the activity arrows corresponds to the activity name or identification.

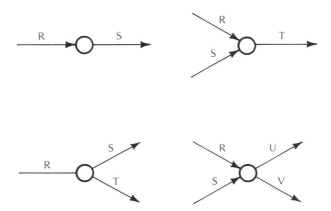

Figure 11.2 Arrow notation network.

The use of the arrow notation network for modeling a project some-times necessitates the use of a dummy activity to properly model the activity logic. Consider the following activity logic:

Activity C follows activity A
Activity D follows activity B
Activity C follows activity B

When using the arrow notation network, the only correct way to represent this activity logic is shown in Figure 11.3. The dashed arrow in the figure is referred to as a dummy activity. A dummy activity has zero cost and zero time associated with it. It is used to represent the proper logic that exists between project activities.

The dummy activity is also used to avoid two activities that start at the same node (event) and terminate at yet another node (event). To avoid the "loop" formed by the two activities, a dummy activity is introduced. This use of the dummy activity is shown in Figure 11.4.

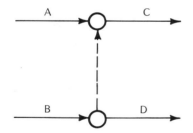

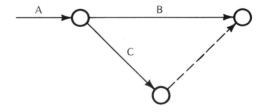

Figure 11.4

Figure 11.3   Need for a dummy activity.   Using a dummy activity to avoid a loop.

A circle notation network may also be constructed to represent the logic between a project's activities. In the circle notation network an activity is represented by a circle. The logic between the activity circles is shown by connecting the circles with arrows. As in the arrow notation network, the actual length of the arrow is of no significance. Figure 11.5 illustrates some activity relationships by means of a circle notation network. The letter in each circle corresponds to the activity name or identification. When using a circle notation network to model activity logic, there is no need to intro-duce a dummy activity. However, to define a single starting datum and ending datum, it is sometimes convenient to create START and END ac-tivities as shown in Figure 11.5.

Obviously, a given construction project may be modeled by either an arrow notation or a circle notation network. Arrow notation has the ad-

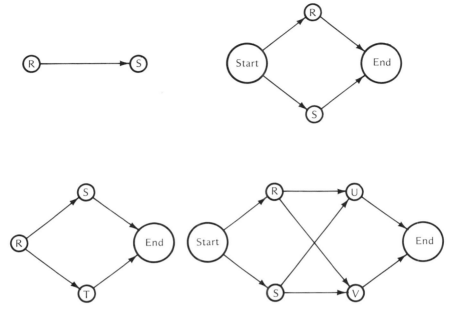

Figure 11.5 Circle notation network.

vantage of providing a better visual representation of the activity logic than the circle notation network. When activity logic becomes complex, it becomes difficult to visually follow a circle notation network. Another advantage of the arrow notation network is that it is relatively easy to transform the network into a time scale. This will be discussed in a later section. Owing to its visual effectiveness, the arrow notation network will be used in this book to represent activity logic.

The circle notation network has the advantage of being easier to construct than the arrow notation network. There is no need for the use of the dummy activity. The circle notation network is especially advantageous when changes in the activity logic must be made. These logic changes are frequent when performing the task of resource allocation.

Since project planning, as discussed in this chapter, does not address the task of resource allocation, the only parameter we will discuss in this chapter is the activity duration or time. These activity durations are assumed to be determined in the activity planning task. Actually, the durations of the various activities may not be deterministic but stochastic; i.e., when discussing the duration of an activity, the duration may be subject to change.

There is a probability associated with the duration of an activity. If the probability of an activity duration is one, then the activity duration is deterministic. Thus, the parameter of the project planning task, as discussed in this chapter, is either deterministic or stochastic. The two different types of problems (deterministic versus stochastic parameters) require two different types of modeling ability. •

In addition to the duration parameter being deterministic or stochastic, the actual logic that exists between project activities may also be deterministic or stochastic. There is a probability associated with one activity following another. If this probability is known to be equal to one, then the structure of the activity logic is deterministic. If it is less than one, the network structure is subject to change, i.e., it is stochastic. As is true of the different modeling abilities required to model the deterministic and stochastic activity duration parameter, different types of modeling ability are required to model stochastic versus deterministic network structures.

Given the possibility of deterministic or stochastic activity logic network structure and the possibility of deterministic or stochastic parameters, the type of problem in question and an appropriate model are summarized in Figure 11.6. For example, the critical-path method (CPM) models the project that has deterministic activity logic structure and deterministic activity durations. On the other hand, project evaluation and review technique (PERT) models the project that has deterministic activity logic structure but stochastic activity durations.

This chapter assumes that the probabilities associated with a network's structure and its parameters may actually be determined. If these probabilities are unknown, yet another type of modeling ability would be required.

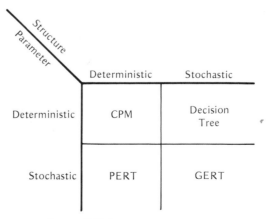

Figure 11.6   Four network possibilities.

THE CRITICAL-PATH METHOD (CPM)

One of the first network models developed and presently the most widely used construction project planning model is the critical-path method (CPM). The original intent was to develop a planning and scheduling tool for the construction and maintenance of chemical-processing plants.

CPM has become so widely accepted today as a planning and scheduling tool that many construction project owners require contractors to submit a CPM plan of the project along with their bid. Although CPM may be used to model any type or size of project, the benefits received from its use are best realized on projects that are rather large in terms of complexity and the number of required activities and projects that are "one of a kind." For very small projects that have been constructed several times in the past so that the contractor knows a best way of performing the project's activities, it may prove infeasible to spend the time or money associated with developing a CPM model. However, in general, the CPM model may be constructed for a project so that the benefits the contractor receives from the model's use far outweigh its cost of preparation.

Besides some of the more obvious benefits from the use of CPM, which are discussed in the following section, a CPM approach to project planning is useful in that it forces the contractor to divide a proposed project into several project activities. This in itself is useful since the contractor becomes better acquainted with the various components of the project. Observe that this practice of dividing the project into several activities is consistent with the identification of system or problem components as part of the systems approach.

The CPM model assumes a deterministic activity network structure and deterministic activity parameter (duration). Given an activity network such as that shown in Figure 11.7, CPM assumes that if activities A and B are completed, activity C can and will occur. There is no chance (a probability of 0) that activity C will not occur given that activities A and B are completed.

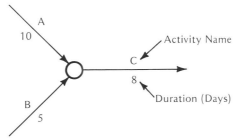

Figure 11.7   Example CPM diagram.

As in all the project planning models discussed in this chapter, the parameter in question is duration. Given activity durations as determined in the activity planning task, one of the objectives of CPM is to determine project duration. When using CPM, it is assumed that each project activity's duration is known with certainty. Given that an activity (e.g., activity A, shown in Figure 11.7) has a duration of 10 days, there is no probability of the activity taking 9 or 11 days. This is the assumption of the CPM calculation procedure.

When the project network is drawn in arrow notation, it is common to place the duration of an activity alongside the activity arrow as shown in Figure 11.7. The units of time (e.g., hours or days) are often not placed on the arrow unless the time units vary from one activity to the next. Rather, the time unit used in the networks may be stated in the upper right-hand corner of the network's drawings.

Given the deterministic nature of the CPM network and the activity durations, the project duration is found by merely summing activity durations. However, when adding activity durations, the fact that an activity cannot start until the logic of the network is satisfied must be considered. In Figure 11.7 activity C cannot start until activity A and activity B are both finished. Since activity A takes 10 days and activity B takes 5 days, activity C cannot start until the end of the tenth day. Given that activity C takes 8 days, the project duration is then calculated as follows:

$$
\begin{aligned}
\text{Project duration} \ &= \ \text{maximum [duration (A); duration (B)]} \\
&+ \ \text{duration (C)} \\
&= \ + \ 10 \text{ days} + 8 \text{ days} = 18 \text{ days}
\end{aligned}
$$

CPM CALCULATIONS

Determining the project duration is not the only purpose of the CPM model. Determining an activity's possible delay time and determining which activities are critical (in that they dictate the project duration) are equally important objectives. To satisfy such objectives, it becomes necessary to generalize the CPM calculation procedure.

Regardless of the size of the project network in question or the type of network notation, whether arrow or circle notation, the objectives of the basic CPM calculations and the actual calculation procedure remain unchanged.

There are three objectives to be satisfied by basic CPM calculations. They are as follows:

1. Determine the completion time or duration of the construction project.
2. Determine which activities of the project are critical; i.e., which activities determine the completion time of the project.
3. Determine how much time each of the project activities may be delayed without affecting the completion time of the project as determined in step 1.

To satisfy these three objectives, the contractor must perform the following:

1. Define project activities.
2. Determine project activity durations.
3. Determine technological logic between activities.
4. Perform CPM calculations.

Determining project activities and their durations is part of the estimating function. Determining the technological logic was discussed in the preceeding section of this chapter. Let us now consider a somewhat simple example project to demonstrate the CPM calculation procedures.

A contractor must prepare a project plan for a project that consists of placing a large culvert. He divides the project into the following project activities:

Activity	Activity Identification
Dig hole	A
Obtain subbase material	B
Obtain pipe	C
Move pipe to site	D
Fine-grade soil in hole	E
Place subbase material	F
Compact subbase material	G
Place pipe and level it	H
Remove excess subbase material from site	I
Backfill with soil	J

Observe that each of the activities is assigned a letter. This is done only to shorten the identification of the activities for the CPM network model.

The contractor next identifies the technological logic that exists between the activities and, recognizing his somewhat limited resources for the project, establishes activity durations. The defined logic and the activity durations are as follows:

Activity A can be done initially and takes 8 working days.
Activity B can be done initially and takes 16 working days.
Activity C can be done initially and takes 24 working days.
Activity D can be done after C and takes 2 working days.
Activity E can be done after A and takes 5 working days.
Activity F can be done after B and E and takes 4 working days.
Activity G can be done after F and takes 8 working days.
Activity H can be done after D and G and takes 6 working days.
Activity I can be done after F and takes 2 working days.
Activity J can be done after H and takes 5 working days.

The project activity durations are all in terms of working days. Thus, all calculations and solutions to the three CPM objectives will be in terms of work days. Of course, in other projects, activity durations may be given in hours, months, etc. The important requirement is that a common unit of time be used for all the activity durations. The CPM arrow notation network model for the defined construction project is shown in Figure 11.8. The numbers in the nodes, or events, are used only to identify the particular events. They have no bearing on the CPM calculations.

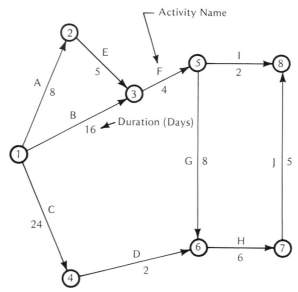

Figure 11.8   Example CPM project.

The contractor wants to determine the completion time (in days) of the project, the critical activities, and the possible delay time of the non-critical activities. To satisfy these objectives, CPM calculations must be performed. These calculations are performed in two steps; the first is known as the forward pass, and the second, the backward pass.

Let us consider the forward pass. This is also referred to as the earliest start-time schedule, since the calculations performed will yield information pertaining to the earliest time that the project activities can possibly start and finish.

The earliest start-time calculations may be made by means of several definitions. The earliest event time (EET) of an event, or node, is defined as the earliest time that the event can possibly occur. To identify the value of an EET on the project network, its value is shown in a five-sided figure pointing to the right, which is placed next to the event's node, as shown in Figure 11.9. The direction of the EET figure indicates that its value was determined by a left-to-right sweep of the network.

From the definition of an EET, the EET of event 1 in the project network in Figure 11.9 may be determined. It is obvious that its value is 0. The project may start as soon as possible.

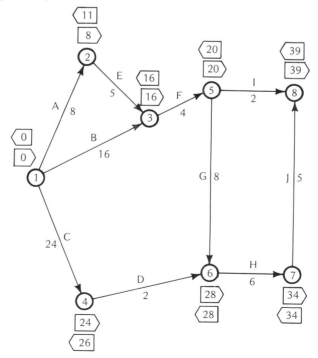

Figure 11.9   CPM calculations

The earliest start time (EST) of an activity is defined as the earliest possible time the activity can start. For example, activities A, B, and C, in the project network in Figure 11.9 can all start immediately. Thus, the ESTs for A, B, and C are all equal to 0, which is the value of the EET of the event or node at which they originate. This makes sense in that these activities cannot start until the event preceding them has occurred. The reader should observe that the EST, in addition to any other times discussed, is referenced to the end of the previous day rather than the beginning of the present day.

The earliest finish time (EFT) of an activity is defined as the activity's earliest start time plus its estimated duration. Therefore, the EFT of activity A is 0 plus its duration of 8 days. Therefore, A's EFT is 8 days. The EFTs of activities B and C may be found in the same manner.

To calculate the remaining EFTs for the nodes or events in the network, the definition of an EET is used. The definition states that the EET of an event or node is the earliest time the event could occur. An event cannot occur until the activities immediately preceding it have finished. Therefore, the EET of the remaining nodes may be found by determining the maximum EFT for the activities immediately preceding them. For example, node 2 only has one activity immediately preceding it. Therefore, its EET is 8, which is the EFT of activity A. Node 3 has both activities B and E immediately preceding it. The EFT of E is 8 + 5, or 13; the EFT of B is 0 + 16 or 16. Therefore, the EET of node 3 is 16. The EFTs for the remaining nodes, and the ESTs and EFTs for the remaining activities, are calculated in the same manner as described for the previous event and activity times. The EETs for all of the events are shown in Figure 11.9. Activity ESTs and EFTs are shown in Figure 11.10.

The EET of node 8 has special significance. This event time, which corresponds to the end of the 39th day, is equal to the completion time of the project. By definition of an EET, this is the earliest possible time for the event to occur. Since it is the last node of the network, it represents the end of the project. Therefore, one of the objectives of the CPM calculations has been satisfied, i.e., the completion time of the project is found to be 39 working days.

Additional information may be obtained from the completed earliest start-time schedule. The EET of each event or node is determined by the activity, or activities, that have the largest EFT. As such, not all the activities may determine the value of the EET of the node at which they terminate. The activities that do not determine the EET of the node at which they terminate may be delayed without affecting the EET value. The amount of time a particular activity may be delayed without affecting the EET of the

Activity	DUR	EST	EFT	LST	LFT	FF	FFP	TF
A	8	0	8	3	11	0	3	3
B	16	0	16	0	16	0	0	0
C	24	0	24	2	26	0	2	2
D	2	24	26	26	28	2	0	2
E	5	8	13	11	16	3	0	3
F	4	16	20	16	20	0	0	0
G	8	20	28	20	28	0	0	0
H	6	28	34	28	34	0	0	0
I	2	20	22	37	39	17	17	17
J	5	34	39	34	39	0	0	0

Figure 11.10   Answers for CPM network.

node at which it terminates is the difference between the EET at which the activity terminates and the activity's EFT. This possible delay time is often referred to as free float. The free float (FF) of activity E in the example network is $16 - 13$, or 3 days. The free float of activity A is $8 - 8$ or 0 days. Activity A's free float is zero because the activity's EFT determined the EET for node 2. The free floats for all of the activities are shown in Figure 11.10. Although giving a measure of possible activity delay time, free float is often a conservative measure of an activity's actual possible delay time. Therefore, the objective of determining possible activity delay times is not completely satisfied by the earliest start-time CPM calculation.

In addition, the objective of determining the critical activities (the activities that dictate the project duration) remains to be satisfied. Admittedly, an inspection of the network may identify the critical activities. However, such a visual identification becomes difficult as the number of activities in the network increases. It is desired to determine the critical activities by means of calculations rather than by trying to determine them by a visual inspection of the network.

Note that if one desires to ignore the existence of events on the arrow CPM network, one may still perform the required CPM calculations necessary to satisfy the three objectives. The earliest start time (EST) of an activity merely becomes the maximum EFT of the activities that immediately precede the activity in question. The ESTs of the originating activities of the project are equal to 0 by definition. The EFT of an activity is merely the sum of its EST and the activity's duration. The project duration is equal to the maximum EFT of the activities that terminate the project. Finally, the free float of an activity is merely the difference between the activity's EFT and the EST of the activity immediately following it.

Thus, it becomes possible to ignore the existence of event times (EETs) when obtaining the project activities' ESTs, EFTs, and free floats in addition to the project duration. Depending on whether or not one discusses events as being part of the CPM network, one may or may not refer to event times (EETs) as being part of the CPM calculation procedure.

The backward calculation pass on the CPM network is referred to as the latest start-time schedule. This is because the calculations performed yield information pertaining to the latest time activities can possibly start and finish. As in the earliest start-time schedule calculations, the latest start-time schedule calculations are made by taking advantage of several definitions.

The latest event time (LET) of an event is defined as the latest possible time the event can possibly occur without delaying the completion time of the project (as determined either by the earliest start-time schedule or as fixed by the planner). From this definition, the LET of node 8 in the network in Figure 11.9 is determined as 39, by the EET of node 8. This means that the latest possible time for the event 8 is equal to the earliest possible time for it in order to complete the job in 39 days. The datum, or starting node, for the backward pass is the terminating node for the forward pass. The LETs for nodes are placed in five-sided figures pointing to the left, as shown in Figure 11.9.

The latest finish time (LFT) of an activity is defined as the latest possible time that an activity can finish without delaying the completion time of the project. The LFT of an activity is equal to the LET of the node or event at which the activity finishes. This is true because of the definition of LET. As such, the LFTs of activities I and J in Figure 11.9 can be found directly to be equal to the LET time of node 8 (39), which corresponds to the completion time of the job.

The latest start time (LST) of an activity is equal to the activity's LFT minus the duration of the activity. In the example in Figure 11.9, the LST of activity I is 39 − 2, 37, and the LST of activity J is 39 − 5, or 34. As in the earliest start-time schedule, these times refer to the end of the given work day.

The LETs for the remaining nodes may be determined from yet another definition of an LET—the LET of a node or event is equal to the minimum of the LSTs of the activities that originate at that node. Therefore, the latest event time for an event is dependent on the activities that originate at the event. For node 7, activity J is the only activity originating at the node. Therefore, the LET of node 7 is equal to the LST of activity J, which is 34. Similarly, the LET for node 6 is 28.

Activities I and G originate at node 5. The LST of I is 39 − 2, or 37, and the LST of G is 28 − 8, or 20. Therefore, the LET of node 5 is 20. The LETs for the remaining nodes, and the LSTs and LFTs for the remaining activities, may be found from the stated definitions. The LETs are shown in Figure 11.9 and the LSTs and LFTs in Figure 11.10.

Obviously, every activity may not determine the LET of the node at which it originates. The activities that do not determine the LETs of their originating nodes may be delayed in starting without affecting the value of any LET of the network. The amount of time that an activity may be delayed may be calculated as the difference between the activity's LST and the LET of the node at which the activity originates. This possible delay time is sometimes referred to as a free-float prime (FFP) or backward float, versus free float or forward float as determined in the forward pass. In our example in Figure 11.9, activity I has a free float prime of $37 - 20$, or 17 days. Activity J has a free-float prime of $34 - 34$, or 0. Activity J has a free-float prime of 0 because it determines the LET of its originating node. One might think of free-float prime as the possible amount of time that the start of a particular activity may be delayed; free float is the possible amount of time the finish of a particular activity may be delayed. The free-float primes for all the activities of the culvert project are shown in Figure 11.10. Free-float primes give a measure of possible activity delay times. However, as in the case of free floats, this measure of possible activity delay time is often too conservative.

It should also be observed that, as in the earliest start-time schedule calculations, one can ignore the existence of event or node times in the CPM calculations associated with the latest start-time schedule. The latest finish time (LFT) of an activity merely becomes the minimum LST of the activities that immediately follow it. The LFTs of the terminating project activities are defined as being equal to the project duration as determined by the earliest start-time schedule or as fixed by the project planner. The latest start time (LST) of an activity is defined as its LFT minus its duration. Finally, the activity free-float prime is equal to the maximum LFT of the activities that immediately precede the activity in question, minus the activity's LST.

Free float and free-float prime, although useful regarding several of the resource allocation algorithms, do not indicate the actual possible delay time associated with performing an activity. The possible delay time associated with an activity is a function of both the earliest start-time schedule and the latest start-time schedule.

Another type of project float is referred to as a total float. Total float (TF) is a function of both the earliest and latest start-time schedules. Total float of an activity is defined as the difference between the LST and EST of the activity, or the difference between its LFT and EFT. Either of these calculations will yield the same total-float value. In the example in Figure 11.9, activity I has an LST of 37, whereas its EST is 20. This means that it may start at the end of day 37 and not delay the completion time of the project. On the other hand, activity I may start as early as the end of the twentieth day. As such, activity I may be delayed as much as 17 days. This is proved by a calculation of the total float, which yields 37 − 20, or 17 days. If the calculation is based on the LFT and EFT of the activity, we find the total float to be 39 − 22, or 17. The total floats of the remaining activities of the network are shown in Figure 11.10. The total float of an activity is, therefore, the amount of time the activity may be delayed without delaying the project completion time as determined by activity technology logic.

If an activity has an EST equal to its LST, then it must begin as soon as possible. It cannot be delayed. Of course, this is true if an activity's EFT is equal to its LFT. These activities, which cannot possibly be delayed (so that the projected completion time is not delayed), are called critical activities. Critical activities that form a continuous path from the start to the end of the project form what is known as the project's critical path. A project always has one or more critical paths. To control the duration of the project, the contractor must direct his efforts to the activities on the critical paths. Admittedly, if activities that have total float are not completed within their allowable float time, they too may become critical. In other words for a project to be completed according to the project duration as determined by the activity technology, each and every activity must not exceed its calculated total float.

At this point, the contractor has satisfied all three of his objectives. The possible project completion time, the critical activities, and the possible delay time of the activities have been determined.

AN EXAMPLE CPM PROGRAM WRITTEN IN BASIC

In this section, we will give an overview description of a CPM computer software program written in BASIC. We will focus our attention only on the programming lines and/or routines that we have not described in previous chapters or are unique and deserve our attention here. It should also be noted that the program described is absent the error routine programming and instructional/procedural routine programming necessary to result in a program usable by an individual that did not write the program.

The CPM BASIC program is illustrated in Figure 11.11. Example data input and program output are illustrated in Figures 11.12 and 11.13, respectively. The program consists essentially of two routines: the input of

CPM network data and the calculation and printing of CPM reports. A third program routine, of lesser significance, enables the user to print the data input.

The program starts with the initializing/dimensioning of the variables used in the program. The variables defined in lines 100 through 120 are used to represent various strings used in the reports generated by the program. Lines 140 through 210 enable the user to continue or exit from the program.

The critical-path data input for a project starts in line 420. Realistically, as is true of most if not all CPM computer programs, the user likely has to sketch/draw the CPM network on a sheet of paper before inputting the requested data to the program. For example, the CPM results illustrated in Figure 11.13 are for the CPM network illustrated in Figure 11.12. The CPM diagram/sketch illustrated in Figure 11.12 consists of circles and arrows. The arrows are used to represent activities. The circles, sometimes referred to as nodes, are used to specify the beginning and ending point of each CPM activity line.

Returning our discussion to the CPM program illustrated in Figure 11.11, the user inputs the project name, location, project owner, and date in lines 420 through 450. This input is subsequently printed as a heading in the calculated CPM results.

The user inputs the number of activities that are to be part of the CPM diagram in line 460. The program then branches to subroutine 1680. This subroutine receives the data input for the various network activities. The activity input is received via the program loop starting with the FOR instruction in line 1710 and ending with the NEXT in line 1920.

Line 1780 requests the user to input the activity code. Any identification code, including inputting work classification, can be input. Similarly, line 1790 requests the input of the activity name.

The beginning and ending node numbers (the numbers in the circles in the CPM network illustration in Figure 11.12) are input in lines 1800 and 1810. Then node numbers are used by the program to "picture or see" how the network diagram looks in Figure 11.12. In effect, the program can tell that an activity follows another activity if the activity starts where the other one ends. The program is written such that the activity's beginning node number must be less than the activity's ending number.

The user inputs an activity's duration in line 1820. After inputting all the activities, the subroutine ends and returns to line 490 via the RETURN instruction in line 1930. The program than immediately branches to the subroutine starting in line 1950. This subroutine is used to sort the activities to enable the subsequent CPM calculations. The sort subroutine is performed via the program loop starting in line 1970 and ending in line 2140. After sorting the activities by node numbers, the subroutine ends and returns via the RETURN instruction in line 2230.

After the input of network data is complete and the sort routine is completed, the program gives the user three options. These options are contained in lines 540, 550, and 560. We will not describe the printing/ listing of data routine referenced in line 540 in that this routine merely consists of PRINT instructions necessary to printing the inputted data.

Instead, we will now focus our attention on the calculation of the CPM results and the printing of the results. This program routine is initiated via inputting a 3 when data input is requested in line 590. The program then branches to line 850 to start the CPM calculations.

As we discussed in the preceding section, CPM calculations and results are obtained by performing two calculation passes through the CPM network, a forward pass and a backward pass. The forward pass calculations are made in lines 870 through 990, and the backward pass calculations are made in lines 1010 through 1180. The float or slack calculations are described in lines 1200 through 1230.

After the CPM program makes the forward pass, backward pass, and float calculations internally, the program prints the results either on the computer monitor or on a hard-copy printer. The user selects a monitor or hard-copy report in lines 1240 through 1260. The monitor printout is obtained via lines 1520 through 1650 and a hard-copy report is obtained via lines 1330 through 1440.

An example hard-copy report obtained via the program for the example CPM network illustrated in Figure 11.11 is illustrated in Figure 11.13. The report illustrates the same type of information obtained via manual calculations described in the preceding section of this chapter.

The benefit to the user of the program illustrated is one of speed. As is true of most, if not all computer applications, we could have obtained the same results via manual calculations. However, these manual calculations require considerable time and are subject to the many errors likely to occur when making manual calculations. Perhaps even more important is the fact that the calculations can be performed in about the same time for a much larger network than the one illustrated in Figure 11.12.

The program illustrated is essentially an example of a data processing/ calculation program. The program as illustrated does not use data files to store any of the inputted data on a data disk. However, the program could be expanded to include this feature of storing the input data on a data disk. This would enable the user to subsequently update, modify, or retrieve any of the data input.

```
100 DIM N$(400)
110 DIM P(50,50)
120 DIM T(50,50)
130 CLS
140 PRINT TAB(18);"ENTER R: TO RUN THE PROGRAM AND ITS OPTIONS"
150 PRINT
160 PRINT TAB(18);"ENTER T: TO TERMINATE THE PROGRAM"
170 PRINT ""
180 PRINT TAB(18)
190 INPUT T$
200 IF (T$="R") THEN 220
210 IF (T$="T") THEN 2240
220 CLS
230 ITOT=100
240 DIM D$(ITOT),C$(100),ST(ITOT),ED(ITOT),D(ITOT),AS(ITOT)
250 DIM TT(2),TD$(2),EF(ITOT),IR(ITOT),ES(ITOT),XS(ITOT),XF(ITOT)
260 REM DEFINITION OF OUTPUT FORMATS
270 D1$="ENTER ACTIVITY CODE, DESCRIPTION,BEG. NODE, END NODE, DURATION
280 D2$="     ACTIVITY          BEGINNING   ENDING   ACTIVITY"
290 D3$="CODE  DESCRIPTION        NODE NO.  NODE NO.  DURATION
300 D4$="\         \
310 D5$="\                \"
320 D7$="     ACTIVITY              DUR-      EARLY     EARLY     LATE"
330 D8$="     LATE       SLACK"
340 D9$="CODE  DESCRIPTION"
350 D0$="     FINISH      TIME"
360 F7$="#######.#"
370 PRINT ""
380 PRINT "THE SCHEDULING PROGRAM HAS NOW BEEN INITIALIZED":PRINT ""
390 PRINT "ENTER C: TO CONTINUE AND RUN THE PROGRAM
400 INPUT C$
410 CLS
420 INPUT "ENTER TITLE OF PROJECT ";T$
430 INPUT "ENTER PROJECT OWNER ";LA$
440 INPUT "ENTER PROJECT LOCATION ";LC$
450 INPUT "ENTER DATE ";DAT$
460 INPUT "TOTAL NUMBER OF ACTIVITIES ";INA
470 IF INA>ITOT THEN PRINT "MUST<= ";ITOT:GOTO 460
480 II=1
490 GOSUB 1680
500 GOSUB 1950
510 CLS
520 CLS
530 PRINT:PRINT TAB(8);"PROGRAM OPTIONS
540 PRINT TAB(10);"ENTER 2: TO LIST DATA ON THE PRINTER
550 PRINT TAB(10);"ENTER 3: TO PERFORM CPM CALCULATIONS
560 PRINT TAB(10);"ENTER 4: TO RETURN TO PROGRAM OPTIONS
570 INPUT "ENTER OPTION";IOP:PRINT
580 IF (IOP=2) THEN 630
590 IF (IOP=3) THEN 850
600 IF (IOP=4) THEN PRINT TAB(15);"END OF PROGRAM";:END
610 REM LIST DATA ON THE PRINTER
620 LPRINT:LPRINT
630 CLS:LPRINT ""
640 PRINT "PLEASE WAIT WHILE THE DATA IS PRINTED ON THE PRINTER....."
650 LPRINT TAB(35);"CPM DATA"
660 LPRINT TAB(35);"PROJECT=";T$
670 LPRINT TAB(35);"DATE=";DAT$
680 LPRINT ""
690 LPRINT "ACT.";TAB(8);"ACTIVITY";TAB(32);"BEGINNING";TAB(46);"ENDING";TAB(58)
;"ACTIVITY"
```

Figure 11.11 Example BASIC CPM program.

```
700 LPRINT "CODE";TAB(8);"DESCRIPTION";TAB(32);"NODE NO.";TAB(46);"NODE NO.";TAB
(58);"DURATION"
710 LPRINT "----";TAB(8);"-----------";TAB(32);"--------";TAB(46);"--------";TAB
(58);"--------"
720 FOR I=1 TO INA
730 LPRINT C$(I);
740 LPRINT TAB(8);D$(I);
750 LPRINT TAB(32);
760 LPRINT USING F7$;ST(I);
770 LPRINT TAB(46);
780 LPRINT USING F7$;ED(I);
790 LPRINT TAB(58);
800 LPRINT USING F7$;D(I)
810 NEXT I
820 LPRINT:LPRINT
830 GOTO 520
840 REM CPM CALCULATIONS
850 CLS
860 PRINT "PLEASE WAIT WHILE THE COMPUTER IS MAKING CALCULATIONS......"
870 REM PERFORM FORWARD PASS
880 IF IFL=1 THEN GOSUB 1950
890 ES(1)=0:EF(1)=D(1)
900 FOR I=2 TO INA
910 IF ST(I)=ST(1) THEN ES(I)=0:EF(I)=D(I):GOTO 990
920 MAX=0
930 FOR L=1 TO INA
940 IF ED(L)<>ST(I) THEN 970
950 IF EF(L)>MAX THEN MAX=EF(L)
960 ES(I)=MAX
970 NEXT L
980 EF(I)=ES(I)+D(I)
990 NEXT I
1000 REM PERFORM BACKWORD PASS
1010 LN=ED(INA)
1020 DX=0
1030 FOR I=INA TO 1 STEP -1
1040 IF ED(I)<>LN THEN 1060
1050 IF EF(I)>DX THEN DX=EF(I)
1060 NEXT I
1070 XF(INA)=DX
1080 FOR I=INA TO 1 STEP -1
1090 IF ED(I)=ED(INA) THEN XF(I)=DX:XS(I)=XF(I)-D(I):GOTO 1180
1100 MIN=999999!
1110 FOR L=INA TO 1 STEP -1
1120 IF ST(L)<ED(I) THEN 1170
1130 IF ED(I)<>ST(L) THEN 1160
1140 IF XS(L)<MIN THEN MIN=XS(L)
1150 XF(I)=MIN
1160 NEXT L
1170 XS(I)=XF(I)-D(I)
1180 NEXT I
1190 REM PERFORM FLOAT CALCULATIONS
1200 FOR I=1 TO INA
1210 AS (I)=XF(I)-EF(I)
1220 NEXT I
1230 PRINT ""
1240 PRINT "DO YOU WANT TO DISPLAY RESULTS ON MONITOR OR PRINTER?
1250 INPUT "ENTER M (FOR MONITOR) OR P (FOR PRINTER) ";Y$
1260 IF Y$<>"M" THEN 1470
1270 CLS
```

Figure 11.11 *Continued*

```
1280 PRINT:PRINT TAB(30);"CPM RESULTS
1290 PRINT TAB(30);T$
1300 PRINT TAB(30);DAT$
1310 PRINT ""
1320 IC=1
1330 PRINT "ACT.";TAB(7);"ACTIVITY";TAB(28);"ACT.";TAB(37);"EARLY";TAB(46);"EARL
Y";TAB(55);"LATEST";TAB(64);"LATEST";TAB(73);"TOTAL"
1340 PRINT "CODE";TAB(7);"DESCRIPTION";TAB(28);"DUR.";TAB(37);"START";TAB(46);"F
INISH";TAB(55);"START";TAB(64);"FINISH";TAB(73);"FLOAT"
1350 PRINT "----";TAB(7);"--------";TAB(28);"----";TAB(37);"-----";TAB(46);"----
--";TAB(55);"------";TAB(64);"------";TAB(73);"-----"
1360 FOR I=1 TO INA
1370 IF I<>(15*IC) THEN 1400
1380 IC=IC+1
1390 INPUT "ENTER C TO CONTINUE ";Y$
1400 PRINT USING D4$;C$(I);
1410 PRINT USING D5$;D$(I);
1420 PRINT USING F7$;D(I);ES(I);EF(I);XS(I);XF(I);AS(I)
1430 NEXT I
1440 PRINT:PRINT "PROJECT DURATION:";DX:PRINT
1450 INPUT "DO YOU WANT THE RESULTS ON THE PRINTER-ENTER Y (YES) OR N (NO) ";Y$
1460 IF Y$<>"Y" THEN 1660
1470 LPRINT TAB(35);"CPM RESULTS"
1480 LPRINT TAB(35);"PROJECT=";T$
1490 LPRINT TAB(35);"DATE=";DAT$
1500 LPRINT ""
1510 LPRINT
1520 LPRINT "ACT.";TAB(7);"ACTIVITY";TAB(28);"ACT.";TAB(37);"EARLY";TAB(46);"EAR
LY";TAB(55);"LATEST";TAB(64);"LATEST";TAB(73);"TOTAL"
1530 LPRINT "CODE";TAB(7);"DESCRIPTION";TAB(28);"DUR.";TAB(37);"START";TAB(46);"
FINISH";TAB(55);"START";TAB(64);"FINISH";TAB(73);"FLOAT"
1540 LPRINT "----";TAB(7);"------------";TAB(28);"----";TAB(37);"-----";TAB(46);"
------";TAB(55);"------";TAB(64);"------";TAB(73);"-----"
1550 FOR I=1 TO INA
1560 LPRINT USING D4$;C$(I);
1570 LPRINT USING D5$;D$(I);
1580 LPRINT USING F7$;D(I);ES(I);EF(I);XS(I);XF(I);AS(I);
1590 IF (AS(I)=0) THEN 1620
1600 K$="-"
1610 GOTO 1630
1620 K$="C"
1630 LPRINT TAB(79);K$
1640 NEXT I
1650 LPRINT :LPRINT "PROJECT DURATION:";DX
1660 PRINT:PRINT TAB(20);"END OF CPM ANALYSIS"
1670 GOTO 520
1680 REM SUBROUTINE:NETWORK DATA INPUT
1690 IC=1
1700 INE=0
1710 FOR I=II TO INA
1720 INE=INE+1
1730 IF INE<>(20*IC) THEN 1760
1740 IC=IC+1
1750 INPUT "PRESS ENTER TO CONTINUE ";Y$
1760 CLS:PRINT "":PRINT "ACTIVITY NO. ";I;
1770 PRINT ""
1780 INPUT "ENTER ACTIVITY CODE: ";C$(I)
1790 INPUT "ENTER ACTIVITY (WORK ITEM) NAME ";D$(I)
1800 INPUT "ENTER BEGINNING NODE NO.: ";ST(I)
1810 INPUT "ENTER ENDING NODE NO.: ";ED(I)
1820 INPUT "ENTER ACTIVITY DURATION";DU$
```

Figure 11.11 *Continued*

```
1830 D(I)=VAL(DU$)
1840 IF ST(I)<ED(I) THEN 1880
1850 CLS
1860 PRINT "BEGINNING NODE NO. MUST BE LESS THAN ENDING NODE NO."
1870 PRINT "REENTER DATA FOR THIS ACTIVITY:":GOTO 1760
1880 CLS
1890 PRINT "DO YOU WANT TO ENTER ANOTHER ACTIVITY/WORK ITEM?
1900 INPUT "ENTER Y (YES) OR N (NO) ";Y$
1910 IF (Y$="N") THEN 1930
1920 NEXT I
1930 RETURN
1940 REM SUBROUTINE: SORT ACTIVITIES USING BEGINNING ACTIVITY NO.
1950 PRINT ""
1960 PRINT:PRINT "PLEASE WAIT...ACTIVITIES ARE BEING SORTED!": PRINT
1970 I1=1
1980 FOR I=I1 TO INA-1
1990 IE=0
2000 FOR L=I+1 TO INA
2010 IF ST(I)<ST(L) THEN 2140
2020 IF ST(I)>ST(L) THEN 2050
2030 IF ST(I)<ED(I) THEN 2140
2040 IF ED(I)=ED(L) THEN 2160
2050 IM=L
2060 IE=1
2070 TT(1)=ST(IM):TT(2)=ED(IM)
2080 TD$(1)=C$(IM):TD$(2)=D$(IM):TD=D(IM)
2090 IF (DU$="V") THEN 5400
2100 ST(IM)=ST(I):ED(IM)=ED(I)
2110 C$(IM)=C$(I):D$(IM)=D$(I):D(IM)=D(I)
2120 ST(I)=TT(1):ED(I)=TT(2)
2130 C$(I)=TD$(1):D$(I)=TD$(2):D(I)=TD
2140 NEXT L
2150 GOTO 2180
2160 PRINT "YOU HAVE INDICATED THE SAME STARTING AND ENDING NODE NUMBERS-YOU CAN
'T TO THAT
2170 PRINT "CHECK DATA FOR ACTIVITY CODES ";C$(I),C$(L)
2180 NEXT I
2190 IF (IE=0) THEN 2220
2200 I1=I1+1
2210 GOTO 1980
2220 IFL=0
2230 RETURN
2240 CLS
2250 PRINT "THIS IS THE END OF THE PROGRAM"
2260 END
```

Figure 11.11 *Continued*

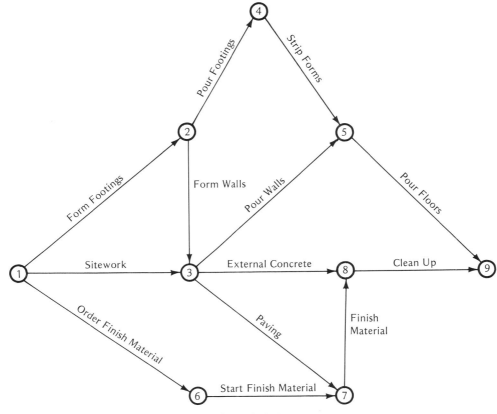

Figure 11.12 Input for example BASIC CPM program.

```
                          CPM RESULTS
                          PROJECT=OFFICE BUILDING
                          DATE=4-5-85


ACT.    ACTIVITY             ACT.    EARLY     EARLY     LATEST    LATEST    TOTAL
CODE    DESCRIPTION          DUR.    START     FINISH    START     FINISH    FLOAT
____    _____          ____    _____     _____    _____     _____    _____

12      FORM FOOTINGS        5.0     0.0       5.0       0.0       5.0       0.0    C
13      SITEWORK             6.0     0.0       6.0       7.0       13.0      7.0    -
16      ORDER FINISH M       6.0     0.0       6.0       12.0      18.0      12.0   -
23      FORM WALLS           8.0     5.0       13.0      5.0       13.0      0.0    C
24      POUR FOOTINGS        11.0    5.0       16.0      19.0      30.0      14.0   -
35      POUR WALLS           9.0     13.0      22.0      30.0      39.0      17.0   -
38      EXTERNAL CONCR       7.0     13.0      20.0      30.0      37.0      17.0   -
37      PAVING               13.0    13.0      26.0      13.0      26.0      0.0    C
45      STRIP FORMS          9.0     16.0      25.0      30.0      39.0      14.0   -
59      POUR FLOORS          12.0    25.0      37.0      39.0      51.0      14.0   -
67      START FINISH M       8.0     6.0       14.0      18.0      26.0      12.0   -
78      FINISH MATERIA       11.0    26.0      37.0      26.0      37.0      0.0    C
89      CLEAN UP             14.0    37.0      51.0      37.0      51.0      0.0    C

PROJECT DURATION: 51
```

Figure 11.13 Output from example BASIC CPM program.

12: Equipment Management Applications

INTRODUCTION

If one is to objectively critique a construction firm's estimating of the costs for a proposed project, one should be critical of the manner in which the majority of construction firms estimate the equipment costs for a project. All too often the construction firm determines the equipment cost to be included in the project estimate as a percentage of some other cost. For example, the contractor might calculate the equipment cost for a project by means of multiplying the estimated labor cost by a percentage.

A much more precise and accurate means of establishing the equipment cost for a project is to determine an actual cost per hour for using a piece of equipment and in turn multiply this hourly cost times the estimated required hours of use. Perhaps the only difficulty with such an approach is the substantial amount of paper work and calculations needed to establish and maintain an accurate hourly cost for each piece of equipment. Data must be collected, processed, and stored daily regarding equipment usage, maintenance, repair, and other ownership costs for each and every piece of equipment.

While a computer does not alleviate the contractor's problems or shorten time related to collecting the above-noted equipment information, it can significantly alleviate the problems regarding the processing and storing of the data. Given the wide ranging mathematical capacity of the computer, hourly rates can be kept up to date. In addition, computerized equipment systems can be used to locate each and every piece of equipment, maintain a historical cost picture of each piece of equipment, and calculate the optimal maintenance and replacement program for the equipment.

In effect, one might suggest that the use of a computer enables the contractor to properly "manage" his equipment. This may in fact make the difference between a profitable and nonprofitable construction firm, especially if the firm is a heavy-equipment or highway firm that maintains substantial equipment.

Before illustrating a computerized equipment estimating/control system, we will first discuss the design and accounting process for a manual equipment system. This will enhance our understanding of the computerized system.

EQUIPMENT ESTIMATING SYSTEM

Depending on the type of construction project, equipment costs can comprise a significant portion of the total project cost. Equipment costs are especially important to heavy-equipment and highway types of projects.

Equipment costs incurred at a project site are direct project costs. However, too often a contractor uses an application process to estimate the equipment cost component of his estimate. For example, a contractor may determine the labor and material direct cost for a project and subsequently multiply this cost by a percentage to determine the estimated equipment cost. This application process may lead to an under- or, overestimate of the actual project equipment cost.

An alternative to treating project equipment costs as an application is to implement an equipment estimating and control system. The objective of such a system is to trace equipment expenditures to individual pieces of equipment and to enable the contractor to treat equipment expenditures as direct costs to projects. Ultimately, the system should provide the contractor a means of evaluating the profitability of owning an individual piece of equipment and also enable the contractor to better determine the profitability of individual projects. This section illustrates the basics of developing an equipment system that serves both an estimating and control objective. There are six steps in this process.

Establishing Hourly Rates per Piece

Step 1 in an equipment estimating/control system is to establish an hourly rate per piece of equipment to be included in the system. Not every piece of equipment should be included. As a guideline, only equipment that is considered to be manageable in regard to time or cost by field personnel should be included. Small or minor pieces of equipment like small saws, compressors, etc., should be handled on a project application process. These types of equipment are often budgeted for an entire project, and the equipment is left at the project for its entire duration.

Once the equipment to be included in the system is identified, an hourly rate for each piece of equipment must be established. This calcuation is illustrated in Figure 12.1.

Establish Hourly Rate per Piece of Equipment

$$\text{Hour Rate} = \frac{\text{Depreciation} + \text{Maintenance \& Repair}}{\text{Annual Estimated Hours}}$$

Example:
Cat 977 K Loader, Account 023

$$\text{Rate} = \frac{3555 + 2745}{900} = \frac{6300}{900} = \$7/\text{hr}$$

Figure 12.1 Determination of an hourly rate for a piece of equipment.

The initial hourly rate used in the system for a piece of equipment is subject to uncertainty. Lacking actual usage hours and maintenance and repair costs, the initial rate has to be estimated based on only a subjective evaluation. However, as data are collected regarding actual use and expenditures, the intent of the system is to determine an accurate hourly equipment rate based on past data.

The calculation of the hourly rate for any piece of equipment must recognize the depreciation of the equipment and its expected annual maintenance and repair. The depreciation charge for a year may be calculated by dividing the initial cost of the equipment by its expected life, whether or not the equipment is fully depreciated. Independent of the calculation of an hourly rate that recognizes depreciation and expected maintenance and repair, an hourly rate not related to the calculation can be used. For example, while a rate based on depreciation and maintenance and repair costs may indicate $20 per hour for a piece of equipment, the company may override this with a $30 hourly rate to reflect market conditions.

Establishing Hours of Use per Piece

Step 2 in developing an equipment estimating and control system concerns estimation of the equipment hours of use by individual piece of equipment for a project. In other words the contractor estimates usage of a piece of equipment in the same way that he estimates the direct labor hours for a project. This step is illustrated in Figure 12.2.

New Project Estimated—Job 124

Estimated Equipment Hours for Cat 977 K for Job 124 = 200
Estimated Equipment Budget for Cat 977 K for Job 124 = $1,400

Figure 12.2 Estimating usage of equipment.

In establishing required equipment hours, there is a question of whether the contractor should base the system on productive hours of usage or hours during which the equipment is at a project site. Given the fact that equipment may be idle for a significant amount of time when it is at a job site, the difference between productive and total equipment hours at a project can be significant.

The calculation of the estimated hours illustrated in Figure 12.2 assumes productive hours. The use of productive hours, and the calculation of an hourly rate in step 1 based on productive hours will likely give the contractor more control potential than a system built on total hours.

Accounting for Use of Equipment

Let us now assume that the contractor initiates a project. The accounting for the use of equipment at the project is illustrated in Figure 12.3. It has the effect of charging the project for the use of the equipment and in effect

Job Starts. Productive Hours for Cat 977 K Input. Assume 180 hours in total. Entry made as follows. (Note: 180 × 7 = $1260)

Equipment 023 (Expense)		Job 124 (Expense)	
D	C	D	C
	1260		1260

Figure 12.3
Recording use of equipment.

recognizing revenue for the equipment account. One might think of this process as one of renting the equipment from the general ledger account to the project.

Recording Actual Cost per Piece

Step 4 in the process, illustrated in Figure 12.4, recognizes the actual expenditures for a piece of equipment as an equipment account expense and not a specific project cost. The theory behind this process is that an equipment expenditure, such as for the repair of tires, is one that will benefit future projects as well as the project on which the actual maintenance was performed. Equally important, the project manager or superintendent can usually control the use of the equipment, whereas he likely cannot control the actual maintenance or repair expenditure. The system is consistent with the principle that a manager should only be accountable for expenditures he can control.

Maintenance and repair cost for Cat 977 K incurred during year equal $800 in total. Individual expenses recognized as occur. In total, entry would be as follows:

Cash		Equipment 023 (Expense)	
D	C	D	C
	800	800	

Figure 12.4 Recording actual equipment expenditures.

Assignment of Total Equipment Expenses

In step 5 all equipment expenses should be assigned to the equipment account; this includes periodic recognition of depreciation entries such as shown in Figure 12.5.

Analyzing Equipment Accounts

Step 6 involves analysis of the accuracy of equipment rates and the profitability of each piece of equipment. This should be done at periodic points in time, perhaps quarterly, or at least annually. This step is illustrated in Figure 12.6. This analysis may result in the contractor deciding to rent a

End-of-year (or quarterly) depreciation entry made for each piece of equipment. For example, for Cat 977 K, depreciation entry would be made as follows:

Equipment Asset Acct.		Equipment 023 (Expense)	
D	C	D	C
	3555	3555	

Figure 12.5 Recording depreciation expense.

Year-end summary entries made. Prior to adjustment equipment and job expense accounts would be as follows:

Equipment 023 (Expense)		Job 124 (Expense)	
D	C	D	C
800	1260	1260	
3555	2800	2800	
4355	4060		
295			

Jobs other than
124

The net equipment 23 debit balance of $295 would be adjusted to zero by crediting equipment 023 in amount of $295 and debiting Underapplied Equipment Job Expense $295. In the subsequent year the budgeted hourly rate for the Cat 977 K would be adjusted upwards.

Figure 12.6 Equipment account analysis.

specific piece of equipment rather than buying it, or adjusting the hourly rate for a specific piece of equipment to more properly reflect its ownership cost and accurately determine project costs.

The process illustrated in steps 1 through 6 is an ongoing process. As the process continues, the system is refined to yield a more scientific means of estimating and controlling equipment costs.

EXAMPLE EQUIPMENT MANAGEMENT AND
ESTIMATING PROGRAM WRITTEN IN BASIC

In this section we will illustrate an example computer software program written in BASIC that can be used for managing and estimating equipment costs. Such a program would be especially useful to a construction firm that maintained considerable equipment as part of running its firm.

The software program illustrated is essentially a data base program; a program that makes considerable use of the storing and subsequent retrieving of cost data regarding a specific piece of equipment. The program is a relatively complex program relevant to the other programs illustrated in this book. The complexity stems from the amount and type of data that are stored on a data disk.

The equipment management/estimating system software program is illustrated in Figure 12.7. We will not describe each and every line of this rather lengthy program. Instead, we will focus on an overview of the program and the unique instructions of program routines. As with other programs illustrated in the book, we have not included the program error routines or user instructions necessary to a complete and thorough program.

The equipment management/estimating systems consist of the following three somewhat interdependent program routines:

I: to initialize names/accounts of equipment for the system
H: to enter historical equipment usage or cost data for a previously defined equipment name/account
L: to list/print hourly rate and cost data for a piece of equipment

These routines are accessed via program lines 120 through 170. The program is initialized by entering F in lines 260 and 460. The user enters the date in lines 560 and 570. The date is stored in a data file starting in program line 600.

The data file titled DATE is used to keep track of the year of the data disk, and the data file named NUMBER is used to keep a running total of the number of equipment classifications defined on the data disk. The program illustrated is designed to enable the user to define ten equipment names/accounts for as many as ten defined equipment classifications.

The user inputs his first equipment classification in lines 790 and 800. The program then proceeds to store the classification name on a data disk using the data file named CLASS in line 920. The field variable (in line 930) CC$ is used to store the classification name, and the variable WI$ is used to store (keep track of) the number of equipment names/accounts initialized/named for the classification.

After initializing an equipment classification, the user is given an option to initialize/enter an equipment name for the defined classification, define another classification, or return to the program options. These options are given to the user in lines 1290 through 1320. If the user inputs C, indicating he wants to input another equipment classification, the program branches to a program routine (line 1420) that enables the user to enter another classification.

If the user should decide to enter/setup an equipment name/account, the user has to identify the classification name for which he wants to enter an equipment name. He does this by entering the classification number listed in front of the classification. The program then tests to determine which classification has been selected. This is done in lines 1360 through 1380. The program then branches to line 1300 where the selected classification name/account is printed.

Assuming the user decides to proceed (rather than exit the program), the program branches to line 1440. Here the user is requested to input the equipment name/account, the initial purchase cost, the useful life, and the estimated annual depreciation charge. This initial setup data is requested in lines 1700 through 1770.

Once this data is input, it is stored on a data disk via the program. This is done in lines 1810 through 1980. The data file opened is named W and the value is R (which is the classification number). For example, if the equipment name/account happens to be in classification 2, the data file for the name/account would be labeled W2. This initial setup data is stored to enhance subsequent equipment account data input. The data file named CLASS is updated in lines 2050 through 2090 to reflect the number of equipment names/accounts defined and stored for a given classification. This is kept via the variable WI$ in line 2080.

After the inputted data is stored in the above-noted data files, the program encounters line 2260 and branches to line 2380. Starting at line 2330 the user is requested to input starting maintenance, repair, depreciation, and usage data. The program is designed with the intent that the user keeps one year's data on a data disk. The purpose of the initial or starting entry requested on lines 2330 through 2380 is to input on a new data disk the cumulative cost and usage totals from prior years. After the data is entered, the data is stored on the data disk via the programming in lines 2460 through 2550, and the program branches back to line 2000.

Line 2010 informs the user that the data is stored, and returns the user to the program options. This is done in line 2030.

```
100 KEY OFF
110 CLS
120 PRINT "":PRINT TAB(29);"PROGRAM EXECUTION OPTIONS":PRINT ""
130 PRINT "ENTER I: TO INITIALIZE THE SYSTEM OR ADD EQUIPMENT ACCOUNT NAMES
140 PRINT ""
150 PRINT "ENTER H: TO ENTER HISTORICAL EQUIPMENT USAGE OR COST DATA
160 PRINT ""
170 PRINT "ENTER L: TO LIST/PRINT HOURLY RATE AND COST DATA FOR A PIECE OF EQUIP
MENT
180 PRINT ""
190 PRINT "ENTER M: TO RETURN TO THE PROGRAM MAIN MENU
200 PRINT ""
210 INPUT T$
220 IF (T$="M") THEN 100
230 IF (T$="I") THEN 1000
240 IF (T$="H") THEN 2570
250 IF (T$="L") THEN 3620
260 PRINT "ENTER F: TO SPECIFY THAT THIS IS THE INITIAL SET UP OF THE SYSTEM FOR
 A
270 PRINT "          NEW DATA DISK
280 PRINT ""
290 PRINT "ENTER A: TO SPECIFY THAT YOU WANT TO ADD MORE EQUIPMENT NAMES TO A PR
EVIOUSLY
300 PRINT "          INITIALIZED EQUIPMENT DATA DISK
310 PRINT ""
320 PRINT "ENTER P: TO EXIT THIS OPTION AND RETURN TO THE PROGRAM EXECUTION OPTI
ONS
330 INPUT Y$
340 IF (Y$="P") THEN 400
350 IF (Y$="F") THEN 1100
360 IF (Y$="A") THEN 530
370 CLS
380 PRINT "YOU HAVE INDICATED THAT THIS IS THE INITIAL SET UP OF THE SYSTEM-ARE
YOU SURE?
390 PRINT ""
400 PRINT "IF THIS IS NOT THE INITIAL SET UP AND YOU HAVE A PREVIOUSLY INITIALIZ
ED
410 PRINT "EQUIPMENT ESTIMATING DATA DISK IN THE DRIVE, YOU MAY ERASE THE DATA D
ISK
420 PRINT "IF YOU EXECUTE THIS OPTION.
430 PRINT ""
440 PRINT "THEREFORE YOU WILL NOW BE REQUESTED TO ENTER YOUR OPTION AGAIN
450 PRINT ""
460 PRINT "ENTER F: IF THIS IS THE INITIAL SET UP FOR THIS EQUIPMENT ESTIMATE DA
TA DISK
470 PRINT ""
480 PRINT "ENTER A: IF THIS IS NOT THE INITIAL SET UP AND YOU WANT TO ADD EQUIPM
ENT
490 PRINT "          ACCOUNTS/NAMES
500 INPUT Y$
510 IF (Y$="F") THEN 550
520 IF (Y$="A") THEN 530
530 GOSUB 1000
540 GOTO 1090
550 CLS
560 PRINT "ENTER YEAR/DATE FOR THIS DATA DISK
570 INPUT YA$
580 CLS
590 PRINT "PLEASE WAIT WHILE THE DATA DISK IS INITIALIZED...."
600 OPEN "DATE.DAT" AS #1 LEN=10
```

Figure 12.7   An example BASIC program for equipment accounting.

```
610 FIELD #1, 10 AS DY$
620 LSET DY$=YA$
630 PUT #1,1
640 CLOSE #1
650 OPEN "NUMBER.DAT" AS #1 LEN=6
660 FIELD #1, 6 AS Z$
670 LSET Z$="0"
680 PUT #1,1
690 CLOSE #1
700 GOSUB 1000
710 XX=ZA+1
720 PRINT ""
730 PRINT "ENTER C: TO ENTER YOUR FIRST EQUIPMENT CLASSIFICATION
740 PRINT "ENTER P: TO RETURN TO THE PROGRAM EXECUTION OPTIONS
750 INPUT C$
760 IF (C$="C") THEN 780
770 IF (C$="P") THEN 400
780 CLS
790 PRINT "ENTER EQUIPMENT CLASSIFICATION NO. ";XX;" =";
800 INPUT NA$
810 CLS
820 PRINT "THE PROGRAM WILL NOW SET UP THE EQUIPMENT CLASSIFICATION ON A DATA DI
SK
830 PRINT "MAKE SURE YOU HAVE THE INITIALIZED EQUIPMENT DATA DISK IN THE DISK DR
IVE
840 PRINT ""
850 INPUT "ENTER C TO CONTINUE ";C$
860 ZA$=STR$(XX)
870 OPEN "NUMBER.DAT" AS #1 LEN=6
880 FIELD #1, 6 AS Z$
890 LSET Z$=ZA$
900 PUT #1,1
910 CLOSE #1
920 OPEN "CLASS.DAT" AS #1 LEN=50
930 FIELD #1, 45 AS CC$, 5 AS WI$
940 LSET CC$=NA$
950 LSET WI$="0"
960 PUT #1,XX
970 CLOSE #1
980 GOTO 1090
990 GOTO 7770
1000 CLS
1010 PRINT "PLEASE WAIT WHILE THE DATA DISK IS READ...."
1020 OPEN "NUMBER.DAT" AS #1 LEN=6
1030 FIELD #1, 6 AS Z$
1040 GET #1,1
1050 ZA=VAL(Z$)
1060 CLOSE #1
1070 PRINT "YOU HAVE PREVIOUSLY DEFINED   ";ZA;" EQUIPMENT CLASSIFICATIONS"
1080 RETURN
1090 CLS
1100 PRINT "YOU HAVE THE FOLLOWING EQUIPMENT CLASSIFICATIONS ON THE DATA DISK
1110 PRINT "CLASS. NO.";TAB(15);"CLASSIFICATION NAME ";TAB(65);"NO.OF ACCOUNTS"
1120 PRINT "------------";TAB(15);"--------------------";TAB(65);"-------------"

1130 OPEN "NUMBER.DAT" AS #1 LEN=6
1140 FIELD #1, 6 AS Z$
1150 GET #1,1
1160 ZA$=Z$
1170 CLOSE #1
1180 Z=VAL(ZA$)
```

Figure 12.7 *Continued*

```
1190 FOR N=1 TO Z
1200 OPEN "CLASS.DAT" AS #1 LEN=50
1210 FIELD #1, 45 AS CC$, 5 AS WI$
1220 GET #1,N
1230 NA$=CC$
1240 NW$=WI$
1250 CLOSE #1
1260 PRINT TAB(3);N;TAB(15);NA$;TAB(70);NW$
1270 NEXT N
1280 PRINT ""
1290 PRINT "ENTER EQUIPMENT CLASS NO.: TO SET UP AN EQUIPMENT ACCOUNT/NAME FOR A
GIVEN
1300 PRINT "                              EQUIPMENT CLASSIFICATION
1310 PRINT "ENTER C             : TO SET UP ANOTHER WORK CLASSIFICATION
1320 PRINT "ENTER P             : TO RETURN TO PROGRAM OPTIONS
1330 INPUT C$
1340 IF (C$="C") THEN 1420
1350 IF (C$="P") THEN 400
1360 R=VAL(C$)
1370 FOR J=1 TO Z
1380 IF (R=J) THEN 1410
1390 NEXT J
1400 GOTO 1090
1410 GOTO 1440
1420 XX=Z+1
1430 GOTO 780
1440 CLS
1450 PRINT "YOU HAVE SELECTED THE FOLLOWING:
1460 OPEN "CLASS.DAT" AS #1 LEN=50
1470 FIELD #1, 45 AS CC$, 5 AS WI$
1480 GET #1,R
1490 NA$=CC$
1500 NW$=WI$
1510 CLOSE #1
1520 PRINT "CLASSIFICATION= ";NA$
1530 PRINT "NO. OF EQUIPMENT ACCOUNTS/NAMES PREVIOUSLY DEFINED = ";NW$
1540 NG=VAL(NW$)
1550 IF (NG=0) THEN 1580
1560 PRINT "":PRINT "THE EQUIPMENT ACCOUNTS DEFINED ARE AS FOLLOWS:"
1570 GOTO 2040
1580 PRINT ""
1590 PRINT "ENTER E: TO ENTER YOUR FIRST EQUIPMENT ACCOUNT FOR THIS CLASSIFICATI
ON
1600 PRINT "ENTER P: TO RETURN TO THE PROGRAM OPTIONS
1610 INPUT C$
1620 IF (C$="P") THEN 400
1630 IF (C$="E") THEN 1660
1640 GOTO 1520
1650 CLS
1660 NG=NG+1
1670 CLS
1680 PRINT "CLASSIFICATION= ";NA$
1690 PRINT ""
1700 PRINT "ENTER EQUIPMENT ACCOUNT/NAME NO. ";NG;" : ";
1710 INPUT EQ$
1720 PRINT ""
1730 INPUT "ENTER PURCHASE COST (NO $ SYMBOL OR COMMAS) = ";EC
1740 PRINT ""
1750 INPUT "ESTIMATED USEFUL LIFE (IN YEARS) = ";EY
1760 PRINT ""
1770 INPUT "ESTIMATED ANNUAL DEPR. CHARGE (NO $ SYMBOL OR COMMAS) = ";ED
```

Figure 12.7 *Continued*

```
1780 PRINT ""
1790 CLS
1800 PRINT "YOU MUST HAVE THE EQUIPMENT DATA DISK IN THE DRIVE...DO THAT NOW
1810 TAW$="W"
1820 TAX$=STR$(R)
1830 TAZ$=TAW$ +TAX$
1840 OPEN TAZ$ AS #1 LEN=90
1850 FIELD #1, 5 AS RX$, 40 AS QN$, 20 AS QC$, 5 AS QL$, 20 AS QD$
1860 LSET RX$="O"
1870 LSET QN$=EQ$
1880 LSET QC$=STR$(EC)
1890 LSET QL$=STR$(EY)
1900 LSET QD$=STR$(ED)
1910 PUT #1,NG
1920 CLOSE #1
1930 OPEN "CLASS.DAT" AS #1 LEN=50
1940 FIELD #1, 45 AS CC$, 5 AS WI$
1950 LSET CC$=NA$
1960 LSET WI$=STR$(NG)
1970 PUT #1,R
1980 CLOSE #1
1990 GOTO 2430
2000 CLS
2010 PRINT "THE EQUIPMENT ACCOUNT DATA IS NOW STORED ON THE DATA DISK.
2020 INPUT "ENTER C TO RETURN TO OPTIONS ";C$
2030 GOTO 1090
2040 PRINT ""
2050 OPEN "CLASS.DAT" AS #1 LEN=50
2060 FIELD #1, 45 AS CC$, 5 AS WI$
2070 GET #1,R
2080 K=VAL(WI$)
2090 CLOSE #1
2100 TR$="$$###,######.##"
2110 PRINT "EQUIPMENT NAME/ACCOUNT";TAB(50);"INITIAL EQUIPMENT COST"
2120 PRINT "-----------------------";TAB(50);"---------------------"
2130 TAW$="W"
2140 TAX$=STR$(R)
2150 TAZ$=TAW$ +TAX$
2160 OPEN TAZ$ AS #1 LEN=90
2170 FIELD #1, 5 AS RX$, 40 AS QN$, 20 AS QC$, 5 AS QL$, 20 AS QD$
2180 FOR T= 1 TO K
2190 GET #1,T
2200 QC=VAL(QC$)
2210 PRINT QN$;
2220 PRINT TAB(50);
2230 PRINT USING TR$;QC
2240 NEXT T
2250 CLOSE #1
2260 PRINT ""
2270 INPUT "ENTER C TO ENTER EQUIPMENT NAME/ACCOUNT ";C$
2280 GOTO 1650
2290 CLS
2300 PRINT "YOU MUST NOW ENTER STARTING COST AND USAGE DATA FOR THE EQUIPMENT.
2310 PRINT "ENTER O'S (THE NUMBER) OR PREVIOUS YEAR'S CUMULATIVE TOTALS.
2320 PRINT ""
2330 INPUT "ENTER REGULAR MAINTENANCE ";MA
2340 INPUT "ENTER IRREGULAR MAINTENANCE ";MB
2350 INPUT "ENTER REPAIR COST ";MC
2360 INPUT "ENTER DEPRECIATION COST ";MD
2370 INPUT "ENTER HOURS OF PROD. USAGE ";ME
2380 INPUT "ENTER HOURS OF STANDBY USAGE ";MF
```

Figure 12.7 *Continued*

```
2390 CLS
2400 E$="$$###,######.##"
2410 PRINT ""
2420 GOTO 2390
2430 SAW$="S"
2440 SAX$=STR$(R)
2450 SAZ$=SAW$ + SAX$

2460 OPEN SAZ$ AS #1 LEN=90
2470 FIELD #1, 15 AS NA$, 15 AS NB$, 15 AS NC$, 15 AS ND$, 15 AS NE$, 15 AS NF$
2480 LSET NA$=STR$(MA)
2490 LSET NB$=STR$(MB)
2500 LSET NC$=STR$(MC)
2510 LSET ND$=STR$(MD)
2520 LSET NE$=STR$(ME)
2530 LSET NF$=STR$(MF)
2540 PUT #1,NG
2550 CLOSE #1
2560 GOTO 2000
2570 CLS
2580 CLS
2590 PRINT "TO ENTER USAGE OR COST DATA FOR A PIECE OF EQUIPMENT, YOU MUST FIRM
IDENTIFY
2600 PRINT "THE EQUIPMENT NAME/ACCOUNT"
2610 PRINT ""
2620 INPUT "ENTER C TO LIST/LOCATE THE EQUIPMENT NAME/ACCOUNT ";C$
2630 CLS
2640 GOSUB 7140
2650 PRINT ""
2660 PRINT "ENTER EQUIPMENT NAME ACCOUNT NO. : TO ENTER USAGE OR COST DATA FOR T
HE EQUIPMENT
2670 PRINT "ENTER P:                          TO RETURN TO HISTORICAL DATA OPTI
ON
2680 INPUT A$
2690 E=VAL(A$)
2700 IF (A$="P") THEN 2570
2710 FOR U=1 TO K
2720 IF (U=E) THEN 2770
2730 NEXT U
2740 CLS
2750 INPUT A$
2760 GOTO 2690
2770 CLS
2780 PRINT "PLEASE WAIT WHILE THE DATA DISK IS READ...
2790 PRINT ""
2800 OPEN TAZ$ AS #1 LEN=90
2810 FIELD #1, 5 AS RX$, 40 AS QN$, 20 AS QC$, 5 AS QL$, 20 AS QD$
2820 GET #1,E
2830 CR$=RX$
2840 CN$=QN$
2850 CC$=QC$
2860 CL$=QL$
2870 CD$=QD$
2880 CLOSE #1
2890 CD=VAL(CD$)
2900 RU=VAL(CR$)
2910 RZ=RU+1
2920 CLS
2930 PRINT "EQUIPMENT NAME/ACCOUNT= ";TAB(40);CN$
2940 QC=VAL(QC$)
2950 PRINT "EQUIPMENT COST=";TAB(40);
2960 PRINT USING TR$;QC
```

Figure 12.7 *Continued*

```
2970 PRINT "EQUIPMENT LIFE= ";TAB(40);CL$;"YEARS
2980 PRINT "ANNUAL DEPR. CHARGE=";TAB(40);
2990 PRINT USING TR$;CD
3000 PRINT ""
3010 PRINT "EMTER C: TO ENTER COST DATA AND/OR USAGE DATA
3020 PRINT "ENTER P: TO RETURN TO HISTORICAL DATA OPTION"
3030 INPUT K$
3040 IF (K$="P") THEN 2570
3050 IF (K$="C") THEN 3080
3060 PRINT "YOU HAVE AN INPUT ERROR, YOU MUST ENTER C OR P
3070 GOTO 3000
3080 PRINT ""
3090 PRINT "RECORD (WEEK) NO.= ";RZ
3100 PRINT ""
3110 INPUT "ENTER TODAY'S DATE ";RR$
3120 INPUT "ENTER REGULAR MAINTIENANCE COST ";RA
3130 INPUT "ENTER IRREGULAR MAINTIENANCE COST ";RB
3140 INPUT "ENTER REPAIR COST";RC
3150 INPUT "ENTER DEPRECIATION COST ";RD
3160 INPUT "ENTER PROD. USAGE HOURS ";RE
3170 INPUT "ENTER STAND-BY USAGE HOURS ";RF
3180 CLS
3190 PRINT ""
3200 M$="$$##,#######.##"
3210 CLS
3220 PRINT "YOU MUST PUT THE EQUIPMENT DATA DISK IN THE DRIVE NOW......"
3230 PRINT "ENTER D: TO STORE THE RECORD ON THE DISK DRIVE
3240 PRINT "ENTER P: TO EXIT AND RETURN TO OPTION MENU
3250 INPUT X$
3260 IF (X$="D") THEN 3310
3270 IF (X$="P") THEN 2570
3280 CLS
3290 PRINT ""
3300 GOTO 3230
3310 CLS
3320 PRINT "PLEASE WAIT WHILE THE RECORD IS BEING STORED....
3330 OPEN TAZ$ AS #1 LEN=90
3340 FIELD #1, 5 AS RX$,40 AS QN$, 20 AS QC$, 5 AS QL$, 20 AS QD$
3350 LSET RX$=STR$(RZ)
3360 QN$=CN$
3370 QC$=CC$
3380 QL$=CL$
3390 QD$=CD$
3400 PUT #1,E
3410 CLOSE #1
3420 PP$="K"
3430 PA$=STR$(R)
3440 PB$=STR$(E)
3450 PC$=PP$ + PA$ + PB$
3460 OPEN PC$ AS #1 LEN=105
3470 FIELD #1, 15 AS LL$, 15 AS LA$, 15 AS LB$, 15 AS LC$, 15 AS LD$, 15 AS LE$,
15 AS LF$
3480 LSET LL$=RR$
3490 LSET LA$=STR$(RA)
3500 LSET LB$=STR$(RB)
3510 LSET LC$=STR$(RC)
3520 LSET LD$=STR$(RD)
3530 LSET LE$=STR$(RE)
3540 LSET LF$=STR$(RF)
3550 PUT #1,RZ
3560 CLOSE #1
```

Figure 12.7 *Continued*

```
3570 PRINT ""
3580 PRINT "THE RECORD IS NOW STORED ON THE DISK DRIVE.
3590 PRINT ""
3600 INPUT "ENTER C TO RETURN TO HISTORICAL DATA OPTION ";C$
3610 GOTO 2570
3620 CLS
3630 PRINT "TO LIST/PRINT A REPORT, YOU MUST FIRST IDENTIFY THE EQUIPMENT NAME/A
CCOUNT
3640 PRINT ""
3650 INPUT "ENTER C TO LIST/LOCATE THE EQUIPMENT NAME/ACCOUNT ";C$
3660 CLS
3670 GOSUB 7140
3680 PRINT ""
3690 PRINT "ENTER EQUIPMENT NAME ACCOUNT NO. : TO LIST/PRINT A REPORT FOR THE EQ
UIPMENT
3700 PRINT "ENTER P                        : TO RETURN TO LIST/PRINT OPTION
3710 INPUT A$
3720 E=VAL(A$)
3730 IF (A$="P") THEN 3620
3740 FOR U=1 TO K
3750 IF (U=E) THEN 3770
3760 NEXT U
3770 CLS
3780 PRINT "PLEASE WAIT WHILE THE DATA DISK IS READ...
3790 PRINT ""
3800 OPEN TAZ$ AS #1 LEN=90
3810 FIELD #1, 5 AS RX$, 40 AS QN$, 20 AS QC$, 5 AS QL$, 20 AS QD$
3820 GET #1,E
3830 CZ$=RX$
3840 CN$=QN$
3850 CC$=QC$
3860 CL$=QL$
3870 CD$=QD$
3880 CLOSE #1
3890 OPEN "DATE.DAT" AS #1 LEN=10
3900 FIELD #1, 10 AS DY$
3910 GET #1,1
3920 YA$=DY$
3930 CLOSE #1
3940 CLS:PRINT "EQUIPMENT NAME/ACCOUNT= ";TAB(40);CN$
3950 QC=VAL(CC$)
3960 TR$="$$##,######.##
3970 PRINT "EQUIPMENT COST= ";TAB(40);
3980 PRINT USING TR$;QC
3990 CD=VAL(CD$)
4000 PRINT "EQUIPMENT LIFE= ";TAB(40);CL$;"  YEARS
4010 PRINT "ANNUAL DEPR. CHARGE= ";TAB(40);
4020 PRINT USING TR$;CD
4030 PRINT ""
4040 PRINT "NO. OF RECORDS ENTERED FOR YEAR= ";YA$;" IS EQUAL TO=;CZ$
4050 PRINT ""
4060 PRINT "ENTER R: TO PRINT OUT ALL THE RECORDS FOR THIS THIS YEAR FOR THE EQU
IPMENT
4070 PRINT "ENTER P: TO RETURN TO THE LIST/PRINT OPTIONS TO EXIT OR SELECT ANOTH
ER EQUIP.
4080 INPUT M$
4090 IF (M$="P") THEN 3620
4100 IF (M$="R") THEN 4150
4110 CLS
4120 PRINT "YOU HAVE MADE AN INPUT ERROR, YOU MUST ENTER P, R, U, OR T
```

Figure 12.7 *Continued*

```
4130 PRINT ""
4140 GOTO 3910
4150 CLS
4160 PRINT "ENTER H: TO PRINT OUT A HARD COPY REPORT ON A PRINTER
4170 PRINT "ENTER P: TO RETURN TO LIST/PRINT OPTION
4180 INPUT H$
4190 IF (H$="H") THEN 4230
4200 IF (H$="P") THEN 3620
4210 CLS:PRINT "YOU HAVE MADE AN INPUT ERROR, YOU MUST ENTER H OR P
4220 PRINT "":GOTO 4150
4230 CLS
4240 PRINT "PLEASE WAIT WHILE THE HARD COPY REPORT IS PRINTED...."
4250 OPEN "LPT1:" FOR OUTPUT AS #1:WIDTH #1,132
4260 PRINT #1,CHR$(15);TAB(55);"SUMMARY OF RECORDS
4270 PRINT #1,TAB(55);CN$
4280 PRINT #1,TAB(55);"YEAR=";YA$
4290 PRINT #1,"EQUIPMENT COST= ";
4300 PRINT #1,USING TR$;QC
4310 PRINT #1,"ESTIMATED DEPRECIATION LIFE= ";CL$
4320 PRINT #1,"EST. ANNUAL DEPR. CHARGE= ";
4330 PRINT #1,USING TR$;CD
4340 PRINT #1,""
4350 PRINT #1,TAB(45);"SUMMARY OF RECORDS AND TOTALS"
4360 PRINT #1,TAB(45);
4370 PRINT #1,"NO. OF RECORDS THIS YEAR= ";CZ$
4380 PRINT #1,""
4390 PRINT #1,"PRIOR YEAR TOTALS:
4400 PRINT #1,"DATE OF RECORD";
4410 PRINT #1,TAB(19);"REG. MAINTENANCE";TAB(38);"IRREG.MAINTENANCE";TAB(59);"RE
PAIR COSTS";TAB(78);"DEPRECIATION";TAB(95);"PRODUCTIVE HOURS";TAB(115);"STAND-BY
 HOURS"
4420 PRINT #1,"--------------------";TAB(19);"--------------------";TAB(38);"-----------
--------";TAB(57);"--------------------";TAB(76);"--------------------";TAB(95);"-----
----------------";TAB(114);"--------------------"
4430 CLOSE #1:SAW$="S":SAX$=STR$(R):SAZ$=SAW$+SAX$
4440 OPEN SAZ$ AS #1 LEN=90
4450 FIELD #1, 15 AS NA$,15 AS NB$,15 AS NC$, 15 AS ND$, 15 AS NE$, 15 AS NF$
4460 GET #1,E
4470 MA=VAL(NA$)
4480 MB=VAL(NB$)
4490 MC=VAL(NC$)
4500 MD=VAL(ND$)
4510 ME=VAL(NE$)
4520 MF=VAL(NF$)
4530 CLOSE #1
4540 OPEN "LPT1:" FOR OUTPUT AS #1:WIDTH #1,132
4550 PRINT #1,CHR$(15);
4560 PRINT #1,TAB(19);
4570 PRINT #1,USING TR$;MA;
4580 PRINT #1,TAB(38);
4590 PRINT #1,USING TR$;MB;
4600 PRINT #1,TAB(57);
4610 PRINT #1,USING TR$;MC;
4620 PRINT #1,TAB(76);
4630 PRINT #1,USING TR$;MD;
4640 PRINT #1,TAB(98);
4650 PRINT #1,ME;
4660 PRINT #1,TAB(117);
4670 PRINT #1,MF
4680 PRINT #1,""
4690 PRINT #1,"RECORDS ENTERED THIS YEAR:"
```

Figure 12.7 *Continued*

```
4700 PRINT #1,""
4710 CLOSE #1
4720 TDA=0:TDB=0:TDC=0
4730 TDD=0:TDE=0:TDF=0
4740 Z=VAL(CZ$)
4750 PP$="K"
4760 PA$=STR$(R)
4770 PB$=STR$(E)
4780 PC$=PP$ +PA$ +PB$
4790 FOR J=1 TO Z
4800 OPEN PC$ AS #1 LEN=105
4810 FIELD #1, 15 AS LL$, 15 AS LA$, 15 AS LB$, 15 AS LC$, 15 AS LD$, 15 AS LE$,
     15 AS LF$
4820 GET #1,J
4830 DD$=LL$
4840 DA=VAL(LA$)
4850 DB=VAL(LB$)
4860 DC=VAL(LC$)
4870 DD=VAL(LD$)
4880 DE=VAL(LE$)
4890 DF=VAL(LF$)
4900 CLOSE #1
4910 TDA=TDA+DA
4920 TDB=TDB+DB
4930 TDC=TDC+DC
4940 TDD=TDD+DD
4950 TDE=TDE+DE
4960 TDF=TDF+DF
4970 OPEN "LPT1:" FOR OUTPUT AS #1:WIDTH #1, 132
4980 PRINT #1,DD$;TAB(19);
4990 PRINT #1,USING TR$;DA;
5000 PRINT #1,TAB(38);
5010 PRINT #1,USING TR$;DB;
5020 PRINT #1,TAB(57);
5030 PRINT #1,USING TR$;DC;
5040 PRINT #1,TAB(76);
5050 PRINT #1,USING TR$;DD;
5060 PRINT #1,TAB(97);
5070 PRINT #1,DE;
5080 PRINT #1,TAB(116);
5090 PRINT #1,DF
5100 CLOSE #1
5110 NEXT J
5120 CLOSE #1
5130 OPEN "LPT1:" FOR OUTPUT AS #1: WIDTH #1,132
5140 PRINT #1,"-------------------";TAB(19);"-------------------";TAB(38);"-----------
     --------";TAB(57);"-------------------";TAB(76);"-----------------";TAB(95);"------
     --------------";TAB(114);"-------------------"
5150 PRINT #1,"TOTALS THIS YEAR";TAB(19);
5160 PRINT #1,USING TR$;TDA;
5170 PRINT #1,TAB(38);
5180 PRINT #1,USING TR$;TDB;
5190 PRINT #1,TAB(57);
5200 PRINT #1,USING TR$;TDC;
5210 PRINT #1,TAB(76);
5220 PRINT #1,USING TR$;TDD;
5230 PRINT #1,TAB(97);
5240 PRINT #1,TDE;
5250 PRINT #1,TAB(116);
5260 PRINT #1,TDF
```

Figure 12.7 *Continued*

```
5270 PRINT #1,"-------------------";TAB(19);"------------------";TAB(38);"---------
----------";TAB(57);"------------------";TAB(76);"------------------";TAB(95);"----
-------------";TAB(114);"------------------"
5280 PRINT #1,"TOTALS TO DATE";TAB(19);
5290 CDA=TDA+MA
5300 PRINT #1,USING TR$;CDA;
5310 CDB=TDB+MB
5320 PRINT #1,TAB(38);
5330 PRINT #1,USING TR$;CDB;
5340 PRINT #1,TAB(57);
5350 CDC=TDC+MC
5360 PRINT #1,USING TR$;CDC;
5370 PRINT #1,TAB(76);
5380 CDD=TDD+MD
5390 PRINT #1,USING TR$;CDD;
5400 PRINT #1,TAB(97);
5410 CDE=TDE+ME
5420 PRINT #1,CDE;
5430 CDF=TDF+MF
5440 PRINT #1,TAB(116);
5450 PRINT #1,CDF
5460 PRINT #1,"-------------------";TAB(19);"------------------";TAB(38);"---------
--------";TAB(57);"------------------";TAB(76);"------------------";TAB(95);"----
-------------";TAB(114);"------------------"
5470 PRINT #1,""
5480 UA$="$$###,###.##"
5490 PRINT #1,"COST/PROD.HOURS";TAB(19);
5500 IF (MA=0) THEN 5530
5510 BA=MA/ME
5520 PRINT #1,USING UA$;BA;
5530 PRINT #1,TAB(38);
5540 IF (MB=0) THEN 5570
5550 BB=MB/ME
5560 PRINT #1,USING UA$;BB;
5570 PRINT #1,TAB(57);
5580 IF (MC=0) THEN 5610
5590 BC=MC/ME
5600 PRINT #1,USING UA$;BC;
5610 PRINT #1,TAB(76);
5620 IF (MD=0) THEN 5650
5630 BD=MD/ME
5640 PRINT #1,USING UA$;BD;
5650 PRINT #1,TAB(95);
5660 PRINT #1,"(PRIOR YEARS)"
5670 PRINT #1,TAB(19);
5680 IF (TDA=0) THEN 5710
5690 VA=TDA/TDE

5700 PRINT #1,USING UA$;VA;
5710 PRINT #1,TAB(38);
5720 IF (TDB=0) THEN 5750
5730 VB=TDB/TDE
5740 PRINT #1,USING UA$;VB;
5750 PRINT #1,TAB(57);
5760 IF (TDC=0) THEN 5790
5770 VC=TDC/TDE
5780 PRINT #1,USING UA$;VC;
5790 PRINT #1,TAB(76);
5800 IF (TDD=0) THEN 5830
5810 VD=TDD/TDE
5820 PRINT #1,USING UA$;VD;
```

Figure 12.7 *Continued*

```
5830 PRINT #1,TAB(95);
5840 PRINT #1,"(THIS YEAR)
5850 PRINT #1,TAB(19);
5860 IF (CDA=0) THEN 5890
5870 XA=CDA/CDE
5880 PRINT #1,USING UA$;XA;
5890 PRINT #1,TAB(38);
5900 IF (CDB=0) THEN 5930
5910 XB=CDB/CDE
5920 PRINT #1,USING UA$;XB;
5930 PRINT #1,TAB(57);
5940 IF (CDC=0) THEN 5970
5950 XC=CDC/CDE
5960 PRINT #1,USING UA$;XC;
5970 PRINT #1,TAB(76);
5980 IF (CDD=0) THEN 6010
5990 XD=CDD/CDE
6000 PRINT #1,USING UA$;XD;
6010 PRINT #1,TAB(95);
6020 PRINT #1,"(TOTALS TO DATE)"
6030 PRINT #1,""
6040 PRINT #1,"COST/TOTAL HOURS";TAB(19);
6050 IF (MA=0) THEN 6080
6060 QA=MA/(ME+MF)
6070 PRINT #1,USING UA$;QA;
6080 PRINT #1,TAB(38);
6090 IF (MB=0) THEN 6120
6100 QB=MB/(ME+MF)
6110 PRINT #1,USING UA$;QB;
6120 PRINT #1,TAB(57);
6130 IF (MC=0) THEN 6160
6140 QC=MC/(ME+MF)
6150 PRINT #1,USING UA$;QC;
6160 PRINT #1,TAB(76);
6170 IF (MD=0) THEN 6200
6180 QD=MD/(ME+MF)
6190 PRINT #1,USING UA$;QD;
6200 PRINT #1,TAB(95);
6210 PRINT #1,"(PRIOR YEARS)
6220 PRINT #1,TAB(19);
6230 IF (TDA=0) THEN 6260
6240 WA=TDA/(TDE+TDF)
6250 PRINT #1,USING UA$;WA;
6260 PRINT #1,TAB(38);
6270 IF (TDB=0) THEN 6300
6280 WB=TDB/(TDE+TDF)
6290 PRINT #1,USING UA$;WB;
6300 PRINT #1,TAB(57);
6310 IF (TDC=0) THEN 4720
6320 WC=TDC/(TDE+TDF)
6330 PRINT #1,USING UA$;WC;
6340 PRINT #1,TAB(76);
6350 IF (TDD=0) THEN 6380
6360 WD=TDD/(TDE+TDF)
6370 PRINT #1,USING UA$;WD;
6380 PRINT #1,TAB(95);
6390 PRINT #1,"(THIS YEAR)"
6400 PRINT #1,TAB(19);
6410 IF (CDA=0) THEN 6440
6420 WWA=CDA/(CDE+CDF)
```

Figure 12.7 *Continued*

```
6430 PRINT #1,USING UA$;WWA;
6440 PRINT #1,TAB(38);
6450 IF (CDB=0) THEN 6480
6460 WWB=CDB/(CDE+CDF)
6470 PRINT #1,USING UA$;WWB;
6480 PRINT #1,TAB(57);
6490 IF (CDC=0) THEN 6520
6500 WWC=CDC/(CDE+CDF)
6510 PRINT #1,USING UA$;WWC;
6520 PRINT #1,TAB(76);
6530 IF (CDD=0) THEN 6560
6540 WWD=CDD/(CDE+CDF)
6550 PRINT #1,USING UA$;WWD;
6560 PRINT #1,TAB(95);
6570 PRINT #1,"(TOTALS TO DATE)"
6580 PRINT #1,""
6590 PRINT #1,""
6600 PRINT #1,""
6610 PRINT #1,TAB(50);"CALCULATED UNIT COST RATES"
6620 PRINT #1,"DESCRIPTION";TAB(30);"PRIOR YEAR";TAB(60);"THIS YEAR";TAB(90);"TO
TALS TO DATE"
6630 PRINT #1,"-----------------------";TAB(30);"-----------------------";TAB(60);"---
-----------------";TAB(90);"-----------------------"
6640 PRINT #1,"TOTAL COST";TAB(30);
6650 MG=MA+MB+MC+MD
6660 PRINT #1,USING TR$;MG;
6670 PRINT #1,TAB(60);
6680 TDG=TDA+TDB+TDC+TDD
6690 PRINT #1,USING TR$;TDG;
6700 PRINT #1,TAB(90);
6710 TT=MG+TDG
6720 PRINT #1,USING TR$;TT
6730 PRINT #1,"TOTAL PROD. HOURS";TAB(37);
6740 PRINT #1,ME;
6750 PRINT #1,TAB(67);
6760 PRINT #1,TDE;
6770 PRINT #1,TAB(97);
6780 YY=ME+TDE
6790 PRINT #1,YY
6800 PRINT #1,"TOTAL COST/PROD. HOURS";TAB(33);
6810 UU=MG/ME
6820 PRINT #1,USING UA$;UU;
6830 PRINT #1,TAB(63);
6840 YY=TDG/TDE
6850 PRINT #1,USING UA$;YY;
6860 PRINT #1,TAB(93);
6870 PP=(MG+TDG)/(ME+TDE)
6880 PRINT #1,USING UA$;PP
6890 PRINT #1,"TOTAL HOURS";TAB(37);
6900 MH=ME+MF
6910 PRINT #1,MH;
6920 PRINT #1,TAB(67);
6930 TDH=TDE+TDF
6940 PRINT #1,TDH;
6950 PRINT #1,TAB(97);
6960 II=MH+TDH
6970 PRINT #1,II
6980 PRINT #1,"TOTAL COST/TOTAL HOURS";TAB(33);
6990 OA=MG/MH
7000 PRINT #1,USING UA$;OA;
7010 PRINT #1,TAB(63);
```

Figure 12.7 *Continued*

```
7020 OB=TDG/TDH
7030 PRINT #1,USING UA$;OB;
7040 PRINT #1,TAB(93);
7050 OC=TT/II
7060 PRINT #1,USING UA$;OC
7070 CLOSE #1
7080 PRINT ""
7090 PRINT "THE REPORT IS NOW PRINTED....
7100 PRINT ""
7110 INPUT "ENTER C TO RETURN TO LIST/PRINT OPTIONS ";C$
7120 GOTO 3620
7130 CLS
7140 PRINT "PLEASE WAIT ... THE DATA DISK IS BEING READ
7150 OPEN "NUMBER.DAT" AS #1 LEN=6
7160 FIELD #1, 6 AS Z$
7170 GET #1,1
7180 ZA=VAL(Z$)
7190 CLOSE #1
7200 PRINT "YOU HAVE THE FOLLOWING EQUIPMENT CLASSIFICATIONS ON THE DATA DISK
7210 PRINT "CLASS. NO. ";TAB(15);"CLASSIFICATION NAME ";TAB(65);"NO.OF ACCOUNTS"

7220 PRINT "----------- ";TAB(15);"------------------- ";TAB(65);"----------------"

7230 OPEN "NUMBER.DAT" AS #1 LEN=6
7240 FIELD #1, 6 AS Z$
7250 GET #1,1
7260 ZA$=Z$
7270 CLOSE #1
7280 Z=VAL(ZA$)
7290 FOR N=1 TO Z
7300 OPEN "CLASS.DAT" AS #1 LEN=50
7310 FIELD #1, 45 AS CC$, 5 AS WI$
7320 GET #1,N
7330 NA$=CC$
7340 NW$=WI$
7350 CLOSE #1
7360 PRINT TAB(3);N;TAB(15);NA$;TAB(70);NW$
7370 NEXT N
7380 PRINT ""
7390 PRINT "ENTER EQUIPMENT CLASS NO.: TO LIST THE EQUIPMENT NAMES/ACCOUNTS FOR
7400 PRINT "                           A GIVEN EQUIPMENT CLASSIFICATION
7410 PRINT "ENTER P                  : TO RETURN TO THE PROGRAM OPTIONS
7420 INPUT C$
7430 IF (C$="P") THEN 400
7440 R=VAL(C$)
7450 FOR J= 1 TO Z
7460 IF (R=J) THEN 7480
7470 NEXT J
7480 PRINT ""
7490 OPEN "CLASS.DAT" AS #1 LEN=50
7500 FIELD #1, 45 AS CC$, 5 AS WI$
7510 GET #1,R
7520 MM$=CC$
7530 NN$=WI$
7540 CLOSE #1
7550 K=VAL(NN$)
7560 TR$="$$###,#####.##"
7570 CLS
7580 PRINT "EQ.NO. ";TAB(8);"EQUIPMENT NAME/ACCOUNT";TAB(50);"INITIAL EQUIPMENT C
OST
```

Figure 12.7 *Continued*

```
7590 PRINT "--------";TAB(8);"------------------------------";TAB(50);"-------------
----"
7600 TAW$="W"
7610 TAX$=STR$(R)
7620 TR$="$$###,#####.##"
7630 TAZ$=TAW$ +TAX$
7640 OPEN TAZ$ AS #1 LEN=90
7650 FIELD #1, 5 AS RX$, 40 AS QN$, 20 AS QC$, 5 AS QL$, 20 AS QD$
7660 FOR T=1 TO K
7670 GET #1,T
7680 QC=VAL(QC$)
7690 PRINT T;TAB(7);
7700 PRINT QN$;
7710 PRINT TAB(50);
7720 PRINT USING TR$;QC
7730 NEXT T
7740 CLOSE #1
7750 PRINT ""
7760 RETURN
7770 CLS
7780 PRINT "THIS IS THE END OF THE PROGRAM"
7790 KEY ON
7800 END
```

Figure 12.7 *Continued*

Once the user has set up an equipment name/account on the data disk, he can elect to enter cost or usage data for a defined equipment name/ account. This is done by inputting an H when requested in line 220. The program then branches to line 2430.

The program is designed with the intent that the user would enter equipment cost or usage data on a weekly basis (although this is not necessary). In order to enter data, the user must first identify the equipment name/account. This is done by having line 2500 branch to the subroutine starting in line 210. This subroutine enables the user to select an equipment classification and then equipment name/account. The equipment name/ account is identified via input to line 2680.

After selecting the equipment name/account, the data disk is read and the initial equipment setup is shown to the user on the monitor. This is done in lines 2780 through 2990. Assuming the correct equipment name/ account has been selected, the user is requested to input the date of the record being re-entered, the maintenance costs, the repair cost, the depreciation cost, and the productive and stand-by hours of usage. After receiving the data, the program then stores the inputted data record on the data disk. This is done via the data filing programming in lines 3320 through 3560. The data file name that receives the data is named/identified via the variables R and E in lines 3430 and 3440. R corresponds to the equipment classification number and E corresponds to the equipment name/account number. Using this system of naming the data file, each equipment name/account is given its own name. The individual records (if one is made each week, there would be 52 records on a data disk) are kept in a specific data file. Note that when entering costs or hourly usage for a specific record, the user can input a 0 if there is no activity in the period.

After the data/record is stored in a data file (via lines 3320 through 3560), the user is informed that the data is stored via line 3580. The program then returns the user to the program options. An overview flowchart of the program is illustrated in Figure 12.8.

Once the user has initialized an equipment name/account, and entered cost or usage data for the equipment, he can then use the program to print an hourly rate report for a piece of equipment. An example of such a report is illustrated in Figure 12.9.

The user is given the opportunity to print a report for a given equipment name/account by entering an L in line 170. The program then branches to line 3620.

To print a report for a given equipment name/account, the user must first locate/identify the equipment name/account. This is done via the same process used to locate/identify an equipment name/account. Via line 3670, the program branches to subroutine 7140. Using this subroutine and the programming in lines 7200 through 7380, the equipment name/account is located and read from the data disk. The initial equipment setup is printed on the monitor to enable the user to determine if he has identified the proper account.

If the user indicates that the correct equipment name/account has been selected, the program proceeds to print the equipment report (an example of which is illustrated in Figure 12.9).

The printing of the report is achieved via the programming in lines 7580 through 7760. The printer is activated in line 7580. After printing the report, the program returns the user back to the program options.

The equipment report illustrated in Figure 12.9 serves several purposes. For one, the constructor can use the report to determine the cost of a given piece of equipment as a function of time. In this manner the constructor can determine when and if a piece of equipment should be replaced or overhauled. The calculating and printing of the hourly cost of a piece of equipment as a function of time also enables the user to prepare an equipment estimate for a proposed project.

The equipment management/estimating program illustrated makes considerable use of data file programming. By expanding the program, the user can use the program to plot cost curves for the equipment as a function

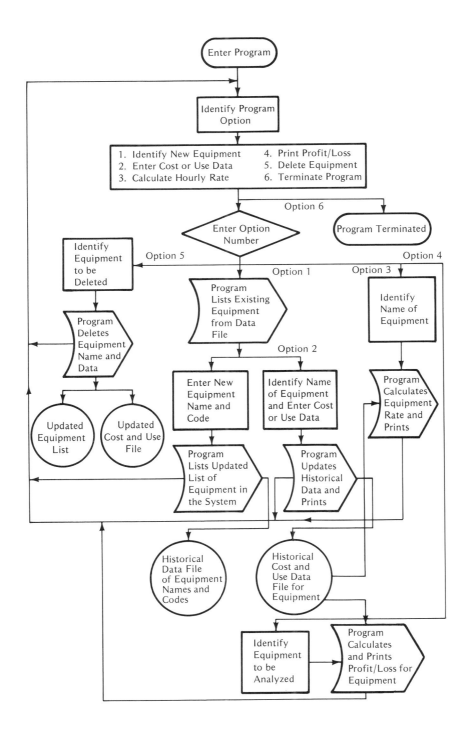

Figure 12.8 Flowchart of computer program for equipment accounting.

of time, set out a preventive maintenance program, etc. Using programs such as the one illustrated, the tedious but important task of keeping track of the real cost of owned equipment becomes a more manageable task.

```
                            SUMMARY OF RECORDS
                            TOWER
                            YEAR=1985
EQUIPMENT COST=      $56,500.00
ESTIMATED DEPRECIATION LIFE=  12
EST. ANNUAL DEPR. CHARGE=       $4,500.00
```

```
                    SUMMARY OF RECORDS AND TOTALS
                    NO. OF RECORDS THIS YEAR=  3
```

PRIOR YEAR TOTALS:

DATE OF RECORD	REG. MAINTENANCE	IRREG.MAINTENANCE	REPAIR COSTS	DEPRECIATION	PRODUCTIVE HOURS	STAND-BY HOURS
	$1,200.00	$1,450.00	$2,540.00	$1,500.00	345	565

RECORDS ENTERED THIS YEAR:

DATE OF RECORD	REG. MAINTENANCE	IRREG.MAINTENANCE	REPAIR COSTS	DEPRECIATION	PRODUCTIVE HOURS	STAND-BY HOURS
4-5-85	$350.00	$540.00	$350.00	$400.00	55	65
5-14-85	$545.00	$450.00	$350.00	$860.00	65	45
714-85	$565.00	$1,450.00	$3,445.00	$1,255.00	23	43
TOTALS THIS YEAR	$1,460.00	$2,440.00	$4,145.00	$2,515.00	143	153
TOTALS TO DATE	$2,660.00	$3,890.00	$6,685.00	$4,015.00	488	718

COST/PROD.HOURS	$3.48	$4.20	$7.36	$4.35	(PRIOR YEARS)
	$10.21	$17.06	$28.99	$17.59	(THIS YEAR)
	$5.45	$7.97	$13.70	$8.23	(TOTALS TO DATE)
COST/TOTAL HOURS	$1.32	$1.59	$2.79	$1.65	(PRIOR YEARS)
	$4.93	$8.24	$14.00	$8.50	(THIS YEAR)
	$2.21	$3.23	$5.54	$3.33	(TOTALS TO DATE)

```
                        CALCULATED UNIT COST RATES
```

DESCRIPTION	PRIOR YEAR	THIS YEAR	TOTALS TO DATE
TOTAL COST	$6,690.00	$10,560.00	$17,250.00
TOTAL PROD. HOURS	345	143	488
TOTAL COST/PROD. HOURS	$19.39	$73.85	$35.35
TOTAL HOURS	910	296	1206
TOTAL COST/TOTAL HOURS	$7.35	$35.68	$14.30

Figure 12.9   Example output from equipment accounting computer program.

```
EQUIPMENT NAME=                    TOWER
YEAR=                             1985
EQUIPMENT COST=             $56,500.00
EST. DEPR. LIFE=                    12
EST.ANNUAL DEPR.=           $4,500.00
NO. OF RECORDS THIS YEAR=           3

DESCRIPTION        PRIOR YEARS      THIS YEAR         TOTALS
---------------    ---------------  ---------------   ---------------

REG. MAINT.          $1,200.00       $1,460.00       $2,660.00
IRREG.MAINT.         $1,450.00       $2,440.00       $3,890.00
REPAIR COST          $2,540.00       $4,145.00       $6,685.00
DEPRECTION           $1,500.00       $2,515.00       $4,015.00
PROD. HOURS            345             143             488
STAND-BY HOURS         565             153             718



EQUIPMENT NAME=                    TOWER
YEAR=                             1985
EQUIPMENT COST=             $56,500.00
EST. DEPR. LIFE=                    12
EST. ANNUAL DEPR.=          $4,500.00
NO. OF RECORDS THIS YEAR=           3

                       CALCULATED UNIT COST RATS
DESCRIPTION         PRIOR YEAR       THIS YEAR       TOTALS TO DATE
---------------     ---------------  ---------------  --------- -----

TOTAL COST           $6,690.00       $10,560.00      $17,250.00
TOTAL PROD. HOURS      345             143             488
TOTAL $/PROD.HOURS   $19.39          $73.85          $35.35
TOTAL HOURS            910             296            1206
TOTAL $/TOT.HRS       $7.35          $35.68          $14.30
```

Figure 12.9 *Continued*

13: Bidding Strategy Applications

INTRODUCTION

Many management practices (e.g., the performance of general ledger accounting, job cost accounting, scheduling techniques such as the critical-path method, and the capturing and structuring of historical estimating data) should be performed by a construction firm even if the firm does not have access to a computer. These tasks/practices are critical to the firm. One has a difficult time arguing that the cost or time of performing these tasks exceeds the benefit, independent of whether or not the firm utilizes a computer. The use of a computer merely serves to increase the already favorable benefit/cost ratio of these tasks.

There are some low-priority management practices that may prove to have a cost or time associated with them that exceeds the benefit of their use by the construction firm. This is especially true if the "number crunching" and "number storing" associated with these low-priority techniques are performed manually.

One seldom mentioned benefit of a computer is that it may make an otherwise unfeasible technique (owing to its cost being greater than its benefit) in fact feasible. One example of such a technique for use by the construction firm is bidding strategy.

As discussed in this chapter, bidding strategy is a probabilistic model/ technique that relates to a firm developing a bidding strategy based on the calculation of the probabilities of one or more competitors' bids.

Bidding strategy has two apparent problems to the "real-world" constructor. For one, the entire concept or process is based on the premise that the contractor is able to accurately estimate his own costs for a project, and that the competitors of the contractor can accurately estimate the cost of their work and that they follow a definitive pattern in their bidding process.

Perhaps a bigger difficulty of bidding strategy relates to the amount of data collection, data filing, and calculations that is required to effectively implement the technique. If this data collection, filing, and calculating is performed manually, it is questionable if the benefit of using the bidding strategy model outweighs the time and cost of using the technique for the average-sized construction firm.

While perhaps not all that beneficial as a manual technique, the use of a computer to store and calculate the substantial amount of data that is part of the technique may result in bidding strategy being practical for even the small construction firm. The vast amount of memory storage of the computer, coupled with its speed of processing calculations (e.g., probability calculations), results in bidding strategy being a feasible and perhaps profitable tool available to the computer-age construction firm.

Before illustrating bidding strategy computer routines and printouts, we will first present the bidding strategy model via manual calculations. This will enhance our understanding of the computerized bidding strategy model.

BID STRATEGY

The optimal profit that a contractor should add to his bid proposal is partly determined by the contractor competition for the project. This is particularly true in the competitive bidding procedure. A contractor's winning or losing a project contract often depends on how well he has formulated his information about his competitors. A contractor must always search for ways to gain an advantage over his competitors. This includes using new and cheaper construction methods and management practices. One of the ways a contractor might gain an advantage over his competitors is to formulate bidding information about their past performances. The contractor can formulate this information into some type of bid strategy. For our purpose we will consider bid strategy as a combination of various bidding rules a contractor follows for bidding, based on a formulation of information. In our case the information will be past bids of contractors. Formulating the information is often referred to as determining a bidding model.

The profit in a contractor's bid for a particular project is the amount of money he intends to make on the project. For purposes of discussion, let us assume that the contractor's estimated cost of bidding a project is indeed accurate and is equal to his actual building cost. Therefore, on a particular project for which a contractor submits a bid, he will either receive his desired profit (assuming he receives the project) or will receive zero profit (assuming he does not receive the project). It becomes clear that a contractor's long-term profit (average profit over a long period of time) will not only be a function of the profit within his bid but also a function of how many projects he receives from the number of projects for which he submits bids.

Owing to the possibility of two levels of profit (depending on whether a contractor wins or loses the contract for a project), it is necessary to define two different types of profit. A contractor's immediate profit on a project is defined as the difference between the contractor's bid price for the project and the actual cost of building it. If a contractor's estimated cost of a project is equal to its actual cost, then the contrator's immediate profit for the project is also equal to the difference between the contractor's bid price and his estimated cost. If we let X equal the bid and A equal the contractor's actual cost of building the project, then the contractor's immediate profit (IP) on the project is given by the following formula.

$$IP = X - A$$

If a contractor submits a high bid (a large included profit) his chance for receiving the contract in a competitive bidding environment is very small. As he reduces his profit, and therefore his bid, his chance for receiving the contract increases.

If we assign probabilities of receiving the contract to the various bids the contractor considers feasible, we may calculate an expected profit for the various bids. The expected profit of a particular bid on a proposed project is defined as the immediate profit of the bid for the project multiplied by the probability of the bid winning the contract. In a competitive bidding environment, winning the contract implies that the bid is the lowest responsible bid. If we let p represent the probability, the expected profit (EP) of the bid is given by the following formula.

$$EP = p(X - A) = p(IP)$$

Assume a contractor is interested in a certain project, called project ABC. Assume his estimated cost of the project is equal to the actual cost of the project, which is $20,000. The contractor has a choice of submitting three different bids for the project. These bids and their probabilities of winning the project contract are as follows.

Bid Name	Amount	Probability of Winning Contract
B_1	$30,000	0.1
B_2	$25,000	0.5
B_3	$22,000	0.8

The probabilities shown are estimated from the contractor's evaluation of the chance of being the lowest bidder. Of course, bid B_1 has the highest immediate profit ($30,000 − $20,000, or $10,000). However, because of B_1's low probability of winning the contract, it may not be the best bid to make to maximize overall profits. The calculation of the various bids' expected profits is as follows.

Bid Name	Probability × Immediate Profit	Expected Profit
B_1	0.1(10,000)	$1,000
B_2	0.5(5,000)	$2,500
B_3	0.8(2,000)	$1,600

It is observed that bid B_2 has the highest expected profit. Expected profit may be conceived as representing the average profit a contractor can expect to make per project, if he were to submit the same bid to a large number of similar projects. Expected profit does not represent the actual profit the contractor expects to make on a project. In the problem described, the contractor would either make a profit of 0 or a profit of $5000 if he submitted bid B_2, whereas the expected profit is calculated to be $2500. Since immediate profit does not recognize the probability of a bid winning a contract, expected profit becomes the more informative profit. Therefore, because most contractors have an objective of maximizing total long-term profits, expected profit calculations are more meaningful than immediate profit calculations, and should be used to determine the optimal profit and bid. In the example described, therefore, the contractor should submit bid B_2.

By using the discussed expected profit concept in addition to information concerning the past bids of his competition, a contractor can develop a bidding strategy that may optimize his profits. At a competitive bid letting, it is common practice to announce openly all the bids of the respective contractors. The intelligent contractor can record the bid prices of the contractors, along with his own bid and his own estimate of the contractors and his own estimate of the project's cost. If it is possible for him to learn the actual cost of the project (either through building it himself or through information obtained from others), he should also record this information. The intelligent contractor should also take note of any special conditions, such as knowledge about a particular contractor's need for work. Having recorded this past bidding information about his competitors, the contractor may formulate the information into a bidding strategy for future projects. Naturally, the more information the contractor has available, and the more accurate his information, the better is his chance of having his strategy prove successful.

When a contractor is bidding on a project in a competitive bidding atmosphere, he generally finds himself in one of the following states regarding his competition. In the most deterministic or ideal state, the contractor knows who his competitors are, thus he also knows the number of competitors. A somewhat infrequent situation occurs when the contractor knows how many competitors there are for the project, but does not know who they are. Since there is less information available in this case than in the case of known competitors, the bidding strategy will be less deterministic and, therefore, less reliable. A less deterministic and less desirable situation occurs when the contractor knows neither who the competition is nor how many competitors there are. The bidding strategy for this situation will be less reliable than the previous two cases, owing to the lack of more complete information.

Consider the case in which the contractor knows who his competitors will be for a competitive bid project letting. In particular, let us assume that the contractor knows he is only going to be competing against one contractor (contractor XYZ). Assume the contractor has bid against contractor XYZ many times in the past and has kept records of contractor XYZ's bids. For each of the projects, the contractor has also recorded his estimated cost. Having this information, the contractor can calculate the ratio of contractor XYZ's bid price to the contractor's cost estimate for the various projects. The contractor's recorded information is summarized in the following tables.

Having the frequency table of the various ratios, the contractor can calculate the probability of each bid ratio by dividing each bid's frequency of occurrence by the total number of bid occurrences. For example, the probability of a ratio of 1.0 is 7/70, or 0.10. Probabilities of the other ratios are as follows. The probabilities are rounded off to two decimal places.

Having calculated the probabilities of the various ratios, the contractor can calculate the probability of his various bids being lower than contractor XYZ's bids. To eliminate theoretical bid ties, it will be assumed that the contractor will bid different ratios than the computed ratios for contractor

Contractor XYZ's Bid/Contractor's Estimated Job Cost	Frequency of Occurrence
0.8	1
0.9	2
1.0	7
1.1	12
1.2	21
1.3	18
1.4	7
1.5	2
	Total = 70

Contractor XYZ's Bid/Contractor's Estimated Job Cost	Probability
0.8	0.01
0.9	0.03
1.0	0.10
1.1	0.17
1.2	0.30
1.3	0.26
1.4	0.10
1.5	0.03
	Total = 1.00

XYZ. For example, to be lower than contractor XYZ's bid-to-cost ratio of 1.10, the contractor might make a bid with a bid-to-cost ratio of 1.05. Let us assume that the contractor decides upon the following bid-to-estimated-cost ratios as being feasible.

Contractor's Bid/ Contractor's Estimated Job Cost	Probability That Contractor's Bid Is Lower Than Bid of XYZ
0.75	1.00
0.85	0.99
0.95	0.96
1.05	0.86
1.15	0.69
1.25	0.69
1.35	0.13
1.45	0.03
1.55	0.00

The calculated probability of being the lowest bidder, or winning the contract, for any particular bid ratio is found by merely summing all the probabilities of contractor XYZ's ratio being higher than the particular bid. For example, if the contractor is to make a bid with a bid-to-estimated-cost ratio of 1.35, the probability of winning would be the sum of 0.03 (the probability that the ratio of XYZ's bid to the contractor's estimated cost is 1.5) and 0.10 (the probability that the ratio of XYZ's bid to the contractor's estimated cost is 1.4). Thus, the probability of a contractor bid with a bid-to-estimated-cost ratio of 1.35 winning the contract is 0.13.

The contractor may now use this information to form a bidding strategy for bidding against contractor XYZ. He may do this by calculating the expected profits of his possible feasible bids. Expected profit of a bid was defined as the immediate profit of the bid multiplied by the bid's probability of winning the project contracted. Immediate profit for a bid was defined as the bid price minus the actual cost of the project. Let us assume that the contractor's estimated cost of the project is equal to the actual cost. Ideally, the contractor would like his estimator to estimate the actual cost correctly, but this is not always the case. However, owing to the lack of information about the actual cost of the project, let us assume that the estimated cost of the project is the actual cost. The immediate profit for each of the contractor's possible bids then becomes equal to the bid price minus the estimated cost of the project. The bid prices are given in terms of the estimated cost of the project. Letting c equal the estimated cost of the project, the immediate profit of the contractor's possible bids may be stated in terms of c. The immediate profit of the bids may be found by merely subtracting $1.0c$ (the estimated cost of the job) from the respective bids. For example, for a bid of $1.35c$, the immediate profit is $1.35c - 1.0c$, or $0.35c$. The expected profit of the possible bids may then be found by multiplying their immediate profits by their respective probabilities of winning the project against contractor XYZ. For a bid of $1.35c$, the probability of winning against contractor XYZ was calculated as 0.13; therefore, the expected profit is 0.13 multiplied by $0.35c$, or $0.0455c$. The expected profits for the contractor's feasible bids are as follows. They are rounded off to three decimal places.

Contractor Bid	Expected Profit of Bid When Bidding Against Contractor XYZ
$0.75c$	$1.00(-0.25c) = -0.250c$
$0.85c$	$0.99(-0.15c) = -0.149c$
$0.95c$	$0.96(-0.05c) = -0.048c$
$1.05c$	$0.86(+0.05c) = +0.043c$
$1.15c$	$0.69(+0.15c) = +0.104c$
$1.25c$	$0.39(+0.25c) = +0.098c$
$1.35c$	$0.13(+0.35c) = +0.046c$
$1.45c$	$0.03(+0.45c) = +0.014c$
$1.55c$	$0.00(+0.55c) = +0.000c$

It is observed that the bid of 1.15 multiplied by the estimated cost of the project yields the maximum expected profit of $0.104c$. This implies that when bidding against contractor XYZ, over time it would be most profitable for the contractor to submit a bid with a bid-to-estimated-cost ratio of 1.15. For example, if the estimated project cost was $100,000, the bid proposal should be $115,000. Considering the possibility of not winning the contract, the contractor's expected profit for such a bid would be $10,400. Of course, the contractor should keep his bidding information about contractor XYZ current. The best bid ratio for the contractor to use in a future project against contractor XYZ may change, depending upon contractor XYZ's bidding performances.

If a contractor was bidding against several known competitors rather than only contractor XYZ, he could formulate his bidding strategy in a similar manner. Let us assume that a contractor knows he will be bidding against two known competitors on an upcoming job, contractor XYZ and contractor UVW. Assume the contractor's information about contractor XYZ is the same as in the previous example. Let us assume that the contractor has also gathered information about contractor UVW's bidding performances and has calculated the probability of his bids being lower than contractor UVW's. This information along with the probabilities of winning versus contractor XYZ are as follows.

Contractor's Bid/Contractor's Estimated Job Cost	Probability of Contractor's Bid Winning Versus	
	XYZ	UVW
0.75	1.00	1.00
0.85	0.99	1.00
0.95	0.96	0.98
1.05	0.86	0.80
1.15	0.69	0.70
1.25	0.39	0.60
1.35	0.13	0.27
1.45	0.03	0.09
1.55	0.00	0.00

To calculate the expected profit of the feasible bids, the contractor must determine the probability that his bid is lower than both contractor XYZ's and contractor UVW's bids. Both of these events are independent. The probability of being lower than XYZ is independent of the probability of being lower than UVW. From probability theory, one may show that the probability of the occurrence of joint events, which are independent, is given by the product of their respective probabilities. For example, the probability that the contractor's bid of $1.15c$ wins (is lower than XYZ's and UVW's bids) is the product of 0.69 and 0.70, or 0.483. Having found the bid's probability of winning the contract, its expected profit is calculated as 0.483 multiplied by its immediate profit of $0.15c$, resulting in an expected profit of $0.07245c$. The expected profits for all the bids are calculated as follows. They are rounded off to three decimal places.

Contractor's Bid	Expected Profit
$0.75c$	$1.00(1.00)\,(-0.25c) = -0.250c$
$0.85c$	$0.99(1.00)\,(-0.15c) = -0.149c$
$0.95c$	$0.96(0.98)\,(-0.05c) = -0.047c$
$1.05c$	$0.86(0.80)\,(+0.05c) = +0.034c$
$1.15c$	$0.69(0.70)\,(+0.15c) = +0.072c$
$1.25c$	$0.39(0.60)\,(+0.25c) = +0.059c$
$1.35c$	$0.13(0.27)\,(+0.35c) = +0.012c$
$1.45c$	$0.03(0.09)\,(+0.45c) = +0.001c$
$1.55c$	$0.00(0.00)\,(+0.55c) = +0.000c$

Note that the contractor should submit a bid that has a ratio of bid cost to estimated project cost of 1.15. Thus, the contractor should make the same bid he should have made when bidding against only contractor XYZ. However, the expected profit of $0.072c$, when bidding against the two contractors, is less than the expected profit of $0.104c$, when bidding against the single contractor. This is because of the added competition. The more competition a contractor has, the less likely he is to receive the contract. The problem of more than two known competitors is handled in a similar manner. We should not conclude that the optimal bid remains unchanged with increasing competition. In general, the optimal bid will have a tendency to decrease with an increasing number of competitors.

If the contractor knows the number of his competitors but does not know who they are, he must make some adjustments to his bid strategy. Since he has a less deterministic problem than the problem of known competitors, his bidding strategy will be less reliable. The best the contractor can do when faced with the problem of a given number of unknown competitors is to assume that they are average. The contractor collects information from all the contractors he has bid against, and totals the information to derive a theoretical average competitor. Having this average competitor information, the contractor can compute the probabilities that his feasible bids are lower than the average contractor's bids. Let us assume that a contractor has done this and has achieved the following results.

Average Contractor's Bid/Contractor's Estimated Job Cost	Probability That Contractor's Bid Is Lower Than Bid of Average Competitor
0.75	1.00
0.85	0.98
0.95	0.95
1.05	0.85
1.15	0.60
1.25	0.40
1.35	0.20
1.45	0.05
1.55	0.00

Knowing the probabilities of winning against the average bidder and knowing the number of competitors for a particular project, the contractor may now determine his best bid. The probability of having a bid lower than several competitors is the product of the probabilities of the bid being lower than the individual average competitors. The probability of a bid being lower than n competitor's bids may be found by raising the probability of being lower than the average competitor to the nth power. For instance, in the described example, let us assume that the contractor is bidding against five unknown competitors. The probability of the contractor's bid of $1.15c$ being lower than all five competitors is $(0.60)^5$, or approximately 0.078. The expected profit of the bid of $1.15c$ is, therefore, 0.078 multiplied by $0.15c$, or $0.012c$. The expected profits for the contractor's feasible bids against five unknown competitors are as follows. The calculations are rounded off to three decimal places. (See page 272.)

It is observed that the bid of $1.05c$ has the highest expected profit ($0.022c$). Obviously, as the number of competitors increases, the expected profit of a particular bid by the contractor decreases. Although it is not as obvious, the actual best bid often decreases with an increasing number of competitors. Using the information about an average bidder, the contractor's best bid and its expected profit for various numbers of competitors are shown overleaf.

Note that the expected profit of the best bid decreases as the number of competitors increases. It is also noted that the best bid ratio drops as

Contractor's Bid	Expected Profit of Contractor's Bids versus Five Unknown Competitors
$0.75c$	$(1.00)^5(-0.25c) = -0.250c$
$0.85c$	$(0.98)^5(-0.15c) = -0.135c$
$0.95c$	$(0.95)^5(-0.05c) = -0.039c$
$1.05c$	$(0.85)^5(+0.05c) = +0.022c$
$1.15c$	$(0.60)^5(+0.15c) = +0.012c$
$1.25c$	$(0.40)^5(+0.25c) = +0.003c$
$1.35c$	$(0.20)^5(+0.35c) = +0.000c$
$1.45c$	$(0.00)^5(+0.45c) = +0.000c$
$1.55c$	$(0.00)^5(+0.55c) = +0.000c$

Number of Competitors	Contractor's Bid with Greatest Expected Profit	Expected Profit of Bid
1	$1.25c$	$+0.100c$
2	$1.15c$	$+0.054c$
3	$1.15c$	$+0.032c$
4	$1.05c$	$+0.026c$
5	$1.05c$	$+0.022c$
6	$1.05c$	$+0.019c$

the number of competitors increases. This happens because as the number of competitors increases, it becomes more difficult for the contractor to submit the low bid, and he is forced to lower his profit and, therefore, his ratio of bid price to estimated project cost. As the number of competitors becomes very large, one would expect the contractor's expected profit on his optimal bid to approach zero. Also, his best bid ratio would approach $1.0c$.

A contractor is often confronted with the problem of bidding against an unknown number of unidentified competitors. Since the contractor's information is limited, the reliability of his bidding strategy will be limited. If possible, the contractor should estimate the number of competitors and proceed as if they were all average. Using his information about an average bidder, the contractor may then determine his best bid. It should be observed that the best bid does not change rapidly with the number of competitors. The expected profit changes rapidly with the number of competitors; however, the best bid is somewhat stationary. Therefore, if the contractor can even approximate the number of competitors, he can probably determine the best bid. Another alternative is to use past bidding information to determine the probability of the various numbers of expected competitors. The mathematics of the bidding strategy model based on this added information becomes more complex.

In the bidding strategy models discussed, it was assumed that a contractor considered only a finite number of bids as being feasible. In reality, the number of feasible bids is infinite. For example, when attempting to submit a bid lower than a competing contractor's bid-to-cost ratio of 1.15, the contractor could use a bid-to-cost ratio of 1.14, 1.135, 1.13, 1.2, 1.1, etc. The bidding models discussed may be formulated to account for unlimited numbers of feasible contractor bids. However, to avoid the mathematical operation of integration that would be required to formulate the information, this assumes only finite feasible bids. In view of the type of information that would be required to formulate the infinite feasible contractor bids (a probability function), it is more realistic to consider only finite feasible contractor bids.

In the bidding models discussed, it was assumed that the contractor's estimated cost was equal to his actual cost of building a project. However, this is seldom the case. Several attempts have been made to construct bidding models that account for this fact by assuming a probability distribution for the ratio of estimated to actual cost. Other variables, such as the expected number of competing contractors, have been handled in a similar manner. As one increases the number of variables considered in the bidding model, the mathematics becomes more complex. In fact, the complex nature of the mathematics and the detailed information required for such models often makes their use impractical. The usefulness of bid strategy models depends on cost, benefits, and reliability. The feasibility of any bid strategy model depends on the contractor's ability to gather the information it requires.

The bid strategy models discussed determined the optimal contractor bid for a project as a function of competition on the project. The resulting optimal bid did not reflect other projects and contractor characteristics that affect the determination of the contractor's optimal bid. The models discussed did not consider such things as competition's need for work, the dollar value of the contract, the contractor's need for work, etc. If the contractor knows that a competitor definitely needs work, he must either adjust his competitor's past records, or may even find it advantageous to overlook his competitor's past performances. As with the use of any other construction management tool, a contractor cannot use bid strategy models blindly.

AN EXAMPLE BIDDING STRATEGY
COMPUTER PROGRAM WRITTEN IN BASIC

In this section we will describe a computer program that performs the data storage and calculations described in the preceding section on the theory and application of a bidding strategy model. As is true of programs described in previous chapters, we will focus only on the unique features of the program or aspects of the program that have not been described in previous chapters. The program, as illustrated, is absent good error control routines and user instructions.

The program enables the user to store/keep historical bidding data of the user's competitors and subsequently use the historical data to determine the optimal bids to make to beat the competitor in a bid letting and maximize profits at the same time. The program makes the assumption that the program user/contractor has the objective of being low bid and maximize profits.

The bidding strategy program is illustrated in Figure 13.1. The program is essentially a data base program; i.e., it contains a considerable amount of data filing programming.

The bidding strategy program illustrated in Figure 13.1 consists of three somewhat independent program routines. They are as follows:

1. Inputting of names of competitors; i.e., competing contractor firms.
2. Inputting of a historical bid of the competitor. The program stores the ratio of the competitor's bid divided by the user/contractor's estimated cost for the project.
3. Recalling of previously inputted historical data to calculate the user's/contractor's best bid to make for a given bid letting given the identification of the competitor.

In essence, the program follows the bidding strategy process described in the previous section. The benefit offered the user of the program is the efficient and accurate means of handling the considerable amount of data stored and manipulation that is part of bidding strategy model.

We will now proceed to give an overall description of the program illustrated in Figure 13.1. The program starts with the initializing/dimensioning of program variables in lines 110 through 140. After selecting to RUN the program in lines 160 through 200, the program identifies various variables in lines 230 through 470. These variables are used as data file names in subsequent data filing programming.

```
100 CLS
110 DIM NU(50)
120 DIM NU$(50)
130 DIM B$(51)
140 DIM A$(25)
150 CLS
160 PRINT TAB(15);"ENTER R:   TO RUN THE PROGRAM
170 PRINT ""
180 PRINT TAB(15);"ENTER T:   TO TERMINATE THE PROGRAM
190 PRINT ""
200 INPUT A$
210 IF (A$="R")  THEN 230
220 IF (A$="T")  THEN 4140
230 A$(1)="ONE"
240 A$(2)="TWO"
250 A$(3)="THREE"
260 A$(4)="FOUR"
270 A$(5)="FIVE"
280 A$(6)="SIX"
290 A$(7)="SEVEN"
300 A$(8)="EIGHT"
310 A$(9)="NINE"
320 A$(10)="TEN"
330 A$(11)="ELEVEN"
340 A$(12)="TWELVE"
350 A$(13)="THIRTEEN"
360 A$(14)="FOURTEEN"
370 A$(15)="FIFTEEN"
380 A$(16)="SIXTEEN"
390 A$(17)="SEVENTEEN"
400 A$(18)="EIGHTEEN"
410 A$(19)="NINETEEN"
420 A$(20)="TWENTY"
430 A$(21)="TWENTYONE"
440 A$(22)="TWENTYTWO"
450 A$(23)="TWENTYTHREE"
460 A$(24)="TWENTYFOUR"
470 A$(25)="TWENTYFIVE"
480 CLS
490 PRINT TAB(30);"BIDDING STRATEGY PROGRAM"
500 PRINT ""
510 PRINT ""
520 PRINT TAB(35);"EXECUTION MENU"
530 PRINT ""
540 PRINT ""
550 PRINT TAB(8)
560 PRINT "OPTION 1: (ENTER 1)-THIS OPTION ALLOWS YOU TO IDENTIFY A NEW
570 PRINT "          COMPETITOR NAME FOR WHICH YOU WANT TO COLLECT DATA.
580 PRINT ""
590 PRINT TAB(8)
600 PRINT "OPTION 2: (ENTER 2)-THIS OPTION ALLOWS YOU TO ENTER BIDDING
610 PRINT "          DATA FOR A COMPETITOR IDENTIFIED IN OPTION 1.
620 PRINT ""
630 PRINT TAB(8)
640 PRINT "OPTION 3: (ENTER 3)-THIS OPTION ALLOWS YOU TO DETERMINE YOUR
650 PRINT "          BEST BID AGAINST ONE OR MORE KNOWN COMPETITORS."
660 PRINT ""
670 PRINT TAB(8)
680 PRINT "OPTION 5: (ENTER 5)-THIS RETURNS YOU TO THE MAIN MENU"
690 PRINT ""
700 PRINT TAB(8)
```

Figure 13.1   An Example BASIC program for bidding strategy.

```
710 INPUT "ENTER 1, 2, 3, 4, OR 5 TO IDENTIFY YOUR OPTION ";D$
720 IF (D$="1") THEN 800
730 IF (D$="2") THEN 1900
740 IF (D$="3") THEN 4190
750 IF (D$="5") THEN 150
760 CLS
770 PRINT "YOU HAVE MADE AN INPUT ERROR."
780 INPUT "ENTER C TO RETURN TO THE OPTIONS TO REENTER ";C$
790 GOTO 480
800 CLS
810 PRINT "YOU MUST ANSWER A QUESTION REGARDING WHETHER OR NOT THIS IS THE
820 PRINT "FIRST TIME YOU ARE RUNNING THE PROGRAM-THAT IS; IS THIS THE FIRST
830 PRINT "COMPETITOR?"
840 PRINT ""
850 PRINT "[CAUTION]-YOU MUST ANSWER THE FOLLOWING QUESTION CORRECTLY"
860 PRINT "OTHERWISE YOU COULD DAMAGE YOUR PREVIOUSLY ENTERED DATA."
870 PRINT ""
880 PRINT "IF THIS IS THE FIRST COMPETITOR NAME TO BE INPUTED, ENTER (FIRST)
890 PRINT "OR HIT THE RETURN IF THIS IS NOT THE FIRST COMPETITOR NAME.
900 PRINT ""
910 PRINT "ENTER (FIRST)-NO BRACKETS- OR HIT THE RETURN IF THIS IS NOT
920 INPUT "THE FIRST COMPETITOR ";E$
930 IF (E$="FIRST") THEN 950
940 GOTO 1240
950 CLS
960 PRINT "YOU HAVE ENTERED (FIRST)
970 PRINT "[CAUTION]-IF YOU ENTER (FIRST) THIS WILL DISTROY ANY PREVIOUS DATA
980 PRINT "YOU HAVE ON THE DATA DISKETTE"
990 PRINT ""
1000 PRINT "ARE YOU SURE THIS IS THE FIRST COMPETITOR NAME YOU WANT TO ENTER"
1010 PRINT ""
1020 PRINT "ENTER (FIRST)-NO BRACKETS-AGAIN IF THIS IS THE FIRST NAME
1030 PRINT "OR HIT THE RETURN IF THIS IS NOT THE FIRST COMPETITOR NAME
1040 PRINT ""
1050 PRINT "NOW ENTER (FIRST) OR HIT THE RETURN TO ENTER MORE COMPETITOR NAMES"
1060 INPUT F$
1070 IF (F$="FIRST") THEN 1090
1080 GOTO 1240
1090 CLS
1100 CLS
1110 PRINT "PLEASE WAIT WHILE THE DATA FILES ARE INITIALIZED..."
1120 OPEN "UNT.BAS" AS #1 LEN=5
1130 FIELD #1, 5 AS D$
1140 RSET D$="0"
1150 PUT #1,1
1160 CLOSE #1
1170 OPEN "AVERAGE.BAS" AS #1 LEN=5
1180 FOR K=1 TO 51
1190 FIELD #1, 5 AS B$(K)
1200 B$(K)="0"
1210 PUT #1,K
1220 NEXT K
1230 CLOSE #1
1240 GOSUB 1550
1250 CLS
1260 PRINT "YOU NOW HAVE STORED INFORMATION ABOUT ";DD;" COMPETITORS"
1270 PRINT ""
1280 PRINT "YOU NOW HAVE THE FOLLOWING OPTIONS"
1290 PRINT ""
1300 PRINT "ENTER M: TO ENTER ANOTHER COMPETITOR NAME
```

Figure 13.1 *Continued*

```
1310 PRINT ""
1320 PRINT "ENTER E: TO RETURN TO THE PROGRAM EXECUTION OPTIONS
1330 PRINT ""
1340 INPUT V$
1350 IF (V$="M") THEN 1240
1360 IF (V$="E") THEN 480
1370 CLS
1380 PRINT "YOU HAVE PREVIOUSLY ENTERED ";DD;"COMPETITOR NAMES"
1390 IF (DD=0) THEN 1510
1400 PRINT "THEY ARE AS FOLLOWS:"
1410 PRINT ""
1420 PRINT TAB(5);"NUMBER/CODE";TAB(20);"COMPETITOR NAME"
1430 PRINT TAB(5);"-----------";TAB(20);"----------------"
1440 FOR J=1 TO DD
1450 OPEN "NAMES.BAS" AS #1 LEN=45
1460 FIELD #1, 45 AS NA$(J)
1470 GET #1,J
1480 CLOSE #1
1490 PRINT TAB(10);J;TAB(20);NA$(J)
1500 NEXT J
1510 PRINT ""
1520 PRINT "ENTER C TO CONTINUE"
1530 INPUT C$
1540 RETURN
1550 PRINT ""
1560 OPEN "UNT.BAS" AS #1 LEN=5
1570 FIELD #1, 5 AS DE$
1580 GET #1,1
1590 CLOSE #1
1600 DD=VAL(DE$)
1610 GOSUB 1370
1620 DD=DD+1
1630 CLS
1640 PRINT "ENTER THE NAME OF THE FIRM NOW"
1650 INPUT NA$(DD)
1660 CLS
1670 OPEN "NAMES.BAS" AS #1 LEN=45
1680 FIELD #1, 45 AS NN$
1690 PRINT ""
1700 LSET NN$=NA$(DD)
1710 PUT #1,DD
1720 CLOSE #1
1730 DF$=STR$(DD)
1740 OPEN "UNT.BAS" AS #1 LEN=5
1750 FIELD #1, 5 AS DE$
1760 RSET DE$=DF$
1770 PUT #1,1
1780 CLOSE #1
1790 GOSUB 3150
1800 FIELD #1, 5 AS CA$
1810 RSET CA$="0"
1820 PUT #1,51
1830 FOR J=1 TO 50
1840 FIELD #1, 5 AS CA$
1850 RSET CA$="0"
1860 PUT #1,J
1870 NEXT J
1880 CLOSE #1
1890 RETURN
1900 CLS
1910 INPUT "ENTER C TO LIST THE COMPETITOR NAMES YOU HAVE PREVIOUSLY IDENTIFIED
```

Figure 13.1 *Continued*

```
";C$
1920 OPEN "UNT.BAS" AS #1 LEN=5
1930 FIELD #1, 5 AS DE$
1940 GET #1,1
1950 CLOSE #1
1960 CLS
1970 DD=VAL(DE$)
1980 PRINT "YOU HAVE INITIALIZED ";DD;" COMPETITOR NAMES"
1990 PRINT "THE COMPETITOR NAMES ARE AS FOLLOWS:"
2000 PRINT "NUMBER/CODE";TAB(16);"COMPETITOR NAME"
2010 PRINT "------------";TAB(16);"-------------------"
2020 OPEN "NAMES.BAS" AS #1 LEN=45
2030 FOR JJ=1 TO DD
2040 FIELD #1, 45 AS NA$(JJ)
2050 GET #1,JJ
2060 LA$(JJ)=NA$(JJ)
2070 PRINT TAB(5);JJ;TAB(16);NA$(JJ)
2080 NEXT JJ
2090 CLOSE #1
2100 PRINT "ENTER THE NUMBER/CODE OF THE COMPETITOR FOR WHICH YOU WANT TO ENTER
DATA
2110 PRINT "OR ENTER 0 (THE NUMBER) TO RETURN TO THE PROGRAM OPTIONS"
2120 INPUT "ENTER THE NUMBER/CODE OR 0 NOW ";H
2130 HH=H
2140 IF (H=0) THEN 480
2150 FOR L=1 TO DD
2160 IF L=HH THEN 2180
2170 NEXT L
2180 CLS
2190 PRINT "THE COMPETITOR NUMBER/CODE AND NAME YOU HAVE SELECTED IS AS FOLLOWS:
"
2200 PRINT ""
2210 PRINT "NUMBER/CODE    COMPETITOR NAME"
2220 PRINT "-----------    ---------------------"
2230 PRINT TAB(5);HH;TAB(16);LA$(HH)
2240 CLS
2250 PRINT "THE PAST BIDDING DATA YOU HAVE COLLECTED FOR
2260 PRINT LA$(HH)
2270 PRINT "IS AS FOLLOWS:"
2280 PRINT ""
2290 DD=HH
2300 GOSUB 3150
2310 FIELD #1, 5 AS CA$
2320 GET #1,51
2330 CLOSE #1
2340 PRINT "NUMBER OF PAST BIDS YOU HAVE COLLECTED= ";CA$
2350 PRINT ""
2360 GOSUB 3150
2370 FOR BB=1 TO 50
2380 FIELD #1, 5 AS CA$
2390 GET #1,BB
2400 NU$(BB)=CA$
2410 NEXT BB
2420 CLOSE #1
2430 GOSUB 3560
2440 PRINT ""
2450 PRINT "ENTER B: TO INPUT A BID FOR ";LA$(HH)
2460 PRINT "ENTER P: TO RETURN TO THE PROGRAM OPTIONS
2470 INPUT S$
2480 IF (S$="P") THEN 480
2490 CLS
```

Figure 13.1 *Continued*

```
2500 PRINT "YOU WILL NOW BE REQUESTED TO INPUT THE FOLLOWING:
2510 PRINT ""
2520 PRINT "BID MADE BY ";LA$(HH)
2530 PRINT "YOUR ESTIMATED COST FOR THE JOB"
2540 PRINT ""
2550 PRINT "WHEN ENTERING THE AMOUNTS, ENTER NUMBERS BUT DO NOT INPUT A $ SIGN O
R COMMAS
2560 PRINT "BUT DO ENTER THE DECIMAL POINT IN THE PROPER LOCATION."
2570 PRINT ""
2580 PRINT "FOR ";LA$(HH)
2590 INPUT "ENTER THE BID AMOUNT ";BD
2600 PRINT ""
2610 INPUT "NOW ENTER YOUR COST ESTIMATE FOR THE JOB ";CD
2620 CLS
2630 Z$="$$#,#############.##"
2640 CLS
2650 RD=BD/CD
2660 IF (RD>2) THEN 2680
2670 GOTO 2690
2680 RD=2
2690 UI=RD-1
2700 XI=UI*25
2710 YI=XI+25
2720 ZI=INT(YI)
2730 ZI$=STR$(RD)
2740 IZ$=LEFT$(ZI$,5)
2750 PRINT "THE RATIO OF THE BID OF ";LA$(HH)
2760 PRINT "TO YOUR ESTIMATED COST IS EQUAL TO = ";IZ$
2770 PRINT ""
2780 PRINT "ENTER D: TO STORE THIS BID RATIO ON THE DISK
2790 PRINT "ENTER P: TO RETURN TO THE PROGRAM OPTIONS
2800 INPUT EE$
2810 IF (EE$="P") THEN 480
2820 CLS
2830 PRINT "THE BID TO COST RATIO IS NOW STORED
2840 PRINT "THE UPDATED PAST BIDS OF ";LA$(HH);" ARE AS FOLLOWS:
2850 GOSUB 3150
2860 FIELD #1, 5 AS CA$
2870 GET #1,ZI
2880 CB$=CA$
2890 CLOSE #1
2900 CB=VAL(CB$)
2910 CB=CB+1
2920 CA$=STR$(CB)
2930 NU$(ZI)=CA$
2940 GOSUB 3150
2950 FIELD #1, 5 AS D$
2960 RSET D$=CA$
2970 PUT #1,ZI
2980 CLOSE #1
2990 GOSUB 3560
3000 PRINT ""
3010 GOSUB 3150
3020 FIELD #1, 5 AS BA$
3030 GET #1,51
3040 BB$=BA$
3050 BB=VAL(BB$)
3060 BB=BB+1
3070 BB$=STR$(BB)
3080 RSET BA$=BB$
3090 PUT #1,51
```

Figure 13.1 *Continued*

```
3100 CLOSE #1
3110 GOSUB 4300
3120 PRINT ""
3130 INPUT "ENTER C TO RETURN TO THE PROGRAM OPTIONS ";C$
3140 GOTO 480
3150 IF (DD=1) THEN 3170
3160 GOTO 3190
3170 OPEN "ONE.DAT" AS #1 LEN=5
3180 GOTO 3550
3190 IF (DD=2) THEN 3210
3200 GOTO 3230
3210 OPEN "TWO.DAT" AS #1 LEN=5
3220 GOTO 3550
3230 IF (DD=3) THEN 3250
3240 GOTO 3270
3250 OPEN "THREE.DAT" AS #1 LEN=5
3260 GOTO 3550
3270 IF (DD=4) THEN 3290
3280 GOTO 3310
3290 OPEN "FOUR.DAT" AS #1 LEN=5
3300 GOTO 3550
3310 IF (DD=5) THEN 3330
3320 GOTO 3350
3330 OPEN "FIVE.DAT" AS #1 LEN=5
3340 GOTO 3550
3350 IF (DD=6) THEN 3370
3360 GOTO 3390
3370 OPEN "SIX.DAT" AS #1 LEN=5
3380 GOTO 3550
3390 IF (DD=7) THEN 3410
3400 GOTO 3430
3410 OPEN "SEVEN.DAT" AS #1 LEN=5
3420 GOTO 3550
3430 IF (DD=8) THEN 3450
3440 GOTO 3470
3450 OPEN "EIGHT.DAT" AS #1 LEN=5
3460 GOTO 3550
3470 IF (DD=9) THEN 3490
3480 GOTO 3510
3490 OPEN "NINE.DAT" AS #1 LEN=5
3500 GOTO 3550
3510 IF (DD=10) THEN 3530
3520 GOTO 3540
3530 OPEN "TEN.DAT" AS #1 LEN=5
3540 GOTO 3550
3550 RETURN
3560 PRINT "BID/COST FREQ.";TAB(16);"BID/COST FREQ.";TAB(32);"BID/COST FREQ.";TA
B(48);"BID/COST FREQ.";TAB(64);"BID/COST FREQ."
3570 PRINT "------------------";TAB(16);"------------------";TAB(32);"------------------";
TAB(48);"------------------";TAB(64);"------------------"
3580 FOR KA=1 TO 10
3590 KB=KA+10
3600 KC=KA+20
3610 KD=KA+30
3620 KE=KA+40
3630 AK=KA*.04
3640 BK=KA*.04+.4
3650 CK=KA*.04+.8
3660 DK=KA*.04+1.2
3670 EK=KA*.04+1.6
3680 AK$=STR$(AK)
```

Figure 13.1 *Continued*

```
3690 BK$=STR$(BK)
3700 CK$=STR$(CK)
3710 DK$=STR$(DK)
3720 EK$=STR$(EK)
3730 A$=LEFT$(AK$,4)
3740 B$=LEFT$(BK$,4)
3750 C$=LEFT$(CK$,5)
3760 D$=LEFT$(DK$,5)
3770 E$=LEFT$(EK$,5)
3780 PRINT TAB(3);A$;"=";TAB(10);NU$(KA);TAB(19);B$;"=";TAB(26);NU$(KB);TAB(35);
C$;"=";TAB(42);NU$(KC);TAB(51);D$;"=";TAB(58);NU$(KD);TAB(67);E$;"=";TAB(74);NU$
(KE)
3790 NEXT KA
3800 RETURN
3810 CLS
3820 PRINT "YOU WILL NOW HAVE AN OPTION THAT WILL ENABLE YOU TO ENTER YOUR ESTIM
ATED"
3830 PRINT "COST FOR THE JOB AND HAVE THE PROGRAM CALCULATE THE ACTUAL EXPECTED
PROFITS
3840 PRINT "IN DOLLAR AMOUNTS FOR THE FEASIBLE BIDS"
3850 PRINT ""
3860 PRINT "ENTER C: IF YOU WANT TO ENTER A COST AND HAVE THE PROGRAM CALCULATE
PROFITS"
3870 PRINT "ENTER P: TO RETURN TO THE PROGRAM OPTIONS"
3880 INPUT XX$
3890 IF (XX$="C") THEN 3910
3900 GOTO 480
3910 CLS
3920 PRINT "ENTER YOUR ESTIMATED COST FOR THE PROJECT BEING ESTIMATED"
3930 PRINT "(DO NOT ENTER THE $ SIGN OR THE COMMAS, BUT DO ENTER THE DECIMAL POI
NT"
3940 PRINT ""
3950 INPUT "NOW ENTER THE ESTIMATED COST ";CT
3960 CLS
3970 PRINT "YOUR FEASIBLE BIDS AND EXPECTED PROFITS FOR THE PROJECT WITH AN ESTI
MATED
3980 PRINT "COST EQUAL TO ";CT;" ARE AS FOLLOWS:"
3990 PRINT ""
4000 PRINT "     YOUR FEASIBLE BID";TAB(40);"EXPECTED PROFIT"
4010 PRINT "     --------------------";TAB(40);"---------------"
4020 M$="$$#,###############.##"
4030 FOR YY=1 TO NH
4040 BD=FB(YY) * CT
4050 PR=FE(YY)*CT
4060 PRINT USING M$;BD;
4070 PRINT TAB(30);
4080 PRINT USING M$;PR
4090 NEXT YY
4100 PRINT ""
4110 INPUT "ENTER C TO RETURN TO THE PROGRAM OPTIONS ";C$
4120 GOTO 480
4130 PRINT "THIS IS THE END OF THE PROGRAM"
4140 CLS
4150 KEY ON
4160 PRINT "THIS IS THE END OF THE PROGRAM
4170 KEY ON
4180 END
4190 CLS
4200 INPUT "ENTER C TO LIST THE COMPETITOR NAMES YOU HAVE PREVIOUSLY IDENTIFIED
";C$
4210 CLS
```

Figure 13.1 *Continued*

```
4220 OPEN "UNT.BAS" AS #1 LEN=5
4230 FIELD #1, 5 AS DE$
4240 GET #1,1
4250 CLOSE #1
4260 CLS
4270 DD=VAL(DE$)
4280 PRINT "YOU HAVE INITIALIZED ";DD;" COMPETITOR NAMES"
4290 PRINT "THE COMPETITOR NAMES ARE AS FOLLOWS"
4300 PRINT "NUMBER/CODE";TAB(16);"COMPETITOR NAMES"
4310 PRINT "-----------";TAB(16);"----------------"
4320 OPEN "NAMES.BAS" AS #1 LEN=45
4330 FOR JJ=1 TO DD
4340 FIELD #1, 45 AS NA$(JJ)
4350 GET #1,JJ
4360 LA$(JJ)=NA$(JJ)
4370 PRINT TAB(5);JJ;TAB(16);NA$(JJ)
4380 NEXT JJ
4390 CLOSE #1
4400 PRINT "ENTER THE NUMBER/CODE OF THE COMPETITOR FOR WHICH YOU WANT TO ENTER
DATA
4410 PRINT "OR ENTER 0 (THE NUMBER) TO RETURN TO THE PROGRAM OPTIONS
4420 INPUT "ENTER THE NUMBER/CODE OR 0 NOW ";H
4430 HH=H
4440 IF (H=0) THEN 480
4450 FOR L=1 TO DD
4460 IF L=HH THEN 4480
4470 NEXT L
4480 CLS
4490 PRINT "THE COMPETITOR NUMBER/CODE AND NAME YOU HAVE SELECTED ARE AS FOLLOWS
:
4500 PRINT ""
4510 PRINT "NUMBER/CODE    COMPETITOR NAME"
4520 PRINT "-----------    ---------------"
4530 PRINT TAB(5);HH;TAB(16);LA$(HH)
4540 PRINT ""
4550 CLS
4560 PRINT "THE PAST BIDDING DATA YOU HAVE COLLECTED FOR ";LA$(HH)
4570 PRINT "IS AS FOLLOWS;"
4580 DD=HH
4590 GOSUB 3150
4600 FIELD #1, 5 AS CA$
4610 GET #1,51
4620 CLOSE #1
4630 PRINT "NUMBER OF BIDS YOU HAVE COLLECTED= ";CA$
4640 CR$=CA$
4650 PRINT ""
4660 GOSUB 3150
4670 FOR BB=1 TO 50
4680 FIELD #1, 5 AS CA$
4690 GET #1,BB
4700 NU$(BB)=CA$
4710 NEXT BB
4720 CLOSE #1
4730 GOSUB 3560
4740 PRINT ""
4750 PRINT "ENTER B: TO CONTINUE WITH DETERMINING YOUR BEST BID
4760 PRINT "ENTER P: TO RETURN TO THE PROGRAM OPTIONS
4770 INPUT S$
4780 IF (S$="P") THEN 480
4790 CLS
4800 PRINT "THE BEST BIDS TO MAKE AGAINST ";LA$(HH)
```

Figure 13.1 *Continued*

```
4810 PRINT "ARE AS FOLLOWS:"
4820 GOSUB 4250
4830 PRINT ""
4840 GOSUB 4270
4850 INPUT "ENTER C TO DETERMINE YOUR BEST BIDS TO MAKE ";C$
4860 CLS
4870 INPUT "NOW INPUT C TO DETERMINE THE BEST BIDS AND THEIR PROFITS ";C$
4880 CLS
4890 PRINT "YOUR FEASIBLE BIDS AND THEIR ECPECTED PROFITS AGAINST
4900 PRINT LA$(HH); " ARE AS FOLLOWS:"
4910 PRINT ""
4920 PRINT "FEASIBLE BID";TAB(15);"PROB. OF BEING LOW";TAB(35);"EXPECTED PROFIT(
TIMES YOUR ESTIMATED COST-C)
4930 PRINT "-------------------";TAB(15);"-------------------";TAB(35);"-----------------
--------------------------------"
4940 T$="#.######"
4950 FD(1)=1!
4960 FZ=1
4970 FOR PP=1 TO NH
4980 FB(PP)=BI(PP)-.02
4990 UU=FB(PP)-1!
5000 FE(PP)=UU*FD(PP)
5010 PRINT USING S$;FB(PP);
5020 PRINT TAB(18);
5030 PRINT USING R$;FD(PP);
5040 PRINT TAB(38);
5050 PRINT USING T$;FE(PP)
5060 LL=PP+1
5070 FC(LL)=FZ-DE(PP)
5080 FD(LL)=FC(LL)
5090 FZ=FC(LL)
5100 NEXT PP
5110 PRINT ""
5120 INPUT "NOW ENTER C TO ENTER YOUR ESTIMATED COST AND DETERMINE YOUR BIDS ";C
$
5130 GOTO 3810
```

Figure 13.1 *Continued*

The user is then afforded the opportunity to select one of four options in lines 560 through 750. Option 1, the initializing of competitors of the user/competitor, must be performed at least once before the other program routines can be selected and executed.

Option 1 enables the user to enter and store on a data disk the names of competing firms. The program is written such that the user can enter competitor names as he confronts them in his bidding activity. In other words the list of names can be updated; it is not necessary to name all of the competitor names at one setting.

When option 1 is selected the first time, the program sets up various data files that are subsequently used in data filing programming. As such, the program asks the user if this is the first time the program is being run. If it is, the user inputs FIRST. Because this initiates a critical branching in the program, the user is requested to input FIRST a second time. Thus, programming is done in lines 810 through 1070. If the user inputs FIRST again, the program branches to line 1090.

Starting in line 1090, the program initiates data files on an inserted data disk. The data file named UNT keeps track of the number of competitor names, and the data file named AVERAGE initializes the frequency of the bid-to-cost ratios of an "average" competitor to 0. (Note: this data file is not used in subsequent program routines because the program, as presented, does not have a program routine to determine the best bid against an "average" competitor as described in the preceding discussion section on bidding strategy. However, the fact that the AVERAGE data file is created would enable the reader to modify the program to perform such a task.)

The program then branches to the subroutine starting in line 1550. Subroutine 1550 informs the user as to how many previous competitor names have been inputted and then enables the user to input a new competitor name. The competitor name is requested in lines 1640 through 1650. The updated number of competitor names is stored in the UNT data file via the programming in lines 1740 through 1780. The competitor name is then stored in a data file. This process starts in line 1790. At this line the program branches to subroutine 3150. This subroutine "opens" a data file for the competitor name. The data file is given a name equivalent to the sequence number of the competitor name; the first competitor name entered is given a data file name FIRST, the second, SECOND, etc. After opening the data file for input, the subroutine returns to line 1800, which stores the competitor name in the data file. Also the frequency table/chart for the competitor's-bid-to-user's-estimated-cost ratios are initialized to 0. The program, as written, keeps track of the competitor's-bids-to-user's-estimated ratios in increments of 0.04. Ratios from 0.00 to 2.00 are calculated and stored on the data disk. After setting up the data files for a competitor, the program returns the user to the program options. An example of an initialized bid to estimated frequency table/chart obtained from a printout of one monitor screen is illustrated in Figure 13.2.

If the user subsequently inputs another competitor name, he would not input FIRST when given the choice. If FIRST is not input, the program branches directly to the requesting of a competitor name program routine.

Once a competitor name has been entered, the user can enter a historical bidding experience for a named competitor. This option/program routine is initiated by inputting a 2 when requested in line 710. The program then branches to line 1900.

```
THE PAST BIDDING DATA YOU HAVE COLLECTED FOR
GOODWORK CONSTRUCTION
IS AS FOLLOWS:

NUMBER OF PAST BIDS YOU HAVE COLLECTED=     0
```

BID/COST	FREQ.	BID/COST	FREQ.	BID/COST	FREQ.	BID/COST	FREQ.	BID/COST	FREQ.
.04=	0	.44=	0	.840=	0	1.24=	0	1.64=	0
.08=	0	.48=	0	.88=	0	1.28=	0	1.68=	0
.12=	0	.52=	0	.92=	0	1.32=	0	1.72=	0
.16=	0	.56=	0	.960=	0	1.36=	0	1.76=	0
.2=	0	.6=	0	1=	0	1.4=	0	1.8=	0
.24=	0	.64=	0	1.04=	0	1.44=	0	1.84=	0
.28=	0	.68=	0	1.08=	0	1.48=	0	1.88=	0
.32=	0	.72=	0	1.12=	0	1.52=	0	1.92=	0
.36=	0	.76=	0	1.16=	0	1.56=	0	1.96=	0
.4=	0	.8=	0	1.2=	0	1.6=	0	2=	0

Figure 13.2   Example Frequency History Table.

In order to enter historical bidding data for a competitor, the user must first identify the competitor name. The program enables the user to do this by first reading the data disk and identifying the previously input competitor names. The reading of the data disk and printing of the competitor names is performed in lines 1910 through 1990. The user then selects the competitor name for which data is to be input in lines 2100 through 2170. Once the competitor name is selected the program reads/gets the historical bidding data table/chart for the competitor from his data files and prints the table/chart on the monitor. This is done in lines 2190 through 2440.

The user is then given the opportunity to input a historical bid for the competitor name. This opportunity/option is given to the user in lines 2450 through 2480. Assuming the user enters B, to enter a bid, the program proceeds to line 2500. The user then inputs the bid amount of the competitor name and also the user's estimated cost for the project. This is done in lines 2590 and 2610.

After receiving the data input, the program calculates and prints the ratio of the competitor's bid to be user's estimated cost for the project. If the user wants to store the bid/cost ratio occurrence in the competitor's data file, he inputs a D when requested in lines 2780 through 2800. Assuming a D is input, the program proceeds to enter the occurrence of the bid/cost ratio in the competitor's bid/cost frequency table/chart. Given the fact that ratios are stored in increments of 0.04, the bid/cost ratio is rounded to an increment of 0.04. The updated frequency table/chart is updated and printed on the monitor. A printout of such a monitor screen is illustrated in Figure 13.3. After updating the frequency bid/cost table/chart, the program returns the user to the program option menu.

```
THE PAST BIDDING DATA YOU HAVE COLLECTED FOR
GOODWORK CONSTRUCTION
IS AS FOLLOWS;
NUMBER OF BIDS YOU HAVE COLLECTED=      6

BID/COST FREQ.  BID/COST FREQ.   BID/COST FREQ.   BID/COST FREQ.   BID/COST FREQ.
---------------  ---------------  ---------------  --------------   ---------------
    .04=    0      .44=    0        .840=   0       1.24=    1       1.64=    0
    .08=    0      .48=    0        .88=    0       1.28=    1       1.68=    0
    .12=    0      .52=    0        .92=    0       1.32=    0       1.72=    0
    .16=    0      .56=    0        .960=   0       1.36=    0       1.76=    0
    .2=     0      .6=     0        1=      0       1.4=     0       1.8=     0
    .24=    0      .64=    0        1.04=   1       1.44=    0       1.84=    0
    .28=    0      .68=    0        1.08=   0       1.48=    0       1.88=    0
    .32=    0      .72=    0        1.12=   2       1.52=    0       1.92=    0
    .36=    0      .76=    0        1.16=   0       1.56=    0       1.96=    0
    .4=     0      .8=     0        1.2=    1       1.6=     0       2=       0

ENTER B: TO CONTINUE WITH DETERMINING YOUR BEST BID
```

Figure 13.3 Frequency History Table with Data.

Assuming the user has previously input a competitor name and has previously entered at least one occurrence of a bid/cost ratio for a defined contractor, it is then possible to use the bidding strategy program illustrated to determine the best (optimal) bid to make against the competitor. This program option is selected by inputting a 3 when given the option in line 710. The program then branches to line 4190.

As with the entering of historical data, the user must first identify the competitor name for which he is to bid against. The program enables the user to identify the competitor name by opening the competitor name data file and printing the names of the previously inputted competitor names. This is done in lines 4220 through 4380.

The user then selects the competitor name via the programming in lines 4400 through 4470. The program then proceeds to print the historical bidding frequency table/chart of the competitor. This is done in lines 4560 through 4740.

By entering B in response to the INPUT instruction in line 4770, the user can proceed to calculate his best bid to make against the competitor. The program first prints on the monitor the probability of the bids of the competitor. A printout of the monitor screen is illustrated in Figure 13.4. The program then proceeds to undercut each of the competitor's bids by

```
            BID/COST RATIO        PROBABILITY
            _____   _____

            1.04                = 0.1667
            1.12                = 0.3333
            1.20                = 0.1667
            1.24                = 0.1667
            1.28                = 0.1667
```

Figure 13.4   Probability of competitor bids.

0.02 times the estimated cost. This is based on the need for the user to underbid the competitor. Based on this assumption, the user's feasible bids are then printed via the programming in lines 4290 through 5100. An example is shown in Figure 13.5.

```
YOUR FEASIBLE BIDS AND THEIR ECPECTED PROFITS AGAINST
GOODWORK CONSTRUCTION                      ARE AS FOLLOWS:

FEASIBLE BID   PROB. OF BEING LOW   EXPECTED PROFIT(TIMES YOUR ESTIMATED COST-C)
_____   _____   _____
1.02              1.0000             0.020000
1.10              0.8333             0.083333
1.18              0.5000             0.090000
1.22              0.3333             0.073333
1.26              0.1667             0.043333
```

Figure 13.5   The contractor's feasible bids.

The program then branches back to line 3810. In this and following program lines the user is offered the opportunity to input his estimated cost for the project being bid. The programming and mathematics is included in lines 4000 through 4090. This calculates the actual feasible bid amounts the user should consider along with their expected profits. An example monitor printout is illustrated in Figure 13.6. The user is then

```
YOUR FEASIBLE BIDS AND EXPECTED PROFITS FOR THE PROJECT WITH AN ESTIMATED
COST EQUAL TO  345645  ARE AS FOLLOWS:

      YOUR FEASIBLE BID              EXPECTED PROFIT
      _____          _____
            $352,557.90                 $6,912.89
            $380,209.50                $28,803.76
            $407,861.10                $31,108.04
            $421,686.90                $25,347.30
            $435,512.70                $14,977.95
```

Figure 13.6   Feasible bids and expected profits.

returned to the program option menu. From this menu he can choose to end the program execution.

In the interest of illustrating a relatively short program, the program shown in Figure 13.1 does not contain program routines that would enable the user to determine his best bid against multiple competitors, all bidding the same job. However, this and other program features could be added by the addition of additional subroutines to the program illustrated.

The program illustrated should give the reader an insight into the many strategy and "gaming" opportunities available by the use of a computer and data file programming. In essence, the data file programming gives the user an efficient means of storing and manipulating vast amounts of data. This, of course, is one of the more advantageous features computers offer the construction industry. There are likely to be many more strategy and gaming applications evolving for the construction industry in the immediate future.

GAMING APPLICATIONS

Perhaps no one application of computer offers the construction industry as much potential for benefits as does what we will refer to as "gaming." Gaming might be viewed as using the computer to simulate playing a game against a competitor.

Gaming is not a new phenomenon. The military has used principles of gaming for many years in its attempt to determine a winning strategy against an enemy in time of war. This was done by using miniature war fields on which the military studied various possible enemy tactics and responded with an action. By means of analyzing various random enemy moves and a response, the military was able to simulate winning or losing a battle. More importantly, based on the actions taken to "win" or "lose" the game, the military was able to determine a "winning" action plan that could then be implemented in real life.

Gaming applications become more prevalent and practical with the advent of the computer. The computer enables the user to play a game against a computer program that is programmed to simulate a real-world situation or event. Consider an Atari® game. A player of an Atari® game like Space Invaders® attempts to shoot various invader-type objects that randomly appear on the computer monitor. The object of the game is to out-wit and out-maneuver the competitor (i.e., the simulated events elected by the computer program). The more times the program user "plays the game," the more experienced he gets at out-maneuvering the game and he improves his score.

Let us now turn our attention to the construction industry. The same principles of gaming apply. If one thinks about the process of building a construction project, one can view it as a game; a game against the real world of uncertainties, including unpredictable weather, labor strikes, material shortages, etc. One can never predict these events with certainty.

A computer program can be written to simulate many of the uncertain events that confront a constructor when he constructs a building. The user can "play" the construction game by making choices and decisions that attempt to keep the project time and cost to a minimum. By also having management tools, such as the critical-path method (CPM) available via the computer program, the user can access these techniques/tools to enable a beneficial decision regarding the project time and cost. The score the user gets for playing the game is expressed as the resulting time and cost of the project.

Such an application of gaming serves very useful purposes for the construction industry and construction firm. For one, gaming provides the user an opportunity to train to manage a construction project. By playing the game, the user can simulate years of on-site project decision making. This would enable a construction firm to train inexperienced superintendents via a computer game before the superintendent had to actually make on-site decisions. In effect, gaming offers the construction industry considerable training benefits.

Gaming also offers the construction industry an opportunity to evaluate the results of various management decisions, via the computer, before the firm has to take the action at a job site. In effect, the computer, via gaming applications, enables the firm to evaluate the results of alternative actions or decisions before the action or decision is taken. Indeed a powerful application; one that offers considerable benefits to the industry.

We will not illustrate any gaming programs. This area of application is in an early phase of development. However, one is likely to witness a significant amount of gaming applications software evolve in the near future.

14: Selection of Hardware and Software

INTRODUCTION

After discussing the process by which a computer works, how to write software programs, and the many applications of computers to construction, perhaps the reader is still left with the question, do I need a computer? If the answer is affirmative, the questions remain as to what computer to buy, what computer software should be purchased, and how does one find the needed software.

The question as to whether the reader should purchase a computer is not independent of the question as to what computer to buy. The very issue of should one purchase a computer is dependent on the availability of computers in different price ranges. If the only computer applicable to a contractor had a cost in excess of $10,000, the contractor's decision to buy or not to buy might be different than if the computer was available at a cost of $3000. In this chapter we will attempt to give the reader direction as to the following three questions:

1. Do you need a computer?
2. What computer should you purchase?
3. What computer software should you purchase and how to find it.

The reader should be forewarned that our discussion will not result in a specific yes or no to the first question, or a specific brand name recommendation in regard to questions 2 and 3. There are just too many relevant factors that prevent giving a definitive yes or no or a brand name.

What might be an optimal recommendation for one firm may prove to be nonoptimal for another. Perhaps the best we can therefore do is to give the reader criteria by which he can make his own decision regarding our three proposed questions.

DO YOU NEED A COMPUTER?

Just how does one go about determining whether or not one needs a computer? Just like any other business decision, the answer to this question can be made only by means of comparing the economic benefits of using the computer and software to the initial and ongoing costs of purchasing and implementing the hardware and software.

The costs of implementing a computer system are usually somewhat easy to establish. Given the abundance of computer hardware vendors, it is relatively easy to establish an initial purchase cost for the hardware the contractor judges appropriate. Today's hardware availability is such that the contractor can usually purchase a computer that will meet his needs for less than $5000.

In regard to the ongoing operating cost, the contractor is likely to incur the following three types of costs annually:

> Software program purchases
> Service contract costs
> Personnel costs to operate the computer

The ongoing software cost obviously depends on the amount and type of software programs the user purchases as a function of time. However, given the continual evolution of new and improved software application programs, it is safe to say that the contractor will want to purchase new programs each and every year. Perhaps the easiest and best way to plan and control this ongoing cost is to budget a set amount each year for purchasing new software programs.

The second ongoing cost, the service contract premium, should be viewed as a necessary annual expenditure. While computers, including the inexpensive personal computers, are surprisingly durable with few mechanical working parts, they can break. Electrical problems, disk drive problems, or perhaps damage caused by liquids spilled onto the machine can all cause the computer to break down. The end result is that most business application users carry a maintenance service contract on their computer. Such a service contract usually results in an annual premium varying from 5 to 20 percent of the initial purchase cost.

A cost often overlooked by a constructor when evaluating the use of a computer system is the salary cost of the individual or individuals employed to operate the computer. While modern day personal computers are relatively simple to use, the fact remains that they do not operate unattended. Similar to a typewriter, an operator is needed to enter data, receive data, and load software programs. Given this fact, the computer should seldom be viewed as a means of cutting one's clerical costs. This seldom happens. Instead, it is more realistic to view a computer as a tool for enabling the implementation of improved management practices rather than viewing it as a cost-saving device.

If we are able to quantify the costs of implementing and using a computer system, how does one then quantify the monetary benefits of a computer to enable one to compare the benefits versus costs? This is unfortunately not quite as easy.

For one, it is somewhat difficult to quantify the monetary benefits of improved management practices or procedures. Second, not all the benefits of computer usage are in fact monetary benefits. For example, one might argue that there is somewhat of a marketing benefit associated with a contractor implementing a computer system. The installation may result in the firm projecting the image of being a "well-managed" contractor (even if the firm isn't). The popularity of computers leads one to believe that a firm is "modern," "up-to-date," by the mere presence of a computer in the firm's office.

It would still be advantageous for a firm to be able to justify a computer installation from a dollars-and-cents calculation. While this might be an unreasonable approach, Figure 14.1 provides the reader a worksheet that attempts to quantify monetary savings that may attach to performing accounting-related functions more efficiently. This is at best a piecemeal approach in that perhaps the primary benefits relate to more timely and improved management practices, including improved cash flow analysis and investment, improved construction estimating accuracy, and a more timely means of detecting a potential project cost overrun via a computerized job cost control program.

Given the fact that the major benefit of a computer system is the improved management practices, another approach to determining if one needs a computer is to have the firm take a quiz to "test" if they need a computer to improve various important duties or functions necessary to performing construction operations. For example, the quiz illustrated in Figure 14.2 can be used as a measure of determining if a firm needs a computer regarding the construction estimating task alone. The more times the reader/firm answers "yes" to the questions, the more likely it is that the firm could justify a computer (for the estimating task alone). As a

	COMPUTER FEASIBILITY	
	MANUAL *Employee Hours* *Month*	COMPUTER *Employee Hours* *Month*
Payroll		
Weekly Cycle		
Union Reports		
Quarterly Reports		
Annual Reports		
Check Reconciliation	—	—
Accounts Payable		
Purchase Journal		
Cash Disbursements		
Vendor Analysis Reports	—	—
Job Costing		
Monthly Reports		
Job Reports		
Miscellaneous Reports	—	—
Inventory		
Job Reports		
Perpetual Records	—	—
Sales and A/R		
Revenue Reports		
Aging Reports		
Cash Receipts	—	—
Job Management		
Scheduling		
Estimating Reports		
Cash Flow	—	—
General Ledger		
General Journal		
Trial Balance		
Monthly Statements	—	—
Total Employee Hours/Mo.		
Total Employee Hours/Yr.		
Times Average Hourly Rate		
Annual Employee Cost	—	—
Equivalent Annual Purchase Cost for Computer	—	—
Annual Maintenance and Repair Costs	—	—
Additional Overhead Cost	—	—
Total Annual Cost	—	—
Computer Savings-Annual (Additional Cost)	—	—
Other Benefits	—	—

Figure 14.1 Worksheet to calculate monetary savings from computer usage.

Question	Yes	No
1. The accuracy of your estimates are such that the actual costs of a project vary by more than 7 percent from your estimated cost.		
2. You do not have an "on-paper" data file of past performance regarding productivity or costs for individual work items.		
3. You do not have an equipment estimating system that enables you to keep track of the cost of owning a piece of equipment.		
4. Your firm's manual record-keeping system is such that the collected information is accurate and would support a computerized system.		
5. You do not keep records of material wastage on a project to enable you to better estimate a future project.		
6. The initial estimate for a project is not revised as the project progresses.		
7. You do not keep track of the cost or productivity trend as a function of jobs and time.		
8. The overhead allocated to individual projects is not determined through analysis of past records.		
9. Job overhead costs are applied to projects rather than determined by analysis of past projects.		
10. The estimating task takes more than 100 man-hours per $1,000,000 of work estimated.		

Figure 14.2   Quiz to determine if computer is justified based on estimating needs.

somewhat arbitrary guideline, one might propose that if the reader/firm answers "yes" more than six times, the firm is in need of a computer to aid it in estimating.

The quiz illustrated in Figure 14.2, and similar ones, is at best only a measure as to whether a firm needs a computer. The question really becomes, "does the firm need more timely data and better management practices?" More often than not the construction firm would answer in the affirmative. This leads us to the next questions; how does one select and implement the best computer hardware and software? These issues are addressed in following sections.

SELECTING COMPUTER HARDWARE FOR
CONSTRUCTION INDUSTRY APPLICATIONS

Once a construction firm commits to implementing a computer, the question remains as to how to select the best computer hardware. No single type or brand of computer is best for each and every firm. Some firms have a need for an inexpensive model that includes minimal capabilities while other firms need larger, more expensive hardware. It will be impossible for us to recommend a single type of hardware. On the other hand, we can identify various concerns the firm should have as it seeks to select the best hardware.

First of all, there are some general concerns that are common to any firm's selection of hardware, independent of whether or not the firm is a construction firm. Perhaps the following three concerns override all others:

> Availability and dependability of service
> Availability of off-the-shelf computer software
> Projected life of hardware

Service is, of course, important when purchasing any type of asset that can break. However, given the fact that a firm computerizes its entire information system, the availability and dependability of service becomes even more critical. A contractor unable to process his payroll because of a "down" computer seldom has relief. He must get his computer fixed fast!

Given the fact that a firm will seldom develop its own software, it becomes critical that off-the-shelf software is available for the selected computer hardware. It is very frustrating for a firm to find out about the availability of a powerful and much needed software program only to find out that the software is not available for the type of hardware the firm has purchased. Part of the solution to this problem is for the firm to first identify needed software and then secure their hardware.

Our third general concern relates to the fact that one might purchase hardware that is soon outdated—computer technology is rapidly changing. Faster computers with more memory capacity and capable of doing more functions continue to evolve. While a firm cannot totally anticipate new and improved machines, it should try to avoid purchasing an old, outdated computer. As a new computer becomes available, software application programmers design programs for the newer machine. A firm with an "old" machine may not be able to run programs designed for the newer machines.

There are, of course, other general concerns to pay attention to when selecting hardware, including availability of peripherals, the potential for hardware "bugs," the feel of the keyboard, etc. However, given the fact that some of these concerns come down to "customer preference," we will not discuss them individually here. Instead, let us turn our attention to some specific concerns that relate to selection of hardware for construction industry applications.

Given the nature of construction industry computer applications, the author views the following as a list of computer hardware concerns that a firm considering a computer should have:

1. Availability of a disk drive.
2. If an application program is to access two data files, the computer should have two disk drives.
3. A minimal of 64K of memory and 128K preferred.
4. A computer that has expandable memory.
5. The availability of a numerical keyboard.
6. The ability to support a printer capable of printing at least 132 characters per line.
7. A monitor screen that can print a minimum of 80 columns of data.
8. The ability to support a version of BASIC that includes the PRINT USING instruction.
9. If individuals have a need to access the same data file, the ability to "network" several of the computers.

The reason for most of the concerns is obvious and needs no further explanation. However, let us expand on a few of the concerns.

As was discussed in an earlier chapter, the use of disk drives enables the user to access data files almost instantaneously. Such an ability is especially critical to the many data management construction application software programs. A disk drive is unsurpassed in its ability to handle data management.

As noted above, a computer should support two disk drives if the user is using a software program that accesses two data files on separate data disks during the execution of the program. For example, a software program application for construction may access a history labor productivity data disk while it is also writing to a separate job estimate data disk. The program that performs this application would be loaded into the computer memory, and each data disk would be inserted in a separate disk drive.

Our concerns about the size of available memory and whether or not the memory of the computer is expandable relates to the fact that data file programs (the majority of construction application programs are data file programs) take considerable memory. The memory of a computer is taken up essentially two ways. For one, the loaded program itself takes part of the memory. Second, inputted or data read from the disk drive during program execution also goes into memory. As such this data takes up some of the memory space. The end result is that a program plus inputted data combine to both use memory. Thus, a considerable amount of computer memory is needed to run relatively complex construction industry application programs.

Our concerns about the number of columns a printer and monitor can print relate to the fact that several construction industry software applications result in a need to print several columns of numbers. For example, construction estimating software applications result in the printing of an estimate spreadsheet. A 40-column monitor (one not recommended for construction industry applications) would limit the user to three or at most four columns of numbers.

The PRINT USING instruction was discussed in our presentation of BASIC in Chapter 4. As noted in that chapter, this is a BASIC instruction that allows the programmer to conveniently format numbers.

For the most part, the BASIC computer language is similar on each computer. However, there are slight differences. One of these slight differences is that some computers support a version of BASIC that includes the PRINT USING instruction while others do not.

Our computer networking concern relates mainly to the medium-sized or larger firm. This type of firm may have several departments within its firm that it desires to have access to a common data base such as a historical labor productivity data file. If this is the case, the firm will want to be able to configure several computers such that they can communicate at the same time to a data file kept in one of the machines. More and more of the newer small business computers are designed to accommodate this networking objective.

There are a few other minor concerns one might have when selecting a given type of computer for construction industry applications. However, these concerns are secondary to our above list. For example, given the vast amounts of data that a construction program likely requires as input, the computer should not only have a numerical keyboard (as noted in our list) but the keyboard should have a ''good feel'' to it; one that results in ease of use but minimizes data entry input errors.

EVALUATION OF COMPUTER SOFTWARE

In an earlier chapter we learned that computer software is as essential to a computer system and computer hardware as is a television program to a television set. We also stressed the importance of a construction firm paying attention to the selection of software application programs before committing to computer hardware. This message should be made loud and clear, independent of the fact that the majority of the time the contractor still commits to hardware first, and then looks for application software. The potential problem with this latter approach is that the contractor may be unable to find desirable software for his in-place computer hardware.

Independent of whether or not the contractor commits to hardware or software first, the question remains as to how does the contractor find and evaluate computer software. Hopefully, the solution to this question in part is made easier by our discussion of the many computer software applications discussed in the previous chapters. The mere fact that the contractor knows what applications there are for computers should better equip him in identifying and securing the appropriate software. However, this in itself is not the solution in total.

The computer software industry is heading more and more toward an off-the-shelf catalog business. The construction firm is likely to purchase software from a retail store or through the mail. In either case the contractor should reserve the right "to test" the software before committing to a purchase. For example, if the software is purchased from a retail establishment, ideally the retail store has available a demonstration computer on which the contractor can test the software. Similarly, if the contractor purchases software through the mail, he should only agree to terms that he has a right to try the software and return it for a refund if he is unsatisfied with its performance.

Given the opportunity to test an off-the-shelf software program, what should the potential user of the construction software program test for? Naturally, he should determine that the program does meet his needs, runs on his hardware setup, and is well documented. However, these are somewhat general statements and do not give the reader an "action plan to test the software." For example, everybody knows that software should be well documented via a manual—but what does this mean?

In an attempt to give the reader very specific procedures (over and above requirements such as the fact that the software should meet his needs), we will discuss several rules to use in testing software. The reader should remember that while there is an abundance of software available, including construction industry software, much of the available software is inefficient in regard to operating it or inputting requested data. All software is not good software. There is a considerable difference between good and bad software. Poorly written software may in fact be so bad that it actually discourages the user from using a computer.

What the author views as 10 good "tests" for evaluating a software program are listed in Figure 14.3. Let us now illustrate, by example, the importance and application of each of these tests. (Note: the tests are not necessarily listed in an order of importance.)

The first test noted in Figure 14.3, that of making sure the software documentation assumes nothing in regard to the user's use of the program, may appear to be a rather minute point. Perhaps it is. However, there is nothing more frustrating to the user of a computer program than to be in a position of not knowing what to do when the program is waiting response or input.

Perhaps the point about the documentation not assuming any prior knowledge (e.g., assuming the user knows to hit the return key) leads us to an even more important point or issue—that of the documentation being complete and written in layman's language. The skills required to write a good computer program are not necessarily the same skills one needs to write a software documentation manual. In fact, a developer of a software program might know a program too well to be able to communicate it to a layman. A good user/documentation manual is often written by a user of the program rather than the developer of the program.

In summary, the potential purchaser of a software program should review the program documentation to determine if it is understandable. A user/documentation manual that is too technical may prove difficult for construction personnel to understand or implement.

Perhaps the most critical and important point or test noted in our list in Figure 14.3 is the second one. This relates to the error routines contained in the program. It is an absolute must that a well-written program contain a complete set of error routines.

A user of a software program will frequently err in entering data or selecting a program option. For example, the program menu illustrated in Figure 14.4 requests the user to input an S, H, P, or T. What if the user inputs an R by mistake. A well-written program should print on the monitor a message similar to that illustrated below:

"YOU HAVE MADE AN INPUT ERROR, YOU MUST ENTER S, H, P, or T"

After flashing this error message, the program ought to enable the user to input the option selection again.

There are numerous types of program errors a user might encounter when executing a program in addition to the above-noted error. For example, in attempting to send data to a data disk, the program may encounter no data disk in the disk drive or may encounter a write-protected

TEN RULES/PROCEDURES FOR
EVALUATING OFF-THE-SHELF SOFTWARE

1. Software manual/documentation should not take anything for granted in regard to the users knowledge of how to use a program or the computer itself. (For example, the documentation should not assume the user will know to hit the "enter" key after inputting data—the manual/documentation should tell the user to hit the return key after inputting information.)

2. The user should "test" the program by intentionally inputting "incorrect" information and observing the response of the system. For example, if the program asks for a dollar amount of labor cost, the user might input a letter or hit the control key. If the program is well written, it should not "go down" when incorrect input is entered; instead the program should inform the user of the error, and let him enter the data again. Perhaps the best way to test a program for error routines is to let a young child, inexperienced in computers, try working the program.

3. A software program should contain several "menus" that enable the user to "branch" to several program options at appropriate places in the program. For example, the program menus should continually enable the user to exit the program via an exit option in the menus.

4. A software program should enable the user to edit or "correct" any input the user enters in response to the program. For example, after inputting a labor cost for a work item in preparing a project estimate, the program should print the inputted data on the monitor and ask the user if the entered data is correct or if the user would like to reenter the data.

5. A software program should never require the user to do something that can be done internal to the computer via the software program. For example, in a real estate feasibility program, after requiring the user to input the land cost, building cost, and equity investment, the program should calculate the mortgage amount rather than require the user to calculate it and input the amount; i.e., the mortgage amount has to equal the land cost plus the building cost minus the equity investment.

6. A software program should never result in the monitor/screen going "blank" while it is performing a function or sending or getting information from the disk drive. A blank screen, even if it is for only a few seconds, may lead the user to believe something is wrong and the user may "panic" and turn the computer off or "pull the plug."

7. To the extent possible, the software program should send or receive data from a disk in a manner that does not "slow down" the user's ability to enter information via the keyboard. Note, most computers are designed such that the keyboard is "dead" or nonoperable while the disk drive is running.

Figure 14.3 Concerns in evaluating/selecting software.

8. When requiring the user to respond to a critical question that directs the program to branch to an important option or lose some inputted information, the program should require the user to input the choice or input twice. For example, if a program gives the user an option of not storing inputted information on a disk, and the user responds that he does not want to store it, the program should respond "are you sure?" and ask him to specify his choice again.

9. A software program that is designed to store inputted data on a disk drive should not have the user put a considerable amount of input data into the computer without periodically placing some of the data on the disk. If hours of data input are all held in memory before the sending of the data to the disk drive, it can all be lost if a electrical problem occurs.

10. A software program should not branch to "instructions" or a "demo" screen reduntantly if such a return is not necessary. For example, a loop that enables a user to input data each time the loop is executed, should not start the loop each and every time with instructions to the user as to how to input the data.

Figure 14.3 *Continued*

```
ENTER S: TO INITIATE THE SET-UP OF THE SYSTEM

ENTER H: TO ENTER HISTORICAL DATA

ENTER P: TO PREPARE A NEW ESTIMATE

ENTER T: TO TERMINATE THE PROGRAM
```

Figure 14.4 Example program menu.

disk. A well-developed software program should anticipate each and every type of error the user may create.

In addition to alerting the user of an error condition, the programmed error routines should also alert the user to the type of error and also enable the user to try again with the correct entry. A program should never "go down" when it encounters an error condition. Instead, the error routines should be such that the program execution resumes.

Next in importance to the program test for error conditions is the necessity of a program to contain many data editing routines. This is especially important in regard to construction industry applications of computers because of the vast amount of data entry that is part of these type of programs. It is very frustrating to a user to enter an incorrect input request, to observe his incorrect entry, and not be able to do anything about it.

To illustrate the need for data editing capability, let us assume that a program requires a user to input a budgeted number of labor hours for a defined work item in preparing an estimate. The program message on the monitor may read as follows:

ENTER LABOR HOURS FOR WORK ITEM

Let us assume that the user wants to input 245.5 hours. However, instead of entering 245.5, he errs and enters 24.55 (i.e., he puts in the decimal point incorrectly). Naturally, if the user detects the data entry error before he hits the return key (which sends the entry to the computer memory), he could backspace via his keyboard and correct his error.

The problem occurs when the user does not see that he made an error until after he hits the return key. With no data editing routine, the user would have to proceed with program execution, knowing that he would get erroneous results because of the data error. This would be frustrating and inefficient. The end result is that it is almost an absolute necessity to include data editing routines in construction industry application programs.

There are essentially three means of programming error routines in a software program. Depending on the purpose and way a program executes, one of these routines may be better than the other. Let us illustrate these three possible editing routines and discuss their benefits and disadvantages.

One of the easiest means of programming a data editing routine would be to have the computer program ask the user if the data entry is correct each time the user enters data. This is illustrated in Figure 14.5. After receiving the data entry, the program prints the entered data and asks the user if the data is correct or if it is incorrect and he wants to reenter it. The user can then proceed by indicating that the entry is correct, or he can loop back and reenter the data if it is incorrect.

Such an approach to data editing is good and bad. It is good from the point of view that the user can correct his entry as soon as he makes it. More often than not, the user recognizes he has made a data entry error right after he has hit the entry or return key. On the other hand, instantaneous data editing is somewhat bad in that the data entry is slowed by the user having to respond to the editing question after each data entry. Equally important is the fact that because the question appears after every data entry, the question becomes routine and this may result in the user

```
VARIABLE:                      ESTIMATED BUILDING COST

ENTER THE BUILDING COST= ?    1000000

ENTERED BUILDING COST=     $1,000,000.00

IS IT CORRECT ?

ENTER C:  IF IT IS CORRECT AND YOU WANT TO PROCEED WITH ANOTHER DATA ENTRY
ENTER W:  IF IT IS INCORRECT AND YOU WANT TO REENTER THE ENTRY
ENTER T:  IF YOU WISH TO TERMINATE/EXIT THE PROGRAM
```

Figure 14.5   Example of data editing routine.

getting in the habit of responding that the data entry is correct even if it is not.

A second type of data editing routine is illustrated in Figure 14.6. The reader will observe that several data entries are printed on the monitor and the user has the opportunity to indicate that there is an error and reenter the data. The problem is that if the user indicates there is an error, the program will loop back to the beginning of the data entry and require the user to reenter each and every one of the data entries shown in Figure 14.6. This, of course, would be inefficient if only one of the entries was incorrect. While such an approach may prove inefficient, certainly it is better than no editing routine.

A third approach to data editing is illustrated in Figure 14.7. In this illustration the program has placed a number in front of each of the several data entries previously inputted. The user can indicate that they are all correct and proceed in the program, or he can enter the number preceding

```
THE INPUTED DATA IS AS FOLLOWS:

LAND COST                   $100,000.00
BUILDING COST             $1,000,000.00
EQUITY INVESTMENT           $220,000.00
LOAN OR MORTGAGE            $880,000.00
LOAN LIFE                        15
LOAN INTEREST RATE              15%
DEPRECIATION METHOD        ACCELERATED
DEPRECIATION LIFE           15 YEARS
INVESTOR'S TAX RATE          40 %

IS THE DATA ENTRY CORRECT ?

ENTER C:  IF IT IS CORRECT AND YOU WANT TO PROCEED WITH DATA ENTRY
ENTER W:  IF IT IS INCORRECT AND YOU WANT TO CORRECT THE DATA ENTRY
```

Figure 14.6   Data editing regarding several items.

```
THE INPUTED DATA IS AS FOLLOWS:

A   LAND COST                       $100,000.00
B   BUILDING COST                 $1,000,000.00
C   EQUITY INVESTMENT               $220,000.00
D   LOAN OR MORTGAGE                $880,000.00
E   LOAN LIFE                             15
F   LOAN INTEREST RATE                   15 %
G   DEPRECIATION METHOD          ACCELERATED
H   DEPRECIATION LIFE                15 YEARS
I   INVESTOR'S TAX RATE                  40 %

IS THE DATA ENTRY CORRECT ?

ENTER LETTER TO CORRECT A SPECIFIC ENTRY
ENTER R: IF THE RECORD IS CORRECT AND YOU WANT TO PROCEED
```

Figure 14.7 Improved data editing.

a single data entry item and the program will enable the user to reenter a single data item entry without having to reenter all of the items.

It would appear that this last data editing approach would be the best; it appears to be most efficient. However, one might argue that by placing all of the data on the screen at one time, as illustrated in Figure 14.7, the user might detect an error on one line but overlook an error on another line.

The end result is that no single data editing routine is without some problems. However, clearly data editing routines are a necessary part of a good program. Perhaps the best approach is combining the first data editing routine we described with the latter routine.

As noted in our number 3 in Figure 14.3, numerous menus are a characteristic of a well-written software program. An example program menu is illustrated in Figure 14.2.

Program menus provide a user an opportunity to branch to several different program routines/options periodically throughout the execution of the program. For example, upon loading an off-the-shelf program into a computer, the first screen the user should encounter should be a menu that enables the user to branch to run the program, terminate the program, or perhaps see a short demonstration or explanation of the program.

The inclusion of several menus in a program is usually an indication that the program is well planned and works efficiently. One of the first steps a good software programmer takes in writing a program is to identify program options and lay out the menu screens that access these options.

Good program menus should also be easy to use. For example, the user entry required to indicate a described option should be short and, to the degree possible, infer the selected option. For example, in the menu illustrated in Figure 14.4, the S refers to the initial *S*etup, the H to enter *H*istorical data, and the P to *P*repare an estimate. The user is less likely to make a data entry error of the requested input character if it is indicative of the option desired.

Similar to the fact that a good software program is well menued is the concern that a program should be written such that it enables a user to use the program menus to backtrack and exit the program. It is frustrating for a user that wants to terminate his use of a program not to have a way to end the program other than turn the computer off.

There is somewhat of an art to a programmer providing menus that enable the user to exit the program. It would be easy for the programmer to include an exit menu in every menu screen that appears on the computer monitor as a program is executed. While such an approach would provide the user a means of exiting the program at many points, such an approach may also prove harmful. If the user is given an opportunity to exit a program when he should not be given an opportunity (e.g., during data input), then the user may erroneously hit the wrong option entry and possibly lose some important input data or perhaps result in him leaving an important program routine that may need to be repeated. In summary, a well-written software program will enable the user to exit the program at convenient and appropriate points in the program execution.

The majority of construction industry computer applications entail the use of data files. In such an application a considerable amount of data is sent to a data disk in the disk drive and/or is received from the disk in the drive. This presents two potential problems in regard to the user's efficient use of a computer. These two problems are referenced in our concerns 6 and 7 noted in Figure 14.3.

To understand one of our problems, we should first mention that the design of most personal computers is such that the computer keyboard is "dead" (inactive) when data is being sent to or received from a disk in the disk drive. This means that the user cannot enter more data if data is being sent to the disk drive. If a program has been poorly designed, data entry can be slowed considerably by untimely frequent sending or receiving of data to or from the drive.

The solution to the above-noted problem would appear simple. Why not have the program store all or most of the inputted data in memory until the end of the program and then have it sent to the disk in the drive at one point in time rather than the periodical sending and receiving of data. There are two major and perhaps critical problems with this latter approach. For one, the holding of a considerable amount of data in the memory takes a lot of memory space. Such an approach may limit the use of the program to applications requiring only small amounts of data.

A second and perhaps more critical problem relates to the fact that should there be an electrical outage or a computer shutdown owing to a clumsy "tripping on the computer cord," any data entry held in the computer memory would be lost.

It would appear that a program designer is caught between two evils, one of slowing up data entry, and one of an efficient use of computer memory and a possible loss of entered data. The end result is that data storage and retrieval has to be well planned out in an effectively designed software program. Perhaps the best approach to data entry and retrieval is to send and receive data frequently within a program, but to make sure the data entry occurs at points in time in the program execution when the user would not be slowed in his data entry. To design such a program, the developer has to put himself in the role of the constructor who is going to enter the data.

There are three other software concerns the reader should remember when testing off-the-shelf software. While these tests (8 through 10 in Figure 14.3) are less critical to the execution of a program than those noted above, lack of attention to these detailed points can negatively impact the efficiency of a program and/or confuse the user when running the program. Given the fact that these tests/points are somewhat self-explanatory by their mere listing in Figure 14.3 we will not discuss them further here.

In summary, the reader's attention is drawn to the fact that there are very few, if any, off-the-shelf software programs that satisfy the 10 tests listed in Figure 14.3 perfectly. However, some programs are much better than others. The reader should afford himself the opportunity to test a program in this regard before he commits to it. The mere fact that a program is capable of printing the type of report the user desires does not mean the program is efficient or for that matter even usable.

SELECTING A VENDOR

Once you decide you need a computer, the problem is not solved. There are numerous hardware and software vendors to choose from when making a computer investment. Purchase of the wrong hardware or software can be as bad as buying a computer too late or too early. One cannot over-emphasize the importance of software. Too many firms commit to the selection of hardware before investigating the availability of software.

Just how does one go about selecting hardware or software from the numerous vendors that have evolved? There are many considerations an individual should recognize when making a decision regarding either hardware or software. The problem of trying to pick the "best" hardware and software for a firm cannot be solved by one individual suggesting that brand X or brand Y is the best. Each and every firm is somewhat different and may therefore need a somewhat different configuration of hardware and software.

While one cannot suggest the best hardware or software vendor for everyone, one can set out key considerations or selection criteria that should be analyzed for selecting hardware or software. See Figure 14.8 which

---

Vendor Selection Worksheet

Consideration	Vendor A	Vendor B	Vendor C
1. Compatibility of hardware and software			
2. Ability to build-up or change configuration as needs change			
3. Availability of service to include number of service people, location of service people, etc.			
4. Financial strengh of vendor			
5. Expected life of equipment before it is expected to become obsolete equipment			
6. Initial cost of the equipment			
7. Operating costs, including annual support staff needed, supplies, and service contract			
8. Ability to interface with other equipment, including communication with other data banks			
9. Ease of using equipment—little training needed			
10. Image the equipment would lend to the firm			
TOTALS			

[Note: rate each item from 1 (unfavorable) to 5 (favorable)]

Figure 14.8   Selecting a vendor.

shows a selection criteria worksheet for the reader to use in selecting either hardware or software.

As indicated, each of the considerations in Figure 14.8 can be rated per vendor. For example, if vendor A has hardware and software available that are compatible and also serve the needs of a firm, one might rate them a 5 in regard to consideration 1. On the other hand, the same vendor might be rated a 1 in regard to consideration 2—the ability to build-up or change a configuration as needs change.

The Vendor Selection Worksheet should be used with common sense. The worksheet is an aid, not a solution. Nonetheless, the worksheet emphasizes the need to perform a complete analysis when committing to hardware or software.

APPENDIX
Computer Terms

Acoustic Coupler. A machine that converts a computer's binary signals into audible tones. In this way the computer can receive and send information via a telephone.

Address. A location in a computer's memory that is used to store information.

ASCII Code. An abbreviation for American Standard Code for Information Interchange. The ASCII code is a binary code (0s and 1s).

Assembly Language. A computer language that replaces the machine language that a computer understands.

BASIC. An abbreviation for Beginner's All-Purpose Symbolic Instruction Code. This is a relatively simple programming language that is used to operate most personal computers.

Bit. A term used to represent a binary digit. This is a computer's smallest unit of information.

Bootstrap. A program stored in a computer's memory that is used for starting the computer.

Byte. A group of eight binary digits or bits.

Cassette. A reel of magnetic recording tape. Data and programs are stored on this tape.

Central Processing Unit (CPU). The "center" of a computer; it acts like a human brain. It commands the processing done by a computer. The CPU contains arithmetic logic as well as control systems that process instructions.

Chip. A "tiny wafer" integrated circuit of silicon that is less than an inch in size. On the surface of a chip are hundreds or even thousands of microscopic electronic components that comprise an integrated circuit.

Code. A method used to represent characters of the alphabet, numbers, punctuation marks, and other symbols with binary numbers.

Command. A symbol or word that instructs the computer to do something.

Control Section. A part of the central processing unit (CPU) that retrieves, decodes, and carries out programmed instructions in a computer.

CP/M. An abbreviation for Control Program for Microprocessors (a trademark). This is an operating system for small computers.

CRT. An abbreviation for cathode-ray tube. This is a video tube (like one in a television). It enables a user to read a program or input or output on a screen.

Cursor. A movable indicator on the screen that illustrates where the next character or symbol will appear.

Daisy Wheel. A typing print wheel that gives an impact print that produces fully formed,

Daisy Wheel *Continued*
high-quality characters. A daisy wheel looks like a bicycle wheel with a central axis and ends of spokes being the letters.

Data.   Information, numeric or nonnumeric, put into and subsequently retrieved from a computer. The term *data* is also a statement in BASIC (see BASIC) used to precede a list on input information (data).

Data Base.   A integrated collection of information used by a computer.

Debug.   A procedure of troubleshooting to eliminate an error in a software program or the hardware.

Digital Computer.   A computer that represents numbers, symbols, and characters with binary numbers.

Disk.   A phonograph type metal or plastic disk that is coated with a magnetic substance used to store information. They are frequently referred to as floppy disks.

Disk Drive.   A powered device that spins a magnetic disk at high speeds. The drive is capable of reading and writing onto the surface of a disk.

Diskette.   Another name for a disk or floppy disk.

Dump Terminal.   A video display unit (like a CRT) and keyboard that can be used to communicate with a computer but that cannot perform computer operations on its own.

Erase.   To remove information stored in a computer's memory.

Execute.   The running of a program in a computer.

Floppy Disk.   A type of disk that is usually plastic.

Hard Copy.   Computer output printed on paper by a printing device connected to a computer.

Hardware.   Physical equipment that forms a computer system, including the computer itself, memory storage devices, and video monitors.

High-Level Language.   A computer language in which each command or statement represents several binary code instructions in machine language. Example

high-level languages include BASIC, FORTRAN, or Pascal. These languages enable a user to use terms they are familiar with in interfacing with a computer.

Impact Printer.   A printer that prints characters by striking a printhead against a carbon or inked ribbon and a sheet of paper. This is done either by impacting an entire character or a pattern of dots.

Input/Output Device.   Equipment used to load information into a computer and to read information from the computer.

Instruction.   A command that a computer can understand.

Integrated Circuit.   An electronic circuit that is imprinted on the surface of a silicon chip.

Interface.   A device or process of linking two parts of a computer or a computer and an accessory.

Interrupt.   A brief interruption in the execution of a program. This interruption is programmed into the computer to enable the computer to handle an external event such as the printing of a character.

K.   An abbreviation for kilo that means approximately 1000 information units (in reality 1024 bytes). Referring to K is a means of referencing the memory storage of a computer. For example, a 64K machine can store approximately 64,000 pieces of information.

Keyboard.   A device similar to a typewriter that permits an individual to input information into a computer.

Language.   A system of words (or numbers or characters) that enable a user to communicate with the computer.

Line Printer.   A printer that produces a complete line of print in one high-speed operation.

Loop.   A sequence of computer instructions that are executed repeatedly until a condition is met.

Machine Language.   A computer's primary or most fundamental language (binary numbers 0 and 1). Advanced programming languages must be converted to this language by the computer.

Matrix Printer. A printer that forms characters from patterns of closely spaced dots.

Memory. The circuits in a computer that store information.

Menu. A list of choices from which a user can store information.

Microcomputer. A computer that uses a microprocessor for a central processing unit. Most personal computers can be considered microcomputers.

Microprocessor. A small integrated circuit that contains the central processing unit of a computer.

Modem. A term used for Modulator-Demodulator. This permits computers to communicate to one another via a telephone.

Network. A means for interconnecting a number of computers by telephone lines.

Nonimpact Printer. A printer that forms characters without striking a carbon or inked ribbon against paper. Instead, often a thermal paper is used by heating patterns of dots on heat-sensitive paper.

Peripheral. An input or output device designed to be connected to a computer.

Personal Computer. A relatively low-cost microcomputer equipped with an input device similar to a typewriter.

Plotter. A machine that is capable of producing a drawing of graphics.

Printer. A machine that produces hard-copy output of programs, program output, or data.

Program. A set of instructions that tells a computer what to do.

Prompt. An instruction from a computer informing the user about an error.

RAM. An abbreviation for random-access memory (see Random-Access Memory).

Random-Access Memory (RAM). A term used to describe computer memory that stores information. A RAM, an integrated circuit, differs from a ROM (read-only memory) in that RAM requires electrical power to remember information. If the computer power is turned off, the information is lost in RAM.

Read. The retrieving of information from a circuit, memory chip, tape, or disk.

Read-Only Memory (ROM). A term used to describe computer memory that stores information. The stored information is permanently stored and cannot be erased and changed or lost even if the electrical power is turned off.

Read-Write Memory. Computer memory whose contents can be erased and changed.

INDEX